THE MONKEY KINGDOM

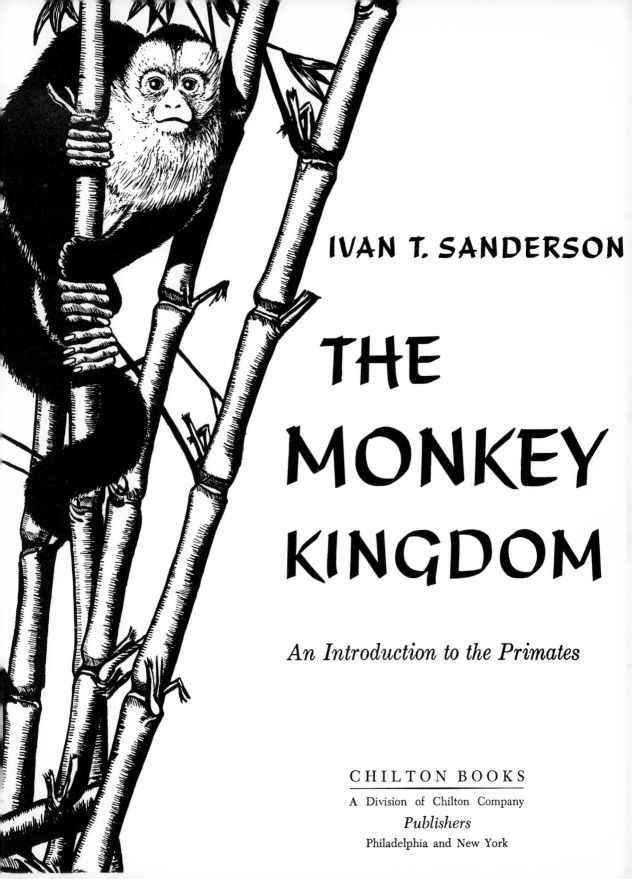

IVAN T. SANDERSON

THE
MONKEY
KINGDOM

An Introduction to the Primates

CHILTON BOOKS

A Division of Chilton Company

Publishers

Philadelphia and New York

Drawings and Maps

*The drawings and the sketch maps throughout the book
are the work of the author.*

Published in Philadelphia by Chilton Company,
and simultaneously in Toronto, Canada,
by Ambassador Books, Ltd.

Acknowledgements

THE PUBLISHERS have been gracious enough to grant me the space to attempt the impossible—the thanking of all those who have aided me in preparing this work.

This book could not have been written without the help and guidance of, and the expenditure of an enormous amount of time by, my close personal friend, Dr. W. C. Osman Hill, F.R.S., presently Prosector of the Zoological Society of London, who is today probably the world's foremost authority on the Primates, and whose monumental work, *Primates,* is now between the publication of its third and the preparation of its fourth volume. Not only did Dr. Hill read the manuscript and make numerous suggestions, criticisms, and emendations; he also checked several sections of the appended *Systematic List,* and he has even permitted me to publish, in advance, his own lists of the Hapaloids, Pithecoids, and Ceboids. Over and above this, he has given me invaluable counsel and advice. For these reasons, this book is dedicated to him.

However, before the completed manuscript was submitted to Osman Hill, two other friends had very kindly reviewed its first draft and had made many pertinent suggestions. These were Mr. T. Donald Carter, Assistant Curator of Mammals at the American Museum of Natural History, and Dr. George G. Goodwin of the same department of that institution. Donald Carter read the whole first draft and urged me to include the detailed systematic list of all species of Primates. Dr. Goodwin read only the three chapters on the tropical American primates, a subject in which he is a recognized expert. But his ultimate contribution was of the essence, for his criticisms together with Donald Carter's led me to recast much of the book.

Finally, I would like to say a word of sincere thanks to these, my long-suffering publishers, and in particular to acknowledge the editorial guidance and production skills of Chanticleer Press.

Having come this far, we may perhaps be permitted to add the ultimate traditional note—thanks to my wife for reading, editing, typing, retyping, and re-retyping the manuscript, and for, somehow, managing to remain orderly about the whole thing until the last period was applied to the Index.

Ivan T. Sanderson

Contents

The Question of Primates

1

OF MEN, MONKEYS, AND OTHERS

M ONKEYS," a famous comedian once said, "are the craziest people." In just what circumstances this remark was made is not on record but, whether it was originally nothing more than a facetious quip or was actually intended as a serious comment on the nature of things, it was a most perspicacious observation and is one that raises a number of interesting questions. For this reason, if for no other, it constitutes a fitting introduction to our story. But this is by no means the end of its worth, for those five simple words also postulate a fundamental hypothesis—namely, that monkeys are people, or vice versa, and this was the basis of the great debate initiated a century ago by Darwin regarding the origin and relationship of man. Finally, it also poses the pertinent question: what is a monkey?

Darwin's hypothesis has now become almost universally acceptable, supported as it is by a wealth of scientific investigation, so that we no longer regard ourselves as the product of a special creation but as a part of the comity of nature, and specifically as members of a particular division of the animal kingdom, known as the Primates, which also includes the creatures we call apes, monkeys, lemurs, and certain other less-known forms. The definition of a "monkey" has not, however, been satisfactorily resolved. This apparently simple question, moreover, requires careful examination before we may proceed to our story, for, although we are not solely or even primarily interested in mere monkeys, we cannot, without its resolution, attempt to discuss the greater galaxy of life-forms to which they belong.

Unfortunately, the only title available for this large and most varied group of animals—namely, the Primates—is hardly used outside of zoological literature, and we have no popularly accepted equivalent in the English language for this, nor any single name for all the kinds of creatures it includes. Furthermore, on the one hand, very few of the English names that have become attached to various kinds, species, or even *genera*, of Primates are really popularly known, while on the other hand the truly popular and widely understood titles bestowed upon them actually have no precise meaning. Neither the designation *ape, monkey,* nor *lemur* has any exact semantic status, and each of these means different things to different people. It is essential, therefore, that we ascertain exactly what we are talking about before we proceed.

One of the major divisions of the Animal Kingdom is known as the *Chordates,* or animals with a spinal chord. The members of several subdivisions of this group have their backbones composed of a string of separate little hinged bones called vertebrae, and are thus known as *Vertebrates*. These are the Fishes, the Amphibians (frogs, toads, salamanders, etc.), the Reptiles (snakes, lizards, tortoises, and crocodilians), the Birds, and finally the Mammals. Mammals may be defined as Vertebrates which, alone among all animals, at the same time have four-chambered hearts, produce milk in their bodies with which to suckle their young, and have true hair—as opposed to other hairlike structures —on their skins. Now, the Mammals may in turn be broken down into nineteen major divisions, or *orders,* as they are known technically, or into eighteen if you choose to include the seals and their kin with the cats, dogs, and their allies.

One of these divisions is called the *Primates* or the First or Top Ones. They were originally so called because men once regarded themselves not only as the end product of Nature but even as the very reason for its existence, so that even mere animals that in any way resembled them in build or behavior were automatically regarded as the nearest approach to perfection and thus of primary or topmost importance. However, a century of proper scientific inquiry and the exercise of sounder logic have brought about a profound change in our philosophical outlook and consequently quite a different opinion upon this matter. The name Primate has nonetheless remained the official designation, and the only one to boot, of the great group of mammals to which we now admit we belong.

Just how to define the Primates is not easy. They have no single externally recognizable physical feature that is common to all, and they vary enormously in size, structure, and behavior. Further, they are divisible into a number of apparently quite distinct types or basic patterns as it were. The reasons for grouping all these together are, in the end, purely anatomical but are often, when critically analyzed, remarkably abstruse. Some forms are, in fact, included more by default than by definition. Nevertheless, members of all of these have certain characteristics in common that they do not share with other mammals, and it can be shown that they are all genetically related. The evidence necessary to demonstrate both these statements is, however, so technical that it is almost if not quite impossible to summarize or interpret it in simple terms or other than by going into a plethora of complicated detail. The range of structure displayed by the Primates is so great, their origin so ancient, and their subdivision so extensive that a precise definition of all of them can be given only in such highly technical terms as the following by Dr. St. G. Mivart:

"Unguiculate, claviculate placental mammals, with orbits encircled by bone; three kinds of teeth, at least at one time of life; brain always with a posterior lobe and calcarine fissure; the innermost digit of at least one pair of extremities opposable; hallux with a flat nail or none; a well-developed caecum; penis pendulous; testes scrotal; always two pectoral mammae."

Though perhaps the most concise definition of the Primates ever given, this is of little use to the average person wishing to know what mammals are primates or what constitutes a primate. To answer these two questions, moreover, there appears to be only one course open to us. This is to list the animals so classed and then to describe each of them as fully as possible, observing, as one does so, why they are considered members of this group and how they differ from other mammals.

There are about 750 known kinds of living Primates, of 244 species, grouped into 80 genera which, in turn, fall into the following twelve fairly well-defined major divisions. These divisions correspond roughly to *Families*, in the technical sense, but they are not all exactly of that status from the taxonomic point of view, and at least one—that of the Pithecoids—is, according to current scientific acceptance, a composite assemblage. They may be summarized as follows:

(1)	*Tupaioids.*	The Feathertail and the Tupaias of the Oriental Region.
(2)	*Lorisoids.*	The Lorises of the Orient, and the Pottos, the Angwantibo, and the Bushbabies of Africa.
(3)	*Lemuroids.*	The True Lemurs of Madagascar.
(4)	*Tarsioids.*	The Tarsiers of the East Indies and the Philippines.
(5)	*Hapaloids.*	The Marmosets, Tamarins, and Pinchés, together with *Callimico*, and the Titis, of South America.
(6)	*Pithecoids.*	The Douroucoulis, Sakiwinkis, Uacaris, Bearded Sakis, and Squirrel-Monkeys of South America.
(7)	*Ceboids.*	The Capuchins, Woolly Monkeys, Woolly Spider-Monkey, Spider-Monkeys, and Howler Monkeys of Central and South America.
(8)	*Cercopithecoids.*	The Swamp Monkey, the Talapoins, the Guenons, and the Red Monkeys of Africa.
(9)	*Cynopithecoids.*	The Mangabeys of Africa, the Macaques of Asia and North Africa, and the Baboons.
(10)	*Coloboids.*	The Guerezas or *Colobus* Monkeys of Africa, and the Langurs, Leaf-Monkeys, Snub-nosed and Proboscis Monkeys of Asia.
(11)	*Simioids.*	Gibbons, Siamangs, and the Orang Utan, Chimpanzee, and Gorilla.
(12)	*Hominoids.*	Men-Apes, Ape-Men, Sub-Men, and Men.

The above is a mere listing of the living primates. Regarding their actual classification, Dr. G. Gaylord Simpson says, in his "Principles of Classification and a Classification of Mammals" (*Bulletin of the American Musuem of Natural History*, Volume 85, 1945):

"Much of the work on primates has been done by students who had no experience in taxonomy and who were completely incompetent to enter the field, however competent they may have been in other respects, and yet once their work is in print it becomes necessary to take cognizance of it. For this reason, if for no other, it is not surprising that most primates have alternative names and that hardly any two students use the same nomenclature for them. The importance of distinctions within the group has often been so exaggerated that almost every color-phase, aberrant individual, or scrap of fossil bone or tooth has been given a separate name, almost every really distinct species has been called a genus, and a large proportion of the genera have been called families."

Dr. Simpson is, of course, speaking primarily of the zoological nomenclature, but, as we shall see, almost the same may be said of the popular.

Not only do a majority of existing Primates have more than one popular name in English, some have half a dozen, others none at all, and still others a variety of native but no English ones. Then again, two entirely different animals may be called by the same "popular" name—like the Squirrel-Monkeys of South America and the Vervet Guenons of Africa, which are both sometimes called Green Monkeys—or one species of a genus may be known by a special name that has no connection whatsoever with the rest of the closely allied species. A notable example is the term "Cinnamon Ringtail," now used indiscriminately for various—and not always the same, be it noted—types of Capuchins. But confusion becomes complete when one Primate is called by the name of another—for example, the African Pottos are sometimes called Bushbabies—or is given such a misleading title as "Tree-Bear."

As was noted above, not even the terms *ape*, *monkey*, or *lemur* have any precise meaning in either scientific or popular parlance. The first two are, to a considerable extent, interchangeable. The name *lemur*, which was devised only about a century ago from the ancient Latin name for certain household gods or spirits, is still not widely known and still less understood. Then, in order to be called a *monkey* in popular parlance, an animal would seem to need certain attributes; but no persons seem ever to have agreed as to just what these should be, and such requisites have certainly never been listed. The average person apparently believes that a monkey should be able to hang by its tail, but the members of only five of the 80 genera of Primates can, in point of fact, do so, and all of these are confined to tropical America and are not even typical monkeys—at least, if that term is to be applied to the primates of the Old World that are customarily so called. Then, the term *ape* should by common sense as well as by scientific definition be confined to the tailless primates (other than men, presumably) of the Old World, all of which belong to a special group or, in technical parlance, superfamily, known as the *Hominoidea*. The term should thus be confined to the gibbons and siamangs and the Orang Utan, the Chimpanzee, and the Gorilla. But there are Dog-Monkeys (Cynopithecoids) that are commonly called Barbary Apes, Japanese Apes, and Black Apes, and the average person often calls monkeys "apes," and apes "monkeys." What is more, even zoologists often refer to the Lorisoids and the Tarsiers as lemurs although they are actually as distinct from the true Lemurs as we are from, say, the Ceboids of South America.

The Marmosets and their allies provide a recurring problem with which nobody seems to be prepared to deal, for they hold a position intermediate between those primates that are usually called "monkeys" and those—the Lorisoids, Lemuroids, Tarsioids, and Tupaioids—that are normally not so called. The Pithecoids (see Chapter 7) cause even more confusion since they stand between the Hapaloids and the Ceboids, and although most naturalists never doubt that they are "monkeys," the average citizen refuses to believe that some of them have any connection with such creatures.

Since, therefore, there is neither a scientific nor a popular definition of a monkey, anybody may presumably stretch this term as widely as desired within the confines of the Primates as a whole, or restrict it to as limited a compass as he wishes. Nevertheless, we would suggest that the title would best be restricted to the Coloboids, Cynopithecoids, and Cercopithecoids of the Old World, and, with some qualifications, to the Ceboids of the New World. The true Lemurs may legitimately be grouped with the Lorisoids, but the Tarsioids and the Tupaioids should be vouchsafed some marked distinction. Likewise, it should be recognized that the Hapaloids and probably the Pithecoids hold a rather special and intermediate position in the scheme of things. This leaves only those creatures classed by zoologists as the *Hominoidea*. These form a distinct and in many ways compact group, all the members of which are closely associated, and which could therefore be called the Anthropoids, or Manlike Ones. However, the group contains two families, that of the Apes or *Pongidae,* and of Men or *Hominidae* and, despite the discovery of a number of extinct creatures which appear to bridge the gap between the two, may at least for the present be split into two parts with the names Simioids and Hominoids.

There is, then, one other aspect of the Primates that requires mention. This is their position on the genealogical tree of mammalian life. In this respect their position has proved to be considerably different from what it was once supposed to be and is by no means that of a branch sprouting from the top. Primates, in fact, are not really very specialized in bodily form—as are, for instance, sloths or elephants. Instead, they have apparently concentrated on something else that we normally, and perhaps rather casually, refer to as "intelligence," though quite what this is nobody has as yet really been able to define. It is manifestly not a single quality but a complexity of distinct aptitudes, each of which can vary much in degree, and the total of which can be manifested in an even greater range of forms. It may truly be said that individual dogs or horses are "intelligent," and many other kinds of animals display "intelligent" behavior. In another context, even the lowly Opossum may be said to show intelligence of a sort, for it has certainly survived unchanged for longer than almost any other mammal, and it is doing very well today in face of a vast invasion of its native territory by swarms of other creatures such as dogs, cats, and

men. But only among the other Primates do we observe the particular quality of intelligence to which we are addicted. This may or may not qualify them for the position of Top Mammals.

From the purely physical point of view, however, Primates are neither the most advanced, complex, nor specialized, nor even the most recently developed, of mammalian groups; in fact, they are, compared to many, rather generalized in that they retain a number of simple and basic features, and they appear to have sprung from near the bottom of the mammalian tree and in very early times. While this was being written a most interesting study of this matter was published in the *Proceedings of the Zoological Society of London,* by P. M. Butler of the Department of Zoology of the University of Manchester, under the unassuming title "The Skull of *Ictops* and the Classification of the *Insectivora.*" In this, a great amount of anatomical evidence is brought together to show the close relationship between the Primates and, on the one hand, a strange, lone form of mammal with furred parachutes found in Malaya and called the Kobego, and, on the other hand, a group of little, mouse-formed insectivorous creatures from Africa known as Elephant-Shrews (see also page 16). The author of this paper further suggests that the common ancestor of these three diverged from the main stem of the Insectivore stock at a very early stage of its development. This places the Primates not too far from some of the most basic and primitive forms of mammalian life.

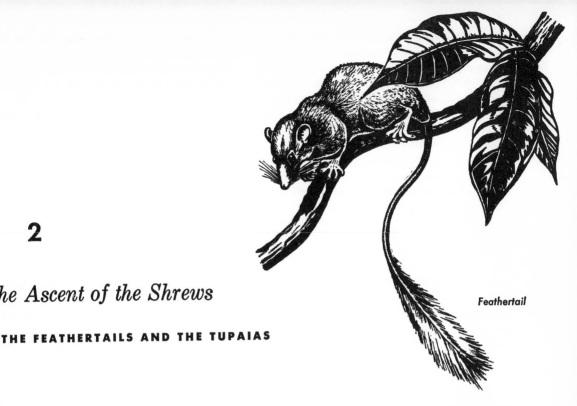

Feathertail

2

The Ascent of the Shrews

THE FEATHERTAILS AND THE TUPAIAS

ALMOST a hundred years ago a certain Hugh Low was staying in the palace of the Rajah of Sarawak, a country on the northwest coast of the great island of Borneo. Unfortunately we have no record of the events of the particular evening that both initiates our story and constitutes such an important milestone in the elucidation of our own history and that of our numerous and remarkably assorted cousins. Published details of the appetites of famous generals before battles are rife, but interesting sidelights on discoveries such as this are invariably unobtainable. All we know is that on this particular night the said Mr. Low obtained the first recorded specimen of a cheery, rat-sized, and somewhat rat-shaped little animal *in* the house of the said Rajah. The animal was preserved and sent to the British Museum in London.

The following year, one Dr. Gray of that institute published a paper in which he described the small beast, giving it the name of "Mr. Low's Feather-tailed One," or, in pseudo-Latin, *Ptilocercus lowi.* This pamphlet noted that the animal was unique in that it had teeth like a shrew, a body like a rat, feet like an opossum, and a tail that more resembled a whisk broom than anything else. At that

date, completely unknown forms of mammals were still turning up with fair regularity, and, although the animal was obviously most interesting, the somewhat new science of systematic zoology was then so busy that nobody did anything particular about the report, and few even commented upon it. In fact, it was sixteen years before a German named Brehm mentioned the animal in an illustrated volume—and misspelled its name, incidentally—and it was a further twelve years before it again got into print—this time in none other than the great Alfred Russel Wallace's monumental work on the over-all distribution of living mammals. A few other specimens turned up from time to time, including one distinctive enough to be given a special name, about 1910, in Kwala Lumpur on the mainland of the Malay Peninsula. A few years later the animal again drew attention sufficient to get itself more properly and fully described, but the describer stated that he could find only a few skins and just one skeleton in all the great museums of the world. Only within the last few years has it been studied in detail, but in the interval it has been elevated to possibly one of the most important positions among mammals. The reason for this needs explanation.

13

If you start going backwards in time, you will note that your ancestors become more and more numerous but that the total number of persons in your "family" becomes less and less. Working backwards, therefore, we should all be related. Of course this, like most theories, does not work out in practice because all sorts of complications mar the neat mathematical picture—in our case, most notably the fact that we very likely have a composite and thus multiple origin, as a species. Nevertheless, centuries of ancestor worship have bequeathed to modern thinking man such a deep interest in his past that it was inevitable he should, sooner or later, start to seek his ultimate origins.

Although some glimmerings of the idea of evolution had been displayed by Aristotle and other perspicacious Greeks centuries before, it was not till the nineteenth century that the idea was finally crystallized by Charles Darwin. During the hundred years following publication of his *Descent of Man,* almost everybody has come to agree that humans are not unique, but are both an offshoot of and at the same time part of a much greater "family"—in the popular sense of that word—of living things known as the Primates. This group of mammals is usually called the "Monkeys," but it includes several other kinds of creatures, ranging from ourselves to, it now transpires, the "Feather-tailed One of Mr. Low." Thus, if we start delving into our own personal ancestry, we may run up against almost anybody; but if we persist, we must eventually hit in succession first some Stone-Age individual of sub-human aspect, and then, in descending order, an ape-like man, a man-like ape, a monkey-like ape, an ape-like monkey, a lemur-like monkey, a monkey-like lemur, and so on until we reach a shrew-like creature displaying the curious combination of features found in the Feathertail. This, however, is not to say that we are descended directly from apes such as we know them, or that apes are descended from monkeys *per se*, or monkeys from true lemurs, but that each of these, together with other types that we shall meet presently, represent general steps in a procession through time. The point in this succession that is of special interest to our story is the one at which the group of mammals to which we belong—the Primates—branched off from all other known groups. And right at that critical point stands the "Feather-tailed One of Mr. Low."

It is, in some ways, humbling to contemplate the fact that we are nothing more than the offspring of

little ratlike creatures with scaly tails, bug eyes, and a special arrangement of bones in their skeletons. That representatives of these lowly creatures should still exist today is perhaps even more remarkable.

The little animal in question has soft, silky-to-woolly fur, a long pointed snout, rather large eyes, ears like a rat, and five fingers and toes. Its hands, though all digits bear claws, are surprisingly human in outline, and the thumb is somewhat opposed, meaning that it stands off at a wide angle from the first finger. The great toe shows the same tendency. The tail is also ratlike and is covered with scales, but its terminal third bears a plume of long, white, feather-like hairs on either side. When the tiny animal composes itself for sleep, which it does during the daylight hours, it curls the tail under its body and holds this fan over its head. Moreover, both while asleep and awake, this fan keeps twitching, involuntarily but most vigorously, when a mosquito or other annoying insect comes buzzing around. It appears to be a sort of built-in fly-swatter. Nothing much has been added to our knowledge of the animal's habits during the past century except that it appears to sleep in hollow branches in a rough nest of leaves, twigs and other dry material, and that it eats mostly insects.

Comparative anatomy, and especially the study of animal bones, is to laymen an abstruse science that professes to be able on occasion to identify and even reconstruct almost a whole animal from a single bone or part of one. The astonishing fact is that it can do so; for time and time again just such a prognostication has been made, and subsequently either a whole skeleton of the animal or even the animal itself, alive, has turned up and proved to fit the description exactly. Thus, when anatomists stated that the Feathertail was related to the Primates because its eyes were completely surrounded by a bony ring, and because of other such minutiae, the statement created great interest.

But examination of this animal's skull and, later, of its skeleton, gave anatomists further great surprises. It proved to have teeth like those of shrews —primitive, terrestrial beasts that swarm all over North America, Europe, Asia, and Africa—but both the skull and the skeleton displayed features that linked it even more closely to animals then known as Tree-Shrews—to which we will now turn.

On either the 25th or 26th of January in the year 1780, a Dr. William Ellis, who was one of the sur-

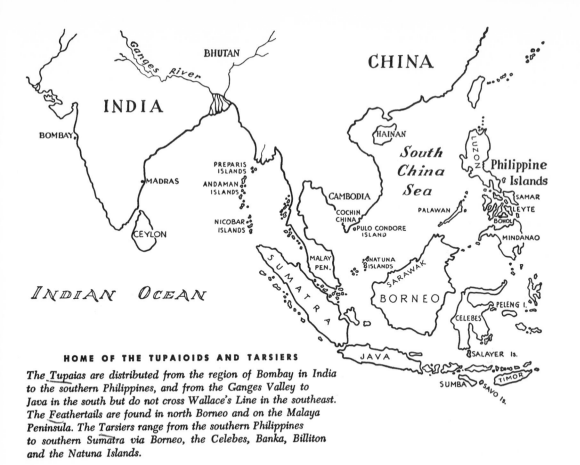

HOME OF THE TUPAIOIDS AND TARSIERS

The Tupaias are distributed from the region of Bombay in India to the southern Philippines, and from the Ganges Valley to Java in the south but do not cross Wallace's Line in the southeast. The Feathertails are found in north Borneo and on the Malaya Peninsula. The Tarsiers range from the southern Philippines to southern Sumatra via Borneo, the Celebes, Banka, Billiton and the Natuna Islands.

geons on the famous Captain Cook's third voyage around the world, recorded in his diary that a party had gone ashore on Pulo Condore Island off the coast of Cochin China—which is the southern province of modern Viet Nam—and shot a few "monkies, squirrels, and a cock and hen." No further details on the monkeys or the fowl are given, but Dr. Ellis made a little drawing of the "squirrel." This drawing has been preserved in his manuscript notes in the British Museum. It is an incredible effort, showing an animal with an elongated rectangular body of about the proportions of a dachshund, four upright, sticklike legs with carefully detailed feet, a fluffy tail going upwards and then straight forwards parallel to the back (possibly on account of a shortage of space at the top of the paper) and a head of rather furious mien with a glaring eye and several nasty-looking teeth showing in the half-opened mouth. Despite the over-all effect, which is rather like that of an elongated electric iron with a handle of exaggerated design, the details are so faithfully drawn that nobody could for a moment call it a

squirrel or doubt that it represents an animal we now know as a Tupaia. Dr. Ellis' diary was never published, so that this little gem remained unknown for many decades.

Then, in 1807, a French traveler named Leschenault de la Tour sent to the *Musée d'Histoire Naturelle* in Paris a stuffed specimen of a similar animal from Java; but this was not even noted until nearly thirty years later when the famous zoologist, Isidore Geoffroy Snt. Hilaire, stumbled across its remains in that museum, and described the animal. However, Sir Thomas Stamford Raffles had in the meanwhile published a delightful tome entitled *A Descriptive Catalogue of a Zoological Collection made on account of the Honourable East India Company in the Island of Sumatra and its Vicinity, etc.*," in which he had described a Tupaia with recognized scientific exactitude. Moreover, the next year another Englishman, Thomas Hardwicke, had done likewise in the *Transactions of the Asiatic Society of Bengal*, so that Geoffroy Snt. Hilaire's "find" in 1835 proved to be somewhat belated.

Matters relative to these animals then proceeded slowly until the first decade of the present century. More and more species were added, coming from as far afield as the region of Bombay in western India; Bhutan; southern China; the island of Hainan; the whole Indo-Malayan region; the islands of Borneo, Sumatra and Java; almost all the smaller islands between these and the mainland; the Nicobars and even the Preparis Islands; though strangely enough not from Ceylon, the Andaman Islands, or Bali. Finally, some very distinct types were found on Palawan, Mindanao, and other southern Philippine Islands. Today, there are some thirty distinct species known, several of them with numerous subspecies, no less than fifty-three of which belong to a single species (*Tupaia glis*). The name Tupaia is derived from the Malayan word for "a little fast animal of the trees," and is used indiscriminately for squirrels and several other animals. The second group, found in a great belt from Sumatra via Borneo to the islands of the South China Sea, is now named *Tana*, which is the specific Malayan name for the Tupaias. A third group comes from India and is known as *Anathana*, there being three distinct kinds found respectively around Bombay in the west, Madras in the southeast, and northeastern India west of the Ganges River. Then there is another genus, of mountain-dwelling forms, named *Dendrogale*, found in Borneo and in Cambodia. Finally, there is a Tupaia in Mindanao and certain of the other southern Philippine Islands to which the name *Urogale* has been given.

The Tupaioids may then be listed as follows:

	SP.	SUBSP.
A. FEATHERTAILS (*Ptilocercinae*)		
(1) Feathertails (*Ptilocercus*)	1	2
B. TUPAIAS (*Tupaiinae*)		
(1) Common (*Tupaia*)	15	74
(2) Great (*Tana*)	9	16
(3) Indian (*Anathana*)	3	3
(4) Tree (*Dendrogale*)	3	3
(5) Philippine (*Urogale*)	1	1

It may be asked why we list these obscure little beasts in such detail, especially when our main story is that of our monkey cousins. The answer is simply that although these animals look like squirrels and were for years called Tree-Shrews, they are not shrews and very few of them live in trees, and they are actually most primitive Primates and

thus direct descendants of our own ancestors and those of all our Primate cousins. They stand, in fact, somewhere on the tree of life between those primitive and ancient mammals that we call Insectivores and the Top Mammals, which include the Lorises, Lemurs, Marmosets, Monkeys, Apes and Men. The reasons for placing them at such a crucial spot on our genealogical tree are numerous but are almost exclusively anatomical, if not entirely so.

In anatomical structure and make-up Tupaias are fairly close to some of the Insectivores, and perhaps most notably to those known as Elephant-Shrews, which hop about on their hind legs and have small trunks and live in Africa. In other respects they are closer to the Lemurs. Like the Feathertails, they have bony rings right round their eyes, usually a small appendix, and above all, a second tongue. This is most puzzling to many people, since they envisage two pink things waggling about side by side in the mouth. Actually, the second tongue is a stiff, often cartilaginous structure shaped like an elongated spoon and lies under the ordinary tongue. In some lemurs it is developed into a sort of comb with which to curry the fur and clean the lower front teeth from behind.

Tupaias are extraordinary little animals and when watched in their wild haunts show many traits that seem to indicate that they are imbued with considerable intelligence. Despite the fact that they were long called Tree-Shrews, most of them spend almost all of their time on the ground, especially on steep slopes; but all can climb with agility, and there are some species that dwell perpetually in the forest canopy and live much the lives of squirrels. Both in the wild and in captivity they display an extraordinary combination of placidity and relaxedness on the one hand, and of violent activity and demonstrativeness on the other. When a Tupaia moves it can go off like a rocket. They are vastly inquisitive, poking their long noses, which bristle with whiskers, into everything, so that if you simply close your hand they will probe and scrape away at it and eventually become almost hysterical in their efforts to open your fingers in order to see what is inside. A pet one I kept for a long time, when it found nothing inside my hand on such occasions, would sit up on my wrist and scream at me in a torrent of insectivorous invective. Because of this curiosity, Tupaias move about a great deal, and they are omnivorous in the widest sense of that word. This is a very significant characteristic and one that has probably played an important part in their history.

There is possibly no such thing as a purely insectivorous, or carnivorous, or herbivorous mammal. True, there are monkeys that seem to live exclusively on leaves and some flowers, bats that appear to eat only insects caught on the wing, and so forth. But insect remains have been found in the stomachs of the former and masses of vegetable fibers in those of the latter. Leopards may relish lettuce, and deer and other hoofed grass-eaters very often eat old bones, rotten meat, snails and other animal matter. The Tupaias, however, seem to eat almost everything digestible, and my pet would even gorge herself on a curry-like Malayan dish known as *nassi goring* that can be made so hot with a sauce called *tzambal* that your eyes water merely from looking too closely at it. In the wild, they eat insects, fruits of many kinds, leaves, snails and other small animals like frogs and lizards, eggs and worms. Tupaias are diurnal animals and sleep during the night either in nests, in holes in the ground —preferably in banks or cliffs—or in tangles of vegetation in the upper tree canopy. To do this, they sit up with their tails protruding forwards between their hind legs and coiled up over their heads, which, in turn, are tucked down onto their bellies. Most of them normally bear two young at a time but sometimes only one, and there are species that normally have either two or three pairs of mammary glands and customarily give birth to four or five young at a time. The gestation period of one species is fifty-six days. However, just because this applies to the species known as *Urogale everetti* found in Mindanao, it need not apply to all or even to any other Tupaias.

Perhaps the most interesting feature of Tupaias is their extraordinary vocabulary. Shrews and other Insectivores make all kinds of noises, from supersonic screams of rage to pleasant murmurs and twitters of joy, but Tupaias chirrup, wheedle, scream, chatter, whistle, utter a long-drawn-out noise like a hawk, mutter, mumble, and, when really excited, give forth with a sound that I can describe only as an explosion. This is not simply a sound but a sort of bursting of the whole animal into violent action, and it has just about the same effect upon a human as the unexpected explosion of a firecracker. My pet first did this on being offered a very large beetle which, to her amazement, bit her on the hand; it took her about an hour to calm down.

Here, then, are the amazing little animals that, in a manner of speaking, are the cause of our story and of much else besides. Tucked away in the Oriental Region of the world for tens of millions of years, and unrecognized for what they really were until recently, they have not only survived countless changes that have eradicated many other more impressive kinds of animals, but have retained an astonishingly virile position in the scheme of things, being extremely numerous in both forms and gross numbers, and being widely distributed. If you have ever kept a Tupaia you will perhaps more readily appreciate the theory of evolution, understand more about the origin of intelligence, and come to know better why we behave as we do; for they, much more so than the apes, display a combination of characters that are on the one hand bestial and on the other rational.

The little Feathertails and the Tupaias point the way from the vast world of mere animal life to a new experiment in living that has culminated in something quite different—ourselves.

3

The Bawling of the Bushbabies

GALAGOS, POTTOS, AND LORISES

Needle-clawed Bushbaby

BETWEEN the Tupaias and the rest of us more monkey-like creatures, there is a great gulf fixed. Somewhere, and sometime certainly more than sixty million years ago, some tupaia-like animals began to change in various and particular ways. It would appear that these changes were brought about for the most part if not wholly as a result of the animals taking to living whole-time in trees.

If you look at a rat head on, you will note that its eyes bulge out on either side of its head. Next, take a look at a squirrel from in front, and you will see that, although its eyes are also on the sides of its head, it looks at you down its nose. If you can find a Tupaia to look at, you will see that it looks almost straight at you, although its eyes are also separated by a long muzzle and are still actually situated on the sides of its head. But if you look straight at the nose of any of the animals we are now about to describe, including also the lemurs, marmosets, monkeys, apes and ourselves, you will find yourself staring straight into its eyes. The shrinking of the muzzle back into the face, as it were, and the movement of the eyes forwards and towards each other over the nose, is useful to an

arboreal leaper since it permits the development of binocular vision whereby everything ahead is seen in a single field. But more of this anon.

If you next look carefully at the hands and feet of a squirrel you will note that, in addition to the long, sharp claws, their palms and soles are naked and are raised into a number of swellings, and that all manner of curious padded lumps or warts are distributed about their surfaces. These aid the animal in obtaining a footing on smooth surfaces where the claws fail to grip. Then again, note the arrangement of the fingers and toes. There are only four fingers, all directed forwards and held alongside each other. The five toes are also held together, but one, the innermost, is shorter, arises farther up the foot and can be somewhat separated from the others. This arrangement of digits suits the squirrel's way of life and aids its galloping movements. The Tupaia's extremities are much the same except that it has five fingers and toes, and the first toe is a little more widely separated, or opposed, as it is called. In the Feathertail, however, both the thumb and the first toe are markedly opposed. Among all the remaining primates both these appendages, if present—for several monkeys have lost their thumbs entirely—are more or less fully opposed, and in some cases so widely that they point directly away from the rest of the digits and give the hands or feet much the appearance of those of parrots. These changes in the basic structure of animals that started with a squirrel-like form are of the utmost importance to our story, but they are not by any means the only ones that took place in the early tupaia-like animals of sixty million years ago when they first took to leading an arboreal existence. But, once these changes had taken place, we had a new form of life on this planet.

What this new kind of animal may have been is not certain, though a number of lowly Primate creatures of various kinds have been found in the form of fossilized skeletons. As so often happens, however, the process was not simple but complex, so that various groups of these animals evolved in various slightly different directions. Countless intervening stages have become extinct without leaving a trace that we have so far found, so that even in the earliest strata we find creatures that look like the originators of at least four major stems of the primate genealogical tree, namely the Lorisoid, Lemuroid, Tarsioid and Hapaloid. Just when or where they branched off the main stem we do not know, but all came off fairly near the bottom of the trunk and each has kept some tupaia-like qualities.

The most primitive appear to be the Lorisoids, which are today found throughout tropical Africa, southern India, Ceylon, and the Oriental Region south of a line drawn from the upper Brahmaputra River in Assam to the Gulf of Tonkin and ranging thence south as far as Wallace's Line but excluding the Philippines and certain other islands (see map). Nothing whatsoever is known of their ancestors. They come in two lines with very different performance records. One is long-tailed, large-eared, and very swift; the other is more or less tailless, small-eared, and slow-moving. The former are entirely African and are known as Bushbabies or Galagos; the latter are spread over both Africa and the Oriental Region and are known as Pottos and Lorises. There are only ten species in all, divided among seven genera as follows:

	SP.	SUBSP.
A. **BUSHBABIES** (*Galagidae*)		
(1) Dwarf Bushbabies (*Galagoides*)	1	7
(2) Typical Bushbabies (*Galago*)		
(a) Lesser Bushbabies (*G. senegalensis*)	1	9
(b) Black-tailed Bushbabies (*G. alleni*)	1	1
(c) Great Bushbabies (*G. crassicaudatus*)	1	11
(3) Needle-clawed Bushbabies (*Euoticus*)	2	2
B. **LORISES** (*Lorisidae*)		
(1) Pottos (*Periodicticus*)	1	5
(2) Angwantibos (*Arctocebus*)	1	2
(3) Slender Lorises (*Loris*)	1	6
(4) Slow Lorises (*Nycticebus*)	1	10

One of the most engaging and in some respects startling of all forms of mammalian life is the tiny Bushbaby of the species known as Demidoff's or the Dwarf Bushbaby (*Galagoides demidovii*). This minuscule, bug-eyed creature can sit on the palm of a man's hand but can also leap a dozen or more feet horizontally or even upwards and in any direction. It is an inhabitant of the true equatorial forests of Africa, and is found in half a dozen recognizable forms throughout a vast area from Senegal in the west to the Rift Valley in the east (see map). It is, however, very seldom seen even by hunters native to those countries, and not only because it is so small. The remains of these animals preserved in museums in the form of skins are various shades of gray, gray-brown, brown and russet, with lighter undersides usually cream in color. In the wild they often display colors that are most startling, being a vivid green above and saffron yellow below. These bright colors, however, fade not only soon after death but even if the animal is kept alive in a cage, and it would appear that the green shades of the uppersides and perhaps also the bright yellow of the under are caused by minute algal spores growing on the hairs of the pelt. These bright colors render the tiny animals almost invisible among the dense foliage, which itself may be a hundred feet above the ground. Secondly, it appears that these animals are more generally diurnal than other Bushbabies and spend much of the night asleep in holes or curled up in thick foliage, so that they are less often spotted by the shine of their eyes in the beam of a flashlight after dark. They are, nonetheless, comparatively common animals in many localities once you have learned where and how to look for them.

They appear to be mixed-diet feeders, eating many insects, tree snails and tree frogs, and other animal food, but also taking a rather special form of vegetable food. This is *green* nuts; that is to say, the kernels of hard-shelled fruits before the shells have hardened, like, for example, green almonds. This food is characteristic of all the Bushbabies and is also of importance to many other monkey-like creatures.

Very little if anything is known about the habits of these Bushbabies, but they are believed to breed twice a year. They have teeth arranged in the typical lorisoid and lemuroid fashion, with tiny upper front teeth pointing downwards and long lower front teeth pointing forwards; although they appear to have two pairs of lower canines or eyeteeth, also sloping forwards, the hindmost of these are elongated premolars. Like all other lorisoids and lemuroids, they have a second cartilaginous tongue under the fleshy normal one, and this combined with the lower front teeth forms a device for currying the fur. The undertongue is then used to clean fine hairs and other material out of the comb formed by the lower teeth. All Bushbabies are most meticulous about their appearance and indulge in lengthy toilettes at regular intervals before and after feeding and then again if handled or otherwise ruffled.

Most astonishing are their hands and feet. The bones of their ankles are enormously elongated so that they form a third section to the limb like that of a bird, and this gives them their tremendous, springlike leaping power. The fingers and toes are long and slender, and both the thumb and great toe are widely opposed and hugely developed. All the digits end below in large, bulblike pads bearing fine striations, and there is a circle of similar pads, bearing "rings" like our fingerprints, arranged around the palms and soles. All the fingers and all but the second or index toe bear small, flat nails. The odd toe bears a long, curved claw that sticks straight up; this latter is found on all lorisoids and is used to scratch the skin. The ears are naked and rather large, and they can be folded up like a fan and moved about separately.

Closely related to the Dwarf Bushbaby is a group of three species forming the genus *Galago* and called respectively the Lesser, the Black-tailed, and the Great Bushbabies, or *G. senegalensis*, *alleni*, and *crassicaudatus* respectively. The first comes in nine recognizable color varieties, one of which is the famous little chinchilla-furred Gogo, or Moholi Galago, that used to be a favorite pet and has even been bred in New York. Lesser Bushba-

bies are inhabitants of the open-canopy forests, of the gallery forests, and of the copses that dot the orchard and savannah belts. They are thus found all the way across Africa (see map) south of the Sahara, from Senegal in the west to Somaliland in the east, thence down the eastern uplands to Mozambique and to the Limpopo and Orange Rivers in South Africa. The little Moholi extends its range west again to the Atlantic coast in Angola.

In most respects and particularly in outward form, the Lesser Bushbabies are not unlike the Dwarfs, but they are twice the size and not quite so agile, and are entirely nocturnal. Their appearance is most typically displayed in the color photograph elsewhere in these pages. Like all galagos they can hang upside down by their feet alone, and in this position they have a habit of moving the body up and down by folding and unfolding the legs. They have an even stranger habit of moistening their hands and feet with their urine to give them a better grip, and they use their fingers as we do, to test things, then often sniffing or licking them before going for the object with the mouth. They are not only bright but appear to be rather intelligent creatures that quickly learn not to be afraid of human beings who are gentle with them, and they have quite a noticeable family organization that in many ways foreshadows the amazing social structure of a tribe of Marmosets. Their conversation is also rather extensive, and their leaders, mothers and babies can each in his own way communicate orders and requests of a wide variety.

Allen's or the Black-tailed Galago is a slightly larger but altogether different animal, coming only from a limited area of equatorial forest about the western curve of Africa between the Niger-Benue and the Congo-Ubangi Rivers (see map). It is probably the greatest leaper of all the Galagos, on occasion literally flying out of tree-heads into clear space over canyons with its arms and legs spreadeagle and its long fluffy tail thrashing behind it almost like a propeller. It is completely nocturnal and usually sleeps in hollow branches at the tops of the largest trees. There is some evidence that the mothers carry the young clinging to their bellies. It appears to be more vegetarian than the Lesser Bushbabies.

The Great or Thick-tailed Galagos are really very different animals, having proportionately somewhat shorter hind limbs, running and galloping rather than leaping, and sometimes descending to the ground, where they hop along without using the front limbs at all. One that we owned for some years spent all day asleep in a small box that had a three-inch circular opening and was placed in a cage. We feed our animals at sundown in the summer and an hour before putting out the lights in their house in winter. This allows the day-feeders time for dinner before darkness comes, and, since they usually leave enough of the meal, they have breakfast waiting for them the next morning after sunup. This arrangement also permits the night-feeders to eat at their leisure during the whole night while the food is still fresh, and this is most important since different kinds of animals feed on entirely different schedules at night, some doing so just after sundown and before dawn, others in the middle of the night, and so forth. We have never seen the Great Galago appear from its box until after all the daytime animals have bedded down for the night and the first contingents of night-feeders have finished their first meals, made their toilettes, and settled down for a nap. This is apparently their habit in forests where they live, for their first appearance therein seems always to coincide with a "flat spot" in general animal activity that always occurs about two hours after dark. When they do appear—in captivity, at least—they put on a most remarkable performance that doubtless replaces the regular nightly activities of these animals in the wild. This consists of sundry precisely regular, often acrobatic, motions performed with machine-like rhythm: up and down, back and forth, round and round, over and under they go, always placing the same foot on the same spot every time around, so that the cage develops highly polished circular areas in all sorts of odd places. After some minutes, or sometimes over an hour of this, the animal brushes itself lightly, then goes and eats, searching through the assorted food with its hands like a monkey, selecting what it wants, and holding this to its mouth. Galagos drink copiously and take alternate sips of milk and water between pieces of food. When about half the food is gone, they retire to an elevated place and spend about an hour currying their fur, cleaning every part of themselves and licking their fingers. They rub their eyes a great deal, and smear saliva all over their large naked ears with their hands. Then they very often go to sleep until shortly before dawn. However, like all nocturnal beasts, they appear to regulate their night's activities by the amount of moonlight, lying low when it is bright and moving about when it is overcast, after the moon has set, or if it is raining.

The Great Galagos, of which there are eleven recognizable forms or races, have a curious distribution spreading down the east coast of Africa and throughout a wide belt in Angola and the southern Congo. They are inhabitants of open and mixed forests, not of the closed canopy. They have very dense, woolly to fluffy fur varying from a delicate, mauvish dove-gray to a rich reddish brown with an orange wash. Their enormous ears can be wrinkled up and turned about in all kinds of strange ways.

A sort of extreme development of the Great Galagos, constituting the genus *Euoticus*, is found in the closed forests from east of the Niger River to the White Nile—at least if an animal named *Galago inustus* is one of these and not just a type of Great Galago. These animals are so distinct that they have been given another name, *Euoticus*, and the common form the specific and rather delightful title of *elegantulus*, or the "Elegant Ones with Nice Ears," which they indeed are. Unlike the other Bushbabies, which have a gentle and often ineffably lovable countenance, these animals, which are also called Needle-clawed Galagos, have somewhat flattened heads with an aggressive, catlike expression and eyes which, when the pupil is contracted to the point of disappearance, stare like those of porcelain monsters and are a bright, glistening orange in color. They are clothed in a short, very dense, woolly fur; their limbs are short and sturdy, and the tail is very long and thickly furred. The ears are naked and pink and stick out of the sides of their heads, while their hands and feet have naked pink flesh and are very large. They give a really ferocious bite for their size, and are most furious and irascible beasts. We kept many alive in West Africa, and they proved to be one of the very few mammals that we have encountered that will wait quietly and then suddenly go for a human being deliberately, latching on with both hands and feet and really chewing, not just biting. We found their stomachs crammed with green nuts and some insect remains, and one of them once caught a live bird, tore it to pieces, skinned it, and ate it. Most notable feature of these animals is their nails, which, instead of being flat and smooth like those of other Galagos and our own, are raised centrally into a sharp ridge that continues forward into a really needle-sharp point or false claw.

This animal constitutes the last member of the

Galagidae, which is one of the two families of Lorisoids. The four remaining animals form the family *Lorisidae,* the first two of which are found in Africa, and are known as the Potto (*Periodicticus*) and the Angwantibo (*Arctocebus*).

The first, an animal about the size of a small cat, has been fairly well known in Europe for a century and has recently been imported into American zoos in fair numbers. It is known by a variety of other names, notably and misleadingly as the "Honey-Bear," "Slow Loris" (which is quite another animal; see below), "Slow Lemur," "Bush-Bear," "Tree-Bear," or even "Bushbaby." Most pleasant of all is undoubtedly the common West African pidgin-English title of "Softly-Softly," which is most appropriate. Where the name Potto comes from we do not know, but even this is now somewhat confusing, since the Latin name of *Potos* has been given to the tropical American relative of the Raccoon known as the Kinkajou but sometimes *also* as the Honey-Bear. The Softly-Softly may be distinguished from all other Lorisoids by its absurd half-a-tail that sticks straight out behind, as well as by a number of other odd features. Pottos are closed-forest equatorial animals and come in five races or subspecies, distributed respectively from Senegal to the Niger River, from there to the Cross River (see map), east of that river to the Congo-Ubangi River, south and east of the Congo and east of the Ubangi, and finally, north of the Congo and thence east to the limits of the forests at the Rift Valley.

In habits they are totally unlike the leaping Galagos, being slow and deliberate in every move, quite unable to jump at all, and almost never letting go with more than one hand or foot at a time. They are nocturnal and sleep all day, sitting up with their heads curved down on their bellies and all four limbs firmly anchored to something. Although slow in movement, they are very active creatures, trundling about the trees at night like small bears but sometimes progressing along the undersides of the branches, upside down like sloths. They are stealthy and make no noise, but they can growl horribly and let out a piercing yell.

There is an unassailable belief throughout the countries where they are found that they are wholly carnivorous and obtain their principal articles of diet—which according to the story are birds and monkeys—by creeping up on them and slowly putting their hands around their victims' necks and strangling them. This is a "nice story" about a nasty

habit, but there is no reliable eyewitness account of it or any other confirmation, though I have seen a Potto give a sleeping monkey a fright so great that it fell into convulsions. It is also true that pottos in captivity will tear up small birds and eat them, and will take all kinds of meat. However, they also eat insects, large quantities of green nuts, fruits, and some leaves.

Pottos have very dangerous sets of teeth and are not to be trifled with—especially since, like all the Lorises, they can move the head almost faster than the eye can follow and present it at almost any point about the body. They also have an unbelievably strong grip with both hands and feet and will not let go. And finally they have another defensive trick that is unique.

Behind the head, the spines of the last neck (cervical) vertebrae and first two chest (thoracic) vertebrae actually penetrate the skin and are capped by horny spines. (There is much debate as to whether these vertebral processes actually penetrate the skin or only raise it into "points" that are capped by the horny spines. Having skinned many dozen fresh specimens, I can affirm that in larger adults the bones actually do penetrate the skin.) If the animal is attacked frontally while trundling along a branch, it rises up to arm's length to await the onslaught. At the last instant, as the assailant closes in, the Potto suddenly brings its head downwards and onto its chest with a rabbit-punch motion, and if the attacker does not stop his onrush in time, he gets the sharp spines between his eyes and down his nose with a raking motion. The effect on a small cat can be well-nigh disastrous. The Potto also has an amazingly thick and tough skin and is clothed in dense, firm, woolly fur which makes it almost immune to the bites of all but larger animals. Then again, the Potto's limbs are strong out of all proportion to its size and are undeniably used for strangling any who insist upon coming to grips with it. The hands and feet are of absurd design, having enormous thumbs and great toes pointing in the opposite direction to the third, fourth, and fifth digits. Further, the second or index finger is reduced to a mere knob without a nail, and the second toe to a sturdy lump bearing the cleaning claw.

Pottos move about the middle strata of the forest as well as in the upper canopy; they sometimes even come down to the ground and make extraordinarily good time there, using a stiff-legged pacing gait that, although deliberate and always cautious, gets them over the ground and to the nearest tree base in short order. They may then simply continue walking straight up the side of the tree with the same gait and at the same pace if the bark is rough enough: an astonishing sight.

The Potto's only known African relative is the Angwantibo (*Arctocebus*), a rare little animal with

to collect zoological specimens we stumbled into an area where these animals were apparently quite common. Several were brought to us alive by natives, and we kept them around our camp and recorded a number of interesting facts about their behavior. However, try as we might and using every trick and device known to us, we could not find

DISTRIBUTION OF THE LORISOIDS

The Lorisoids are divided into two groups, geographically. On the one hand, in Africa, are the Pottos and Galagos of the high forests and the Galagos or Bushbabies of the open tree-dotted orchard bush, extending from Senegal to Kenya and south to the Limpopo River. On the other, in Asia, are the Slender Lorises of southern India and Ceylon, and the Slow Lorises of the Assam, Indo-Chinese, Malaya area and Indonesia west of Wallace's Line.

a rather bright but somehow sad, foxy face, no tail, a bright rust-red woolly coat, small, naked ears, and very small hands and feet bearing tiny, almost vestigial fingers. It is found in the Cameroons area—one form between the Cross River in the west and the Ogowe in the south, and the other from there to the Ubangi in the east. It is a closed-forest animal though it now lives also in secondary growth in some areas and often at no great height above the ground to boot.

Although discovered in 1860 and described scientifically a few years later by none other than the famous Professor Huxley, very little was known about this animal and very few specimens came to hand until quite recently. This is a matter of particular chagrin to the writer because of discoveries made in the northern Cameroons in 1932. While on an expedition with two companions to that country

out exactly where they came from, though we both begged and paid the local people to show us. We even put our own servants and helpers, who came from other districts, to work spying on the local people. We finally came to the conclusion that the local hunters were being perfectly honest when they said that they themselves did not know, other than that they sometimes spotted the animals in trees in various kinds of forest; but they could not say in exactly which kind of environment they normally lived. This is odder than it may sound since every animal favors one or more special niches in its own country, and the Africans are consummate naturalists. They usually can lead you unerringly to almost any animal that exists in their country— that is, unless it is considered religiously, mystically, or jujuistically taboo, or unless they think you are going to clamp a tax upon it. In this case, we were already exonerated by the locals of any fiscal intent, and I never learned of any jujuical connotation in connection with the little Angwantibo.

It appeared to be a strictly nocturnal animal and spent more of its time hanging upside down from branches like a sloth than it did upright or horizontally with face down. Secondly, it appeared to sleep hanging upside down with the hind feet placed in front of the hands, and at such a time, although easily awakened, its limbs could be touched, pinched, or even pricked with a pin without disturbing it. The limbs also appeared to be colder than the rest of the animal, just as if the blood flow therein had been cut down. The limbs were altogether odd in that the animal could be walking along one way under a branch, then suddenly stop, raise its head, bend it upwards and then backwards over its chest and, next, solemnly start walking back the other way with its front legs. This proceeded until the head passed between its back legs and the whole body had pivoted over, so that the face pointed downwards behind the back legs. Having gotten itself in this extraordinary fix, it then let go with first one and then the other hind leg, which flew around in a circle and again attached to the branch above. Thus, the animal now became suspended face downwards, but with all its four limbs going up behind its back. Finally it rolled over, letting go with first one hand, then the opposite foot, then the other hand, and finally the second foot, and thus ended up facing the branch once more with face upwards. They did this time and time again, and when there were two on the same branch their antics became almost incomprehensible.

Angwantibos are much more active than Pottos, and they are much quicker at getting about. However, they are slower in individual bodily movements and appeared to us to be fairly gentle in disposition. They are exceedingly clean little animals and go through a most elaborate toilette, even for a Lorisoid, after every meal, the entire coat being combed with the lower front teeth, and the ears, face and chest being finished off with saliva applied with the hands. They are very sensitive to sound and go instantly into a defensive retreat by ducking their heads down onto their chests at the slightest noise. They proved to be carnivorous and took all types of soft-bodied insects and worms but only licked hard-shelled insects and snails, and they thrived on raw meat, particularly bird meat.

Their hands are an even further exaggeration of those of the Potto, the index finger having vanished altogether.

The other two Lorises and the remaining Lorisoids are found in the Oriental Region. The first to be scientifically described and the one that gave its name to the whole group—the Slender Loris (*Loris tardigradus*)—is found in the forests of southern India up both the west and east sides of that peninsula, and almost all over the island of Ceylon. The name of Loris both in English and in technical Latin is derived from the Dutch word *loeris,* meaning a clown. Hence the delightful German name for its relative—to us, the Slow Loris—which they call the "Plumplori," or "Fat Clown."

The Slender Loris has many qualities in common with the little tailless Angwantibo, though its limbs are much longer and very thin, its ears larger and more rounded, and its eyes so huge that there is practically no room left for any face on the front end of its head. These are arboreal animals, but they are found in all kinds of forests from tangled mountain growth to swampy coastal woodlands, and they vary greatly in both size and coloration, though they form but one interlocking species-group. Like all Lorisoids, they have a strange habit of holding their hands, whenever not actually in use, tight clenched like a diminutive pugilist, but with the thumb inside the fingers. They look like owls and have an owlish way of swaying back and forth as they stare fixedly at you.

They are small animals, measuring at most ten inches when stretched out and apparently never weighing over a pound. They are completely nocturnal, and although appearing slow and very deliberate in their movements, they can get about the trees fairly rapidly and can even run. Their food is varied and forms a well-balanced diet, with some leaves, flowers, shoots, and green nuts, all manner of insects both soft- and hard-bodied, and any eggs they can find or small animals they can catch. To my lasting surprise, I have seen more than one individual eat the feathers of a bird along with the flesh, like an owl—something I have not personally seen done by any other Lorisoid, or any other Primate, for that matter.

They have absurd-looking hands and feet, with short, sturdy, and very widely opposed thumbs and great toes and reduced index fingers; and for second toes they have tiny stubs bearing the invariable Lorisoid scratching claw. All the other

1. Contrast in Primates

A young Chimpanzee from Africa solemnly inspects one of his distant relatives, a full-grown White-eared Marmoset from South America.

2. Common Tupaia (*Tupaia glis*)
A living example, from the Orient, of one of our most ancient ancestors. These creatures form a link between the primitive mammals known as the Insectivores and the group to which we belong.

3. Pigmy Bushbaby
(*Galagoides demidovii*)
A full-grown male, the tiniest of the long-tailed Lorisoids of equatorial Africa. Studies of the embryos of these animals have contributed important clues to our understanding of the evolution of the Primates and thus of our own kind.

4. Potto (*Periodicticus potto*)

A slow-moving Lorisoid with what the Africans descriptively call "half-a-tail," neatly "manicured" finger and toe nails, and thumbs and great toes that point backwards. It mumbles and growls like a dog if molested but can move about soundlessly.

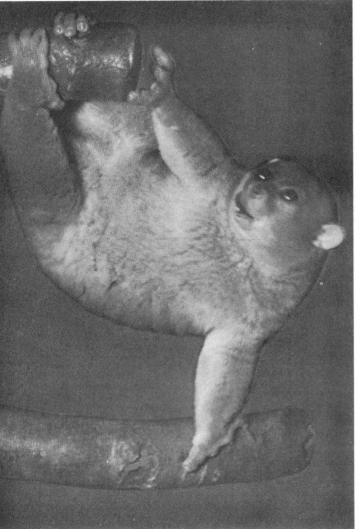

JOHN MARKHAM

JOHN MARKHAM

5. Moholi Bushbaby

(*Galago senegalensis moholi*) This form is found throughout a vast territory in southern Africa, from the Atlantic coast to Lake Nyasa and from the southern Congo to the Orange River. A zoologist once raised a colony of these "Gogos" in New York and studied their "language," which consists of many noises, each used exclusively by males, females, or the young.

6. Slow Loris (*Nycticebus coucang*)

There are several closely related forms of this specie
living in the Oriental Region and on some of the
greater Indonesian Islands. They are tailless Lorisoids of slow, deliberate, and ultracautious habits.
They show marked preferences in their selection of
human friends.

7. Angwantibo (*Arctocebus calabarensis*)

The "Bear-Monkey of the Calabar region" inhabits a
limited area in the notch of western Africa. It is
a virtually tailless relative of the Potto and has a
foxy face. Although known for a century, it has only
recently been captured alive and only once exhibited
—in the London Zoo.

8. Slender Loris (*Loris tardigradus lydekkerianus*)
This form comes from Mysore. These mysterious
little Lorisoids of India and Ceylon are extremely
irascible. They live alone, threaten anything that
approaches them, and even fight their own mates.

9. Lesser Mouse-Lemur (*Microcebus murinus*)
This is one of two kinds and comes from the great island of Madagascar—the exclusive home of the true Lemuroids. The Mouse-Lemurs are as small as and very similar in external appearance to the smaller Bushbabies of Africa.

10. Greater Dwarf Lemur
(Cheirogaleus major crossleyi)
One of three species of small Lemuroids from Madagascar. Natives report that this species always has triplets. When full grown they are enormously fat, but the young are exceedingly scrawny.

11. Ruffed Lemur (*Lemur variegata*)
The largest and most colorful of living Lemuroids, now found only in the heavily forested parts of northeastern Madagascar. It measures up to four feet, of which half is tail. It is nocturnal and builds nests.

12. Ring-tailed Lemur (*Lemur catta*)
The commonest of the true Lemurs. Its home is Madagascar, and this form spends most of its time on the ground in rocky, dry places.

13. Mongoose-Lemur (*Lemur mungoz*)
This small form of Lemur varies in a bewildering way, and some varieties look surprisingly like their near relatives, the Brown Lemurs. It is a diurnal forest animal that makes one of the most docile and charming of all pets.

14. Black Lemur (*Lemur macaco*)
This is an adult female and in color typical of its sex despite its popular name. Males are invariably jet-black, including the ear tufts and the long hairs of the cheeks. All the young of both sexes are, however, uniformly black like their fathers. The eyes of the males are orange; those of the females are, as shown, amber.

15. The Aye-Aye (*Daubentonia madagascariensis*)
One of the greatest mammalian enigmas to early zoologists because it has teeth and claws like a squirrel and a tail like a fox.

digits bear nails. They often hang upside down or rise on the two hind legs alone, and, like the Potto and the Galagos, they often seize their food with both hands. Slender Lorises are solitary and rather touchy creatures that first mumble, then growl, and finally half-heartedly attack any creature, even of their own kind, they may happen to run into. The males do not appear to have any more respect for females even in the mating season; in fact, their whole behavior at that time can only be described as boorish in the extreme. The mothers give birth twice a year, often if not normally to twins, and then carry them for a time about their persons. During this period they are very irritable and must be kept apart from their own kind and left severely alone. They abandon their babies for good if they are once separated from them.

To our way of thinking—and we are perhaps quite mistaken—they are not very pleasant or intelligent beasts. Although they have been tamed, they never seem to display the rather engaging ways or definite personalities of their relative, the larger Plumplori or Slow Loris. Those I have owned always reminded me of Barn Owls with their ugly faces and demeanors, whereas Slow Lorises are more like the gentle Barred Owls with their soulful great eyes and pathetic vocal complaints. The former are, in fact, quite unlike the tragic-appearing, perpetually worried, and solemnly hard-working Slow Loris (*Nycticebus coucang*) of the Indo-Chinese peninsula and the Indonesian Islands.

The Slow Loris is a most remarkable creature and defies almost all the presumed rules of nature, including even those so patiently recorded through two centuries of observation of other Lorisoids. Although slower to get about and more deliberate than any others, its individual bodily movements can be so swift that they can hardly be matched by those of any other mammal. The head can flash out between the hind legs, under an arm, or over the back so quickly that the only indication of its change of position is often the flow of one's own blood and the sudden pain of the bite inflicted. Slow Lorises display individual preferences for humans that are not readily explicable on the ground of accepted logic. One will growl and snap at everybody except one person, who may do anything with him; another can be handled by total strangers, and still another only by women. They

may be enormously susceptible to a certain tone of voice and even when asleep will instantly unroll and come trundling over with measured tread to anybody making exactly the right noises. Also, some of them appear to have a streak of latent showmanship, for they will walk about, rise on their hind legs, pick up objects on command, and generally do all manner of active things provided an audience is present, or if the animal is being photographed, filmed or otherwise made the center of attention. Individuals of all species of animals vary in temperament as much as we humans do, but this is very marked among these extraordinary animals.

Slow Lorises are found in a bewildering variety of sizes and color patterns all over a vast area, from the east and south banks of the Brahmaputra River in the northwest to the Gulf of Tonkin in the east and thence south throughout Burma and Indo-China, Siam, and Malaya to Singapore, and on to the great islands of Borneo, Sumatra (exclusive of the western lowlands), Banka, and Java. In habits they are all very much alike, but they vary somewhat in color, and their faces display a variety of dark markings, from those in the north that have solid, dark rings round the eyes and a dark median-dorsal stripe down the back, to southern forms that have sundry bifurcating frontal head stripes joining the eye rings to the dorsal stripe. In bodily structure, they are heavy and compact, with moderately short limbs; thick, dense fur; pointed faces and large eyes. They have hands with a reduced, opposable thumb and a small index finger, and feet with a small, claw-bearing second toe and a large great toe that points directly away from the others. The ears are small, furry, and buried in the coat. There is often an apology for a tail hidden in the fur of the rump.

Slow Lorises are strictly nocturnal and sleep in holes in trees or other dark and secluded places. At night they are decidedly active and industrious, trundling about the branches both right side up and upside down in search of insects and other small animal food. They also take green nuts and honey, and chew on various special fruits. To obtain their food they may let go with both hands and either hang downwards, stand upright, or project their bodies straight out horizontally, supported only by their powerful legs. Once they have a grip on anything it is extremely hard for that thing, if alive, to get away, and it is almost impossible for less than two grown people to pry the animal loose. As soon as you get one foot unhooked and start on the next, the first one flies back and takes hold again. Slow Lorises are most persistent and can lift enormous weights relative to their own size. A favorite of ours once lifted an electric typewriter off a desk and held it aloft for ten minutes.

These, then, are the living Lorisoids, a strange offshoot of the Primate tree of life but one which, although it has not produced a "man," has given rise to creatures that display some remarkable propensities. The main reason they did not give rise to higher types is probably their concentrated specialization for life in forest treetops. Let us, then, turn to another offshoot that fared somewhat better but which, although diversifying into all manner of forms and producing veritable giants, likewise failed to give rise to anything of a more advanced nature, though for quite other reasons, as will be seen.

Indri

4

The Retreat of the Lemurs

THE TRUE LEMURS OF MADAGASCAR

Going back once more to about the year sixty million B.C., we pick up the tale of another group of our more distant cousins. These are commonly known as the Lemurs, but, because this term is often used to cover also the Lorisoids and the Tarsiers, we will call them the Lemuroids. Incidentally, the name "lemur" was first applied to these animals about the middle of the seventeenth century, but by whom we do not know. It is taken straight from the Roman name for the spirits of the dead, *lemures*, which at certain times were believed to appear at the back of household hearths and stare out at the living through the flames. There is a belief that it was a Frenchman who first applied this name to these animals and that he did so to one of the larger kinds like the Ringtail, the eyes of which sparkle but still manage to look somehow dead and which can, after prolonged mutual staring, give one an unpleasant feeling.

The Lemuroids today form a very varied but compact group of monkey-like or Primate mammals that are entirely confined to the great island of Madagascar and the small nearby Comoro Islands, both of which lie in the southwest Indian Ocean. Sixty million years ago, however, the an-cestors of these animals, together with a vast host of related creatures, were apparently spread all over the world. Whole families (speaking in the classificatory sense) have been unearthed in Europe and in North America. All of them, however, seem to have died out after about twenty millions of years, and from then until the almost immediate present there is a great gulf in our knowledge of their family tree. During this time, the more advanced and more typical "monkeys" were evolved and spread all over the earth, driving out the bird-brained lemurs until the only retreat left to them was the island of Madagascar. And just before the aggressive monkeys got there, too, that island became separated from Africa by a deep channel, and the Lemuroids were saved.

Once safely insulated there, the original immigrants evolved in all manner of ways into an incredible variety of different-looking creatures, the reason for which was probably that they had practically no natural enemies to contend with. They appear to have had a sort of built-in evolutionary energy, and the island of Madagascar happened to lie between exactly the right latitudes and to have a most varied climate, topography and veg-

35

etation—all highly suitable for the development of large numbers of variations among animals, and thus for rapid evolution and specialization. And some of the types the original Lemuroids produced in the course of time are altogether stunning.

Madagascar contains many vast marshes that were once even more extensive than they are today. All kinds of animals were evolved for life in these marshes in the far past, and the bodies of many, on dying, sank into the mud and were preserved. Among these was a gigantic species of lemur with a head and body of about the size of a donkey. Since this creature is presumed to have had a long, fluffy tail somewhat longer than its head and body, it must have been a nightmarish beast. At the same time, other lemuroids appeared that were only about the size of house mice, and some of these still exist. Most interesting of all, however, are other types, designed for life in forests, that came in time to look, in almost every way, like the true monkeys. Of these, also, some remain today—notably the Sifakas. A very conservative professional zoologist who had been on a fossil-hunting expedition to Madagascar once told me that he believed some giant lemurs might still exist in the impenetrable forests clothing certain isolated mountains that happen to be regarded as taboo by the natives and have therefore never been explored. His reason for making this unexpected suggestion was the volume of pure noise behind certain calls that he had heard emanating night after night from those mountains. The noise, he claimed, was much greater than that made by the biggest known lemurs—and the racket these can make is hardly believable, coming from such small animals.

Although there are only twenty-one distinct species of Lemuroids living today on Madagascar and the Comoro Islands, they are so varied in size, structure, and habits that they have to be broken down into four major groups, three of which contain three very distinct subgroups, and the fourth only a single astonishing beast known as the Aye-aye. At the same time, almost all these animals still seem to be in what may be called an evolutionarily virile state; meaning that almost all the species appear in a wide variety of distinct color and color-pattern forms, all of which are so different we are hard put to it to decide just when any one constitutes a mere variation, a true and constant variety, or a really separate species. Finally,

THE RETREAT OF THE LEMURS

All the True Lemurs are today confined to the great island of Madagascar. This island was once divided among three major vegetational zones—tall forest down the eastern half; mixed deciduous forest down the western; and a dry scrub zone across the southern tip. Today most of the first and nearly all of the second have been cleared for agriculture, and the great marshes of the eastern gulf heads have also dwindled.

some of them will interbreed. For those who are interested we herewith offer a simple list of all the living lemuroids.

	SP.	SUBSP.
A. LESSER LEMURS		
(1) Mouse-Lemurs (*Microcebus*)	2	3
(2) Dwarf Lemurs (*Cheirogaleus*)	3	7
(3) The Tanta (*Phaner*)	1	1
B. GREATER LEMURS		
(1) Gentle Lemurs (*Hapalemur*)	2	3
(2) Sportive Lemurs (*Lepilemur*)	2	2
(3) Typical Lemurs (*Lemur*)	6	15
C. MONKEY-LEMURS		
(1) Sifakas (*Propithecus*)	2	10
(2) The Avahi (*Avahi*)	1	1
(3) The Indri (*Indri*)	1	1
D. RODENT-LEMURS		
(1) The Aye-aye (*Daubentonia*)	1	1

Listed thus, this mass of various, varying, and variegated beasts, which few of us will ever see except in films and pictures, will perhaps become a little less confusing. The real problem is to put the proper name on any particular animal.

Since earliest times, when a Malayan people occupied the island of Madagascar, a most persistent onslaught has been maintained against the natural vegetation of that country for both farming and other purposes. This has now reached devastating proportions and is being greatly augmented by the establishment of plantations for the bulk production and export of sundry crops such as coffee and rice. The result is that the original forests are dwindling rapidly, and with them the unique fauna of the island. The French administration has wisely clamped the most rigid restrictions on the killing or taking of any of the indigenous wild animals by any foreigner—even, in some cases, for approved scientific objectives— but they have failed to control the taking of these same animals by the natives for food or other purposes. Worse still, nothing at all is being done to conserve the forests and other natural wild areas in which these animals have lived for millenia and upon which they wholly depend for their very existence. Unless something decisive is done, and quickly, the original vegetational cover of Madagascar is going to be eliminated forever, and with it almost all the Lemuroids.

Following the list given above, we will start with the tiny creatures known as Mouse-Lemurs, which, in some respects, display a number of characteristics that point towards a common ancestry long ago with the Lorisoids. This statement should not, however, be interpreted as indication of any true relationship with, for instance, the Galagos of today. Rather, it means that both they and the Galagos have retained certain physical features common to their joint ancestry.

There are two species of Mouse-Lemurs. The smaller is called *Microcebus murinus* or the "Mouse-sized Tiny Monkey," measures only about five inches from nose-tip to tail-base when fully extended, and has a six-inch tail. There are two noticeably different races, one found on the western lowlands, from Majunga on the northwest coast to the southern tip of the island and then east to Fort Dauphin, and the other, up the whole east coast to Cape D'Ambre and thence south along the northwest coast to Majunga (see map). They look like very small Bushbabies, but their hind limbs are not so exaggerated, nor are their eyes so large. They are clothed in thick, exceedingly soft fur, the hairs of which are black at the base and reddish brown at the tips on the upper and outer sides but white-tipped on the undersides. The hands and feet and a band up the nose are light in color, and there is usually a dark median-dorsal line. They eat insects almost exclusively and live in several types of forest, in open scrub, and even in the great marshes, but they prefer to sleep in holes in trees. The only other species, known as Coquerel's Mouse-Lemur, is much larger and is recorded only from limited areas in the northwest and southwest of the island.

Closely related to the Mouse-Lemurs are the Dwarf Lemurs (*Cheirogaleus*), of which there are also three clearly defined species-groups. These are, respectively, the Greater Dwarf Lemur (*C. major*) of the western seaboard, from Ampasindava Bay (see map) to Fort Dauphin in the southeast; the Fat-tailed Dwarf Lemur (*C. medius*), which is known from isolated areas on the central west coast and about Fort Dauphin; and the Hairy-eared (*C. trichotis*) which is known only from a few specimens collected at widely separated localities, and represents a quite distinct eastern mountain-forest form. All are small, squirrel-shaped and squirrel-sized animals but with fairly large, rounded, naked ears, bushy tails, galago-like hands and feet, and huge eyes placed very close together. The undersides of their hands and feet are surprisingly like those of the little Bushbaby known as *Galagoides,* with pronounced terminal pads on all the digits and large pads on the palms and soles. Apart from the typical lemurine scratching claw on the second toe, all the nails are sharply pointed and very clawlike. In fact, their whole structure is very like that of squirrels, and they lead much the same lives, though they are entirely nocturnal. They sleep in holes in trees and inhabit all kinds of vegetation, from isolated trees on open savannahs to closed forest. Practically nothing is known of the habits of the Dwarf Lemurs, but one curious feature of all of them has been noted, namely that they apparently store large quantities of semiliquid fat in the base of their tails, which may measure as much as an inch and a half in diameter in large specimens at certain times of the year.

The last of the known Lesser Lemurs is called, in one Malagash dialect at least, the Tanta, but has been called the Fork-marked Lemur by foreigners, and is scientifically designated *Phaner furcifer,* a very fancy name that means the "Visible One Bearing a Fork." In some respects it seems to stand between the Mouse- and the Dwarf Lemurs on the one hand, and between both of them and the Greater Lemurs on the other; but it is a very distinct, nocturnal, and purely closed-forest, arboreal animal. It is rather a large, brownish gray lemur, measuring over all about three feet when stretched out, and having large, erect, naked ears. It is known only from the northern fifth of the island. Its curious popular name is derived from its color pattern, which invariably consists of a broad, dark, spinal line that bifurcates on the crown of the head and sends two black tines downwards to join the dark "spectacles" that ring the large, staring eyes. Most startling, however, are the teeth of these animals, for they have two pairs of upper tusks, the foremost being the usual canines or eyeteeth, the second a pair of seizing teeth or premolars that have developed into sizable rapiers.

The first of the Greater Lemurs are, although anatomically quite distinct from the Tanta, only one cubicle removed from that animal and are called the Gentle Lemurs. Slightly larger in size, with furred, round, and close-pressed rather than elongated and erect ears, and with much shorter, more monkey-like faces, they are, nonetheless, in some forms astonishingly like the larger Dwarf Lemurs. Their eyes, in proportion to the whole face, are, however, never so enormous. They also have only two pairs of mammae, one of which is situated on their shoulders; the males have strange, naked, oblong patches covered with spines on the insides of their arms above the wrists. There are two well-defined species known as the Snub-nosed Lemur (*Hapalemur simus*) and the Gray Lemur (*H. griseus*), the former distributed down the northern two-thirds of the eastern coastal area, and the latter throughout the rest of the island except for the northern tip.

Very little is really known about these animals, though they were first described almost two centuries ago. They are both primarily nocturnal, though they have been observed moving about in bright sunlight. They are slow-moving, easily tamed, and truly gentle in disposition. They have lower front teeth that point straight forwards and their cheek teeth are like those of sharks; the purpose of these is, first, to strip the hard outer layers from bamboos, reeds and other canes, and then to crush or cut up the rough fibrous interiors. They wield the lower front teeth like chisels and then do the cutting with the cheek teeth, using them as we would a pair of scissors. The Snub-nosed species inhabits various types of forest and also the open marshes, where it crops the giant reeds and eats their pith. If their natural foods are not available, they will crop grass like rabbits. They have thick, hairy coats, gray or brown above but with lighter undersides, cheeks, jowls and ears.

The animals to which the name of *Lepilemur* has been given have somehow acquired alternate English names each as silly as the other, to wit, the Weasel-Lemurs and the Sportive Lemurs. They have no resemblance whatsoever to weasels except possibly in the first over-all impression of their skulls, which have pronounced upper tusks and evenly interlocking, sharp cheek teeth. They are fairly "sportive" in that they are active, arboreal leaf-eaters; but it would have been better if their scientific name had been directly translated, for it is derived from the Latin *lepidus,* which means "pretty, neat, or graceful." They are bunch-bodied, long-legged leapers with rounded heads, sharply pointed but short muzzles, and small eyes. Again, there are two species, which also, like so many Malagash animals, inhabit respectively the eastern mountainous area from Vohemar to Fort

Dauphin (*L. mustelinus*), and the west coast lowlands, from Ampasindava Bay to and around the the southern tip of the island to Fort Dauphin (*L. ruficaudatus*). None is known from the central belt of plateaux nor from the extreme northern tip of the island. They are pronouncedly gregarious, travel about the trees in rather rowdy parties, and are said to be great jumpers. By day, they are believed to sleep in regular nests, but this seems to be unlikely in view of their semitribalized habits. Mothers, however, make nests in hollow trees where they give birth to a single young once a year, in September.

The remaining Greater Lemurs form a genus to which the name *Lemur* has been given, and for the principal reason that one of their number was the first Lemuroid to become known to science. We tend to regard these animals as typical of the whole group, whereas they are really rather extreme forms, having long-muzzled, foxy faces, exaggerated, bushy tails, and several rather special anatomical features. Although they are comparatively large and rather distinguished-looking animals, they usually present quite a problem to the uninitiated, for they seem to combine the qualities of several different kinds of creatures. There are six species; three of these are quite easy to identify. The best-known of all Lemuroids is the Ringtailed or Cat-Lemur (*Lemur catta*), which is still the commonest of all species and was almost certainly the first one to be brought out of Madagascar alive. It seems possible that this striking animal may have been taken to India by the Arabs over five hundred years ago, or, even earlier still, been carried by the Sabaeans back to the Hadhramaut during Roman times, and thus have become known to the later classical writers. It makes a very exotic and engaging pet, and there are early eighteenth-century French prints that show examples in captivity or apparently running free in the gardens of the chateaux of the wealthy.

In Madagascar this species is confined to the southwestern dry area, south of the Morondava River (see map), but excluding the forested mountainous strip running up the east coast, north of Fort Dauphin.

They are extremely clean and neat about their person and can be house-trained. Unlike monkeys, they almost never knock things over, though they are very inquisitive and show thieving tendencies, especially for certain perfumes, powders of all kinds, and anything long and pointed like a pencil, with which they will play for hours. Most edibles have to be put away when they are loose, but they can be taught to help themselves to certain foods, such as pretzels, that are left about for them, and will never upset the bowl. One belonging to the author wears a belt at all times, and permits a chain to be attached to this when he is to be taken out; once outside, he shows the keenest interest in the passing scene and comments upon it in a wide variety of sounds. When resting at home, he makes a small contented noise which sounds to us exactly like "Who?". This animal responds to his name and has adopted a sort of proprietary attitude to all our other half-hundred assorted pets, going to visit each daily and peering long into their cages, sometimes reaching in to wake them up or simply to hold hands with them. The only time we have seen him truly confounded and annoyed about anything was when he tried to investigate the underside of a hedgehog which, of course, immediately snapped itself into a ball and, in doing so, stabbed him in the palm with its sharp spines. Normally, he allows himself to be handled by us and will even come and take food right out of our mouths; but, on more than one occasion, when tired by being held in one position too long, he has rounded on me and given me a very hard and prolonged bite.

The beauty of the Ringtail is not only its soft mauvish-gray and white fur, or its shapely body, but its fluidity of motion. Some of the poses it adopts, with its long tail wrapped around its neck, send artists and particularly sculptors into transports of delight. Its walk is a kind of strut, with the tail held straight up and curving over slightly backwards at the tip. It can leave the ground, apparently without effort, and just sail to a height of about ten feet and then grip and cling to a wall by nothing more than a half-inch picture molding. Our pet will leap from the floor to a perfectly smooth wall, rebound from this clear across the room, and land safely on the top of a picture frame time and time again without knocking the latter down or doing any other damage. Ringtails are terrestrial and rock-dwelling, not arboreal animals, and they are wholly diurnal. Coming from the drier parts of Madagascar, they are often said not to drink, but all those that I have owned have drunk a great deal, lapping like a dog, and most of them seem to have an inordinate love of water in all forms, often learning to turn on faucets by themselves and then sitting for long periods underneath them with the water running on their bellies.

Their fur is thick and woolly; the naked parts of the nose, hands and feet are jet-black. Their eyes are a bright gold. There are two pairs of very prominent glands on their arms: black and naked and situated in the part of their limbs that is clothed in white fur. People invariably notice these and want to know what they are. One pair is on the front of the shoulders; the other on the inside of the forearm above the wrist. The first, which is found only in the males, is a sac filled with evil-smelling fluid that can be squeezed out and is surrounded by an area of short hairs. The second is a naked patch of black skin with a bump at the lower end from which arises a horny spur that may be forked at the tip.

We go into these odd anatomical minutiae in such detail only because, being so noticeable, they provide an opportunity to bring up and dispose of a much larger subject. There is probably no animal that is devoid of skin or other external glands opening out through the epidermis. We, of course, are covered all over with sweat glands. In other mammals, special large and concentrated glands may be situated almost anywhere about the body, as, for instance, the so-called "pods" of the Musk-Deer, the contents of which is used as a fixative for the most expensive perfumes. In some cases we know the purpose of these glands, such as those of the skunk, which are indubitably for defense, but in most cases we have no idea what their purpose may be. Ring-tailed Lemurs have been observed for years, and the only thing they have been seen to do with these wrist glands is to pass the long bushy tail between them, while rubbing it vigorously between the wrists. However, our pet, like all his kind, has an overpowering interest in long, thin, pointed things such as pencils, and these too he will treat with his wrist patches in the same way. We would like to know what things the animal might handle in this manner in the wild, and for what purposes.

Captive ringtails appear to develop a taste for a very wide variety of foods; in fact, ours will, from time to time, take a little of almost anything we eat. But by all accounts—and there are not many—of these animals in the wild, it appears that they are naturally almost entirely vegetarian, sub-sisting on fruits of the prickly-pear cactus, the green "nuts" of various fig trees and wild bananas, and on sundry roots.

The second species of Greater Lemur is a very large and beautiful creature known as the Ruffed Lemur (*L. variegatus*), which has to be seen to be fully comprehended—as the accompanying illustration demonstrates. Individuals may grow to a length of more than four feet. They have long silky fur, normally colored black and white, but occurring in a great variety of patterns. One of the three subspecies happens also to appear not infrequently in the form of a mutation in which the white areas are replaced by various shades of red. Crosses between these and the standard-colored animals sometimes come out with gold and black pelage. They are treetop forest-dwellers, confined to the coastal strips of both the west and east of the northern tip of the island. They are completely nocturnal but have the strange habit of sun-bathing in the morning. They are the only nest-builders of the group.

The third species is the most commonly seen in zoos, where it often breeds and raises its young successfully year after year. The animal is known as the Black Lemur (*L. macaco*), but this name is very misleading since, although the male is pure black all over, the female is always some shade of brown with light undersides and chest, cheeks, and ear plumes. The species may, however, be readily identified by the long ruffs or plumes on the ears and the very bushy tail, the former feature being unique to these animals. They are treetop dwellers, go about in large, rowdy parties, and are said to be incredibly agile and to move through the trees faster than a man can run over the ground below. They also have a remarkable habit of dropping to the ground from tremendous heights when pursued, then "high-tailing" it through the undergrowth to another tree, and galloping up this to its top. For long they confused naturalists by interbreeding with the next species, producing, as a result, offspring that look surprisingly like some varieties of still another species—namely the Mongoose-Lemur.

The three remaining Greater Lemurs present external features that, combined, are enough to drive any field naturalist out of his mind. The first is known, rather noncommittally, as the Brown Lemur (*L. fulvus*), the second as the Mongoose-Lemur (*L. mongoz*), and the third as the Red-bellied Lemur (*L. rubriventer*). All three are various shades of brown all over, but the amount of variation in the colors and the arrangements of lighter and darker areas about the body vary endlessly and in all manner of ways, so that no two animals (of the first species particularly) seem ever to be alike. The Brown Lemur may, however, be distinguished from the Mongoose-Lemur by its having dark-hued and sometimes almost black cheeks, while the latter always has light cheeks. The little Red-bellied species, in turn, may be identified by its small ears, which are furred all over their back and front sides and all around their edges, and are completely hidden in the thick fur of the head. The Brown Lemur comes in seven racial forms, which are individually recognizable only by experts and are distributed all over Madagascar, except for the southwest and a strip along the mid-east coast, and in the central areas of the north. There is even a form on the Comoro Islands. They are alert, omnivorous animals that appear to be abroad both by day and by night.

The Mongoose-Lemur, which makes a very sweet and gentle little pet, comes from the Comoro Islands, the northern tip of the main island, and a limited area in central Madagascar. It is an active, arboreal and diurnal vegetarian that walks about like the Ringtail, with its tail held erect. The smaller Red-bellied species is found all over the island and in all types of country. It is also gregarious, and apparently diurnal.

When we turn from these animals to the remaining Lemuroids, we encounter some truly remarkable creatures. They may be divided between two quite unlike families (in the technical sense of that word): the first, composed of four animals of three distinct kinds or genera; the second, containing only one extraordinary creature called the Aye-aye or, more happily, the Hi-hi.

The first two of these animals are known as Sifakas, or Monkey-Lemurs. They are indeed more monkey-formed than any other lemurs, and not only in body but also in other respects. Their faces are naked, black in color, and flat, as opposed to being long-snouted and foxy like those of other Lemurs. Their movements are comparatively slow and usually deliberate like those of lorises, and when on the ground they walk erect on their hind legs, or hop along with their hands outstretched. They are essentially arboreal animals, but they not infrequently descend to the ground

to feed or to play about in low shrubs. They go about in small family parties and are exclusively eaters of leaf buds and flowers. There are several recognized races of both species distributed more or less all over Madagascar, but both vary in color and color pattern in the most bewildering manner. There are both completely white and almost entirely black forms of one species—the Diademed Sifaka (*Propithecus diadema*)—and white, gray, and various brown varieties of the other, Verreaux's Sifaka (*P. verreauxi*). It would be very difficult to describe the color variants of each, but the former always has a light fringe across the front of the head. The fur of Sifakas is full and silky.

Unfortunately, these lovely animals do not live in captivity, or rather they have not done so till now, presumably because of their very specialized diet. However, the same used to be true of the Howler Monkeys of South America, the leaf-eating Guerezas of Africa, and the Langurs of Asia. As new methods of feeding are devised it may in time be possible to keep all of these animals alive, and the Sifakas—especially the pure white forms—would make a stunning exhibit in any zoo. The mothers at first carry their babies in their arms but later make the youngsters ride piggy-back.

The Avahi or Woolly Lemur (*Avahi laniger*) has much the proportions of the Sifakas but has somewhat longer hind limbs and huge feet. Its ears are small and furry and are completely hidden in thick fur—which, combined with the very flattened face, makes the whole head almost spherical. The face is clothed in very short hairs, except for the nose tip, which is naked, and the eyes are large, wide-set and staring, so that the animal's countenance resembles that of certain owls. Avahis have the oddest hands and feet, with very short digits of unequal length, huge thumbs and great toes that stick out of the side of the "wrist" and "heel." Avahis were once found all the way down the eastern side of Madagascar from Vohemar in the north to Fort Dauphin in the south and also, in a slightly different form, along a strip on the northeast coast. They are solitary creatures, completely nocturnal and primarily arboreal, performing prodigious leaps and preferring to make use of upright branches on which to land. They sometimes descend to the ground, where they waddle along on their hind legs with their hands and tails held on high. In the trees they keep their tails coiled up like springs except when leaping. They are leaf-eaters.

The remaining members of this, the third family of Lemuroids, are known simply as the Indri (*Indri indri*). They are found only in a limited region of volcanic mountains along the middle section of the eastern coast, but they are said still to be fairly common in parts thereof. They are altogether preposterous-looking beasts, measuring two feet in length with a mere two-inch tail, and having limbs proportioned almost as in ourselves. The name *Indri*, incidentally, is a pure mistake, for it stems from an expression, "*Indrizy*" or "*Indri-izy*," which appears to mean something like "Look at that" or "There he is." The Malagash call the animal the *Babakoto* or the *Amboanala,* the latter meaning Bush Dog or Dog of the Forest.

The face is more prognathous than that of the Avahi or the Sifakas and is, in some respects, doglike. The ears are rather large, rounded, and furred on the back and around their edges, and are carried on the sides of their heads. The eyes have a rather soulful and doglike expression, probably because of the long eyelashes. The face is naked and black and is surrounded by a fringe of fur that hides the ears. The animal is clothed in rather long, dense fur with a variable but always startling arrangement of black and white. Normally, the crown of the head is white and the ears are black, and this coloration continues onto the back and shoulders and thence almost to the elbows; the limbs and underside are white but the hands, the feet, and sort of "chaps" on the front upper legs are black. Most remarkable of all are the comparatively enormous hands and still larger feet; these have such huge and widely opposed thumbs and great toes that they look like pairs of calipers and appear to be thrust into black gloves and socks respectively.

Indris wander about the trees of the forest in small family groups and make the most terrific uproar, calling in unison with a trumpet-like wailing as of human beings or dogs in anguish. They are leaf-eaters but are said to eat also the brains of any birds they can catch, like many and perhaps all other Lemurs. They used to be held in considerable awe by the human inhabitants of the country where they are found; and, probably because of their somewhat human shape and behavior, a high degree of reasoning power was attributed to them. They were even credited with the ability to catch a thrown spear and to direct it back at their attacker. I have heard the same story about baboons in West Africa and about the Howler Monkeys in South America, but throwing, as opposed to mere lobbing, is a purely human invention and has not yet been recorded as a proclivity of any animal.

The last of the Lemuroids is the Aye-aye (*Daubentonia madagascarensis*) an animal that has caused more zoological puzzlement than almost any other mammal known. It was originally discovered by a French explorer in 1780 and was described as a kind of squirrel. This was later also affirmed by some of the most eminent anatomists, even after examination of its skull. The mistake was, in many respects, justifiable, since the arrangement and form of the teeth are astonishingly like those of a squirrel, with a few small cheek teeth having flattened crowns for chewing, a toothless gap along both sides of both jaws, and finally two huge, chisel-shaped teeth in the front of both jaws. Then about 1800, one scientist tentatively suggested that the animal was a Lemuroid, but it was sixty years before any more specimens came to hand and the animal could be properly examined. Even then it continued to worry the specialists, for it had no known relatives, either living or fossil, but showed a strange blending of characters between the Lemurs and certain primitive Primate forms from the dawn of time. It also had features that seemed to blend with those of the Tarsiers. It was obviously a left-over from some side branch of early primate stock that ultimately gave rise to all the Lemuroids.

Its appearance is displayed in the photograph elsewhere in these pages and need not be elaborated upon except to say that the long coat is hairy and coarse and always rather scraggly. Apart from its internal anatomy, the oddity of the beast is concentrated in its hands and feet. Taking the latter first, the great toe is very large and widely opposed, and bears a round, flat nail. The toes are finger-shaped, have swollen terminal pads, and carry claws. The hand, seen from the underside, is basically very human in outline, but the middle two fingers—the third and fourth—are almost double the length of the outer two, and the third is less than half the thickness of the others: all bear claws, including the thumb which, although opposed, is not much used for grasping things. The purposes of the extraordinary hands, and particularly of the long, thin third finger, are at least twofold. First, the latter is used to curry the fur, to clean out the intricacies of the animal's ears, and to pick its teeth. Secondly, it is used for two purposes in feeding.

Aye-ayes are nocturnal and live in trees, notably

in the giant bamboo brakes. They use their curious front teeth to pare the hard outer casings off the bamboos in order to get at the internal pith. Aye-ayes occasionally take other vegetable matter of like nature, but their principal food is insects and especially the larvae or grubs of certain kinds of beetles that bore into wood. To obtain these, Aye-ayes creep along branches with their large and very sensitive ears held close to the bark surfaces, and are thus able to detect any small noises made by the chewing and munching of grubs within. They also tap the wood with their long, thin third finger in order to trace the passageways made by the insects within the wood. When an opening to one of these passages is located, the Aye-aye either thrusts in its third finger, hooks the grub with the long claw, and draws it out, or sets to work with the front teeth to break open the tunnel until it can reach the prize.

Mothers make large spherical nests lined with dry material and give birth to a single young. Aye-ayes are fearless little creatures and will strike at intruders and bite viciously if grabbed, meanwhile uttering a most aggravating noise rather like that produced by scraping ice from a car windshield with a metal tool. Aye-ayes are now found only in two widely separated forest tracts, one about Na-rinda Bay on the northwest coast, the other along the east coast from Antongil Bay south to the Man-goro River (see map). Despite the continued super-stitious respect shown the animal by the natives, they are, like all Lemuroids, fast becoming scarce. Another species, double the size of the living one, has been found in the form of fossilized bones in the southwest of Madagascar.

5

The First of Our Kind

Tarsier

THE TUPAIAS, as we said above, are very bright little animals and show remarkable intelligence. Likewise, each of the Lorisoids, in its own way, displays certain most discerning traits. Then again, the Lemuroids often approach the true monkeys in behavior and sometimes seem even to parody our own activities. When, however, we turn to the tiny mammals now found in the East Indies and the Philippines and known as the Tarsiers, we at once meet some genuine philosophical problems. Tarsiers, like the Tupaias, are exceptionally bright, but they are also something more than that. Coming to them, in fact, we appear to have finally left the world of mere beasts and to have entered our own hegemony.

The Tarsiers are little rat-sized sprites with soft woolly fur, long tails in some cases with a slight terminal tuft, huge eyes, and large hands and feet with long slim fingers and toes terminating in huge clinging pads like those of tree frogs. In habits also they are surprisingly like tree frogs, leaping about dense foliage, mostly at night, and catching insects. There are a dozen recognized kinds of Tarsiers that may be grouped into three distinct species—the Philippine form (*Tarsius syrichta*), the Borneo-Sumatran (*T. bancanus*), and the Celebesean (*T. spectrum*). Their distribution is clearly defined, the first being found only on the islands of Samar, Leyte, Bohol, and Mindanao of the Philippines; the second around the southern end of Sumatra, on the islands of Banka and Billiton, all around Borneo, and on the Natuna Islands in the South China Sea; and the Celebesean species (in five distinct forms) on Salayer Island, in a small area in the center of the main island of Celebes, on its northeastern peninsula, and on Peleng Island off its east coast. Tarsiers have been alleged to have come also from Java and the island of Savu, away to the south between Sumba and Timor, but both these reports are doubtful, and no actual specimens of Tarsiers have ever been found on either of those islands. These animals may be listed as follows:

A. **TARSIERS** (*Tarsius*)
    (1) *Philippines Tarsiers* (*T. syrichta*)
        (a) Samar and Leyte (*T. s. syrichta*)
        (b) Bohol (*T. s. fraterculus*)
        (c) Mindanao (*T. s. carbonarius*)
    (2) *Malaysian Tarsiers* (*T. bacanus*)
        (a) Sumatra and Banka (*T. b. bacanus*)
        (b) Billiton (*T. b. saltator*)
        (c) Bornean (*T. b. borneanus*)
        (d) Sirhassen (*T. b. natunensis*)

(3) *Celebesean Tarsiers* (*T. spectrum*)
   (a) Sangir (*T. s. sangirensis*)
   (b) Spectral (*T. s. spectrum*)
   (c) Central (*T. s. dentatus*)
   (d) Dwarf (*T. s. pumilus*)
   (e) Banggai (*T. s. pelengensis*)

The first time the existence of these little living fossils was made known to our world was sometime in the late seventeenth century; the discoverer was a Jesuit priest named Camelli who, very sensibly and in some respects correctly, called them "the smallest long-tailed monkey of Luzon," though no tarsier has since been found on the island of that name. A description and a hilarious drawing of one was published in 1702 by an English naturalist named Petiver, who stated that its native name was the *Magu*, which is still used for this animal on the island of Samar. The animal remained scientifically unknown for many years but was mentioned by Linnaeus in his famous *Systema Naturae* as a kind of "monkey." Then, the French zoologist Buffon got hold of a preserved specimen, which he described in some detail, but which puzzled him as to whether it was a kind of rodent, related to the jumping Jerboas, or a strange form of Opossum. It was not till 1777 that it was recognized as a kind of Primate. It was then classed as a "lemur," and it has remained so ever since, at least from the popular point of view. However, although it is indubitably a cousin of the monkeys and of ourselves, it is not by any means a lemur. Nevertheless, it is also neither a Tupaioid nor a Lorisoid, and it is certainly not a Hapaloid, a Pithecoid, or any kind of monkey. In fact, the Tarsiers stand all alone on the tree of life but at a most critical juncture. Originally, moreover, they seem to have been developed in, of all places, North America.

The three species of tarsiers living today are all of one genus. They represent the last remaining twig of a previously sturdy branch of primate stock that sprouted off the main trunk at least as long ago as sixty million years, in what we call the Palaeocene Period. Further, the earliest known—from some bones and teeth found in Montana, U.S.A.— were quite typically Tarsiers, and these must themselves have had quite a venerable ancestry, possibly extending back into the last stages of the Cretaceous Period, when the dinosaurs still thundered about the earth.

Quite a large number of different kinds of tarsiers are now known to have lived in North America—

two dozen genera, to be precise—but the last of them seems to have died out or moved away about thirty-five million years ago. Ten other genera are known from Europe, whence they vanished somewhat earlier. Two kinds are known from China, but they are of rather doubtful affinities. None is known from Africa or South America or, of course, from Australia, and none of the fossil genera is known from anywhere later than some thirty million years ago. Yet tarsiers must have been around throughout this vast intervening stretch of time, for they are still around today.

The importance of the tarsiers results from the shape of their noses. This may seem like a very unimportant matter, but, for a large number of reasons which will not be elaborated here, it warrants their being separated from the Lemuroids, Lorisoids, Tupaioids and all lower mammals and being classed with the Hapaloids, Pithecoids, Ceboids, and the true monkeys, apes, and ourselves. The latter are called collectively the *Haplorhini*, which means "ones with simple nostrils"; the former, the *Strepsirhini*, or "ones with twisted nostrils." To be more precise, the former have hair right to the borders of their circular nasal openings and to some extent inside them—as in ourselves—and to the edge of their lips, whereas the latter have naked muzzles and sort of curlicued nasal openings. Actually, the Tarsiers display more anatomical features in common with the lemurs than with the higher primates, but then, on the other hand, if they were regarded as lemurs, they would be exceptional in almost all respects. Thus they really stand all by themselves, and, in view of their simple nostrils, they are better classed with us.

In habits they are extremely odd. They sleep clinging to upright creepers or branches during the day, using not only their exaggerated fingers and toes and four "thumbs" but the naked undersides of their tails, which act as adpression brakes to keep them from slipping. They wake up in the early evening, clean themselves fastidiously, and then leap off after food, which consists mostly of insects but also includes tree snails, tree frogs, and other small animals. They stalk their prey, then pounce on it, and hold it in both hands while they tear it apart and munch it up rather slowly. Most comical is their expression while doing so because their enormous eyes are invariably squeezed tight shut during each bite (as with marmosets), probably to avoid having them stuck by the hard, thrashing limbs of the larger insects. Tame ones will, however, eat an astonishing variety of foods, including a wider range of unnatural comestibles than almost any other animal apart from the common North American Opossum, which will eat anything even vaguely digestible. Like all animals, they show individual preferences. Some are very finicky, scorning certain insects and relishing, for instance, Limburger cheese, while others will eat insects greedily and scream at you if even a mild Camembert is offered. The only thing they won't eat, contrary to an age-old belief apparently held by almost everybody in the Philippines, is charcoal; and this despite the fact that one kind is even called *Tarsius syrichta carbonarius,* or the "Carbon-eater." How this curious belief originated is not known.

A really odd thing about Tarsiers is that, contrary to all that was written in earlier days and also that which one might logically expect, they are not treetop dwellers nor, apparently, denizens of the upper canopy of the tall primaeval forests. Rather, they appear to stay in the lower and middle strata of trees and foliage and are commoner in the dense secondary and tertiary growth of cleared lands. Also, they seem to prefer the lowlands, especially near coasts, so that, while they are found all round the great island of Borneo, they are not known to come from its interior; and this is not entirely due to lack of exploration and proper collecting inland.

They have an odd, squirrel-like or froglike habit of dodging round a limb so as always to be on the opposite side from a potential enemy; at the same time they never take their lustrous eyes off your face, and keep wrinkling and moving their large ears about just like Bushbabies to catch every sound from you or elsewhere that may indicate danger. To add a final touch to their protective mechanism they can turn their heads almost right around on their necks, like some owls, and can therefore look straight backwards. It is just these habits that perhaps originally gave them a headstart in the competition for survival and that may even have ultimately resulted in our own appearance and final dominance.

Our cousins, the monkeys and their ilk, called collectively the Primates or Top Mammals, are said to be more "successful" than all other animals. The word "successful" actually has no more precise meaning than the word "intelligence," but it does signify two facts; first, that there are a large number of different kinds of Primates spread over a huge area of the world today, and secondly, that most of these have proved very adept at survival and are today represented by very large populations of individuals. Success means, first, enhanced power to survive, and secondly (from our point of view), an ability to evolve into a Man. In both, the Primates have obviously succeeded, and when we come to enquire scientifically just why and how they have done so we find ourselves led to some most interesting considerations. Among these the habits of the Tarsiers become highly significant.

These little animals do certain things that, although sometimes also performed by Lemuroids and Lorisoids and even by other such mammals as rodents and opossums, constitute, when taken together, most significant behavior. The reason that mammals (other than the Tarsiers, Marmosets, Monkeys, Apes, and Men) have elongated naked noses beset with whiskers, as described above, is that they customarily use them for searching out their food and then for testing it before picking it up with their mouths. Even a rat or a Tupaia will normally first pick up food with its mouth and then take it with its hands, sit up and chew it. On the other hand Tarsiers, like monkeys, apes, and ourselves, use their eyes rather than their nostrils to identify and locate edibles, grab the food first with their hands, and then bring it up to their mouths. This is extremely important and for several reasons. First, any animal doing this is in less danger from enemies while it is locating and catching food, since all its senses and especially its eyes may, during the process, be used to keep watch. Second, while eating, the same added alertness and availability of all the sense organs are ready to detect danger. Thirdly, the use of the eyes to locate and identify food implies tridimensional vision, or vision in depth, something that is rare among lower animals. For instance, many animals seem to be unable to locate or identify either food or enemies as long as the latter stand perfectly still; they can, in fact, identify only "movement." Fourthly, bringing food up to the face rather than grabbing for it with the mouth affords a better chance of examining it before getting stung, bitten, poisoned or otherwise injured. The results of this simple practice, therefore, all tend to enhance the animal's chance of survival. By extension, they also lead automatically to several other beneficial changes.

By using the hands to hold food, the animal is obliged to sit up on its hind legs and tail, if available. This requires that the head be on top of the body at such times, and this automatically necessitates changes in several physiological processes, such as pumping the blood vertically instead of horizontally. This, in turn, happens to coincide with a demand for an increased supply of blood to the head, which then automatically enhances the chance of enlargement of those areas of the brain that cope with the interpretation of visual impressions. At the same time also, a greater alertness of the muscles and their nerves generally is required to enable the animal to catch and pick up food with its hands. Altogether better coordination is needed by any animal doing this, and the Tarsier long ago adopted all these habits, and so called forth in its body all those responses mentioned above.

Now, insects may be searched for in nooks and crannies or on or under leaves, but they may also be caught on the wing as they fly about among foliage from branch to branch. The Tarsiers, like the Bats, appear to have made a deliberate attempt to do something about the catching of insects on the wing; and this called for special agility as well as very accurate timing, good eyesight, precise judgment of distance, long-range identification of objects, and quite possibly a need for color vision —something obviously quite helpful to an animal that does its hunting by sight but of small use to those that hunt for food only by smell, hearing or touch. These necessities demanded a bigger and more complex brain; and once you have a large brain, you apparently have a mechanism with which to think. In fact, "using your brain" is not only an expression but an automatic result of having one, and the Tarsiers were one of the first animals, if not the very first, to get such a device in any worth-while form. And they certainly put it to use. Indeed, it is believed that some of their descendants specialized in the process, and that these became the ancestors of the monkeys, apes and thus of ourselves.

In character, Tarsiers are outstanding individualists. They are gentle creatures but, although apparently aware of their minuscule proportions, they are by no means either cowardly or rashly bold, like shrews, rodents, and other lower types. They tame easily and they seem to be extraordinarily susceptible to human kindness, but they still rise up, open their mouths, hiss, and make incredibly pugilistic gestures with their tiny clenched fists if they are threatened or deliberately teased or are hungry.

They are, nevertheless, nervous and very sensitive to sudden movements, sounds, and even natural smells. Like almost all mammals, they appear to be highly conservative and are much distraught by any innovations, especially after they have once settled down to life in a limited environment, like a cage or room, the exact arrangement of which they know. It may take them a whole day to get over the shock of finding a piece of furniture moved to a new position.

Among themselves, according to all those who have been privileged to keep and observe them, they appear to be pacific and to tend to pair off rather than to set up a complex social system of etiquette like the Marmosets. Several people have remarked on their habit of stealing food from each other, which results in sparring but never, apparently, in fights such as the Tupaias indulge in at the slightest provocation. Their most notable attribute is their strange way of settling down amongst human beings, who must appear to them, we should not overlook, as monsters equivalent to giants seventy feet in height. They have a most alarming way of turning their little heads and looking you straight in the eye when you call them or, sometimes, when you say something with special emphasis, so that one is often constrained to ask oneself the ridiculous and obviously baseless question as to whether they know what we are saying or feeling.

The hands and feet of the Tarsiers are very odd indeed. The thumb is opposed but is rather long and thin, and like the four fingers terminates in a large, circular clinging pad, and bears a nail. The feet are preposterous, the great toe being widely opposed but very short, carried at the end of a large extension of the foot, and terminating in a monstrous globular pad. The four other toes go off at an angle of about one hundred degrees, are long and thin, bear terminal pads, and have claws on the second and third digits and nails on the fourth and fifth extremities. The "ankle" bones are elongated so that the legs are really four-jointed like those of tree frogs.

Tarsiers are, naturally, very rare in zoos and more especially in private collections and as pets, though they are not excessively rare in their own native haunts. Being tiny, quick, nocturnal creatures and not of any particular interest to the human inhabitants of the countries where they live, they are seldom seen. Moreover, if they are caught, kept alive, and offered for sale to the few foreigners who are interested in them and who may happen to be in those countries where they are found, there are still many reasons why they may not survive in captivity. The natives of the countries where they live do not know what they feed on and have little interest in finding out; thus, we do not really know what their normal diet is, and few have had experience in keeping them in captivity. Nevertheless, they have been kept alive for many months in a few zoos—notably in Philadelphia in the U.S.A., and in London in England. Apparently, these animals need proportionately a rather large cage in which to live, a small nest-box in which to sleep during the day, branches upon which to climb, and a rather long resting and "acclimatization" period before being put on public exhibit. Published accounts imply that they will take, or need, an extraordinary variety of specialized food. A correlation of these statements seems to boil down to a few basic facts. First, they are primarily carnivorous and predominantly insect-eaters, getting along well on a diet of mealy-worms as long as a quota of finely chopped raw meat and other insects, such as cockroaches, grasshoppers and blowflies, is offered. They also take a small amount of green nuts and fibrous fruits, and such unnatural items as milk and cream cheese. They seem to require a lot of water, which they prefer to suck from a clean saturated rag hung from the top of the cage. They sometimes have a passion for salt. Although as susceptible to individual affection as any other animal, they often abhor being handled and go through an elaborate toilet if they are so much as touched.

How they behave in their native environment is not known, and thus their daily routine is still a mystery to us, apart from conjecture. If someone had the inclination, the time and the opportunity to go into the woodlands where they live and observe them over an extended period, such a person could doubtless record a volume on the habits peculiar to these animals.

Tiny and obscure as they are, the Tarsiers hold a unique position in the life of our planet, for they seem to represent living examples of the final turning point between the vast mass of mammalian life that is not truly comprehensible to us and that which is, in however dim a sense, of "our way of thinking." As the Feathertail is the most primitive form of known Primate that is still alive today, the Tarsier is the most basic form of "our kind"—a minuscule hysteric of no practical importance but of enormous scientific interest and value.

6

Hapaloids

The Sprites of the Jungle

THE MARMOSETS AND THEIR KIND

Silver Marmoset

WE COME NOW to a group of most enchanting little monkey-like animals that live in the tropical forests of the New World. Introducing them immediately after the Tarsiers is necessitated by mere expediency and should not in any way be interpreted as implying that they are directly descended from or come next up on the general family tree of Primate life. Just where they did spring from on that tree is not known, and since the few fossil remains of their ancestors that we have tell us little about their origin, we know nothing of it. That they are Primates and related to a considerable host of others of that ilk that also inhabit the New World is clear from their general anatomical make-up, but they are undoubtedly an early off-shoot of that stem. They show some features in common with the other American Primates, but they have many others that are unique; and perhaps most notable among these, to the casual observer at least, are claws, or rather clawlike structures, on all the fingers and toes except on the great toe, which bears a thumblike nail. Of less scientific

value but nonetheless of significance are the general form of their bodies, their stance and methods of movement, their habits, and notably their voices and variety of "vocabulary," their facial expressions, and their over-all behavior—all of which are singular, most distinctive, and unlike those of the other New World Primates.

This grouping of animals may be called the Hapaloids, after the best and probably first known and named type, the Ouistiti or Common Marmoset (*Hapale jacchus*). It is current taxonomic practice to include in this group only the members of the family *Hapalidae* as at present constituted—the Marmosets, the Tamarins, and the Pinchés—and to exclude from that family the members of the two genera called *Callimico* and *Callicebus*. However, the animals contained in these two genera are obviously so closely related to the Marmosets, Tamarins, and Pinchés, and are so unlike the other New World primates, that they must be associated with them and should manifestly be included in the same *family*. These are, first, an animal known as Goeldi's

49

Marmoset (*Callimico*) and second, a host of closely related species known as Titis (*Callicebus*). It should be clearly understood that this association is purely arbitrary and is used here merely for convenience and the sake of simplicity, since no such close association has so far been suggested in proper scientific form with the necessary supporting evidence.

At the present time, speaking from the purely technical point of view, the Marmosets, Tamarins and Pinchés are considered to form a separate and distinct *family* (that of the *Hapalidae*); the *Callimico*, a *subfamily* of the New World "Monkeys" or *Cebidae;* and the Titis, a *genus* of another subfamily of that *family*. Nevertheless, it is our firm opinion that continued investigation will eventually show these forms to be closely related and to form a compact family of the Primate stock. Treated thus, the Hapaloids may be listed as follows:

	SP.	SUBSP.
A. **HAPALINES**		
(1) Marmosets		
(a) Pigmies (*Cebuella*)	1	2
(b) Tufted (*Hapale*)	10	11
(c) Naked-eared (*Mico*)	1	3
(2) Tamarins		
(a) Bald-headed (*Marikina*)	2	2
(b) Black-faced (*Tamarin*)	3	6
(c) Moustached (*Tamarinus*)	12	21
(d) Maned (*Leontocebus*)	3	3
(3) Pinchés		
(a) Pinchés (*Oedipomidas*)	3	3
B. **TITI-TAMARINS**		
(1) Goeldi's Marmoset (*Callimico*)	1	1
C. **TITI-MONKEYS**		
(1) Titis (*Callicebus*)	7	33

The order in which the forms are listed above does not imply that the first is the oldest or most primitive and the last the newest and most highly developed, nor that one arose from another in an orderly procession from first to last. The Titis do seem to be more highly developed and are mostly larger in size than any of the others; Goeldi's *Callimico* or "Beautiful Monkey" is manifestly intermediate between the Titis and the others; but for the rest, one could arrange them in various ways. For reasons that are not easy to define, the Pinchés, isolated in the northwestern forests, seem to form the end of a specialized branch, while the Maned Tamarins of the southeastern Tupi forests

seem to constitute the end product of another. But there are several ways in which we might derive either from the other Tamarins or from the long-legged, leaping *Hapale*. There are also some good and apparently valid arguments for placing the Pinchés in the tamarin group between the Moustached or White-faced and the Maned Tamarins. This would bring the last next to *Callimico*, with which they certainly have several features in common. Further, it is a question where we should draw the line, if any, between the so-called marmosets and the tamarins. *Mico* and *Marikina* more or less bridge this gap, which is really at most only one of degree, and that principally in the size of the eyeteeth. Moreover, old males of some species classed as Marmosets may have these teeth proportionately more developed and tusklike than those of some species designated as Tamarins.

Marmosets have been known to the world at large since the very first voyages of discovery by Europeans to South America. Both the Spaniards and the Portuguese in the sixteenth century found them living as pets among the Amerindians all along the coasts of the tropical areas, and, being fascinated by their rather uncanny appearance and remarkable intelligence as well as by their endless "conversation," took them back to Europe. There they immediately became a rage among the aristocracy, and enormous prices were sometimes paid for healthy specimens by titled men who presented them to their wives and daughters and more especially, for some curious sociological reason, to their mistresses, who carried the tiny mites in their sleeves or other convenient retreats about their raiment. The French especially prized them and gave us our name for them, which in their language is *marmouset*. This old word, meaning originally a small boy or a man of very short stature, later came to denote those grotesque little hunched figures so often carved around the bases of fonts in churches. By the sixteenth century the term had come to mean any grotesque little figure and especially a parody of a human being; and it was just this elfin quality of these animals that brought on their popularity, for in many ways their faces are more expressive than those of any other animals, the apes not excluded. Marmosets are still very popular as pets, though a belief has grown up that they are delicate and hard to keep alive in captivity.

Starting with the minuscule Pigmy Marmosets we encounter a conundrum. These tiny animals, with a head and body only about four inches long when full grown, were originally found in the valley of a tributary of the Amazon known as the Napo, which rises in the Andes in Ecuador less than a hundred miles from the Pacific and then runs through Peruvian territory to a confluence with the Javarí River, at the exact point where Colombia, Perú, and Brazil meet. This meeting of waters actually initiates the Amazon proper. These marmosets have smoothly rounded heads and silky fur that forms a slight mane over the neck and is of a general green tone but has a pepper-and-salt appearance as a result of yellow rings on the individual hairs. They are rather furious little beasts that have a habit of swaying from side to side when you look at them and making threatening expressions by lowering their "eyebrows" and raising the hair on their heads. The males, tiny as they are, will erect the fur all over their bodies and scream at anything, however big it may be.

Since World War II, considerable quantities of them have been coming from the southeast coast ports of Brazil, over two thousand miles away from their only recorded locality of origin. These two locations are as widely separated and as totally disconnected as, say, Morocco and the Congo forests. Moreover, they now appear always to have been available for purchase in Pernambuco. The specimens from the east, however, have white undersides, and the males have little white moustaches divided into two parts on either side of the upper lip. Are we therefore to suppose that these animals are found all across the forest belt of Brazil, or only in two widely separated areas? The southern form is now distinguished as a separate subspecies known as *C. p. niveiventris*. Whatever be the answer, these two kinds of marmosets are very distinct from all others and are most closely related.

Pigmy Marmosets are runners and climbers rather than leapers, but they are so lightning fast that it is sometimes virtually impossible to follow them with the eye even in the unnatural surroundings of a human dwelling. Being of truly pigmy dimensions and having the squirrel- or tarsier-like habit of skipping round to the opposite side of anything to which they are clinging, plus the almost perfect camouflage provided by the color of their fur, they are virtually unobservable in the wild. Moreover, their talk consists of various extremely high-pitched trills and twitterings very like those of birds and in some cases hardly distinguishable from those of certain insects. This vocabulary is enormously varied and proves, from recordings, to range above the normal sensitivity of our hearing into what is called the supersonic. As with most if not all other marmosets and possibly all Hapaloids, twins are the rule. The mother hands them over almost immediately after birth to the father, who carries one on each thigh, and hands them back to her at very regular intervals for nursing; but it is he who finally weans them, teaches them what can only be called table manners, and assigns them their place in the family group or small tribal unit, for these animals are semicommunal in their manner of living.

The Pigmy Marmosets are sufficiently distinct to have been assigned a special name, *Cebuella*. In some respects they stand considerably apart from the other Hapaloids, and they are certainly not closely related to the next genus to be described. This is chosen somewhat arbitrarily and mostly because its members are the next smallest in stature. These are the Typical Marmosets (*Hapale*), a large assemblage that contains the first named Hapaloid, the Oustiti or Common Marmoset (*H. jacchus*). Its members may be divided into two subgroups, the first represented by four species (*penicillata, petronius, flaviceps, aurita*), which are short-legged runners from the southeastern Tupi Forests of Brazil, and the second by half a dozen longer-legged, leaping species that inhabit a vast area from north of the dry Caatinga on the eastern bulge of Brazil, north to the Amazon Basin, and thence far to the west.

A distinguishing feature of the members of this genus is the curious adornment they carry around their ears in the form either of a bunch of very long, drooping hairs that arise in front of the ears, or of corollas of stiff hairs growing all around those organs, like ruffs. In the Black-eared or Black-plumed form (*C. penicillata*) these are prominent; in other forms, such as *C. flaviceps*, they may be shorter but more extensive and spread out to form a fanlike brush in front of the ears; but in *C. aurita* they are reduced in front but are developed all around the ears into a corolla of pure white, plumelike hairs. These marmosets have rather thick and fairly long, soft, almost silky fur that is colored in a most distinctive manner. Basically, it is black—wholly so on the extremities and on the undersides of the body, where the hair is sparse—but the individual hairs on the upper sides and tail are variously banded. These hairs have, centrally, a wide band or ring, usually of yellow or orange; and are tipped with light cream, silver or reddish. When the fur is smoothed back over the dorsum and tail, this banding of the hairs causes a diffuse cross-striping of the body and a slight ringing of the tail. The teeth of these marmosets are of modest proportions, though the canines are developed into little tusks both above and below.

In habits they are somewhat gregarious in that they travel about in gross family parties. If observations of their behavior in the unnatural conditions of captivity are any criterion, they would appear to have a most advanced social organization. Various of these species, notably the Black-plumed and the White-eared, have been kept for long periods and in considerable quantities both in zoos and in the private homes or collections of a number of zoologists, and all their owners have remarked upon this aspect of their behavior. Perhaps the most elaborate and charming descriptions of this are recorded by the late, well-known author, Fletcher Pratt, who kept a family unit of the White-eared for over twenty years in an apartment in New York and reached the eighth generation bred in captivity. The original father of all of these was, at the time of writing, completely bald but otherwise pure white in pelt, and although confined to resting all the time on a heating pad, still ate heartily and appeared not only healthy but happy. It seems that the oldest male in the group disciplines all the others to line up in a particular order at feeding time—"married" males first in order of age, then married females, then unmarried males, then unmarried females, and finally subadults in strict order of age and sex also—and that the Old Man stands by to admonish those attempting to get out of line. These animals appear actually to be monogamous in the true sense and to adhere strictly to their mates, at least for long periods. They also display a very high degree of affection for and concern over the well-being of their partners. Despite several prolonged observations, the precise gestation period of these animals is not known; but it is believed to be as much as four months, and the young seem not to be mature for about a year. During this time they are also carried by the father for a considerable period and weaned by him. They then live amicably with the parents until they show interest in a young member of the opposite sex, at which time the parent of their own sex shows marked aggressive tendencies towards them, presumably indicating that, in the wild state, they would then be driven away from the family group.

A notable aspect of the behavior of these marmosets is their vocalization. All Hapaloids make an astonishing number of different kinds of noises, from high-pitched keening sounds that carry extraordinary distances, have ventriloquial properties, and seem to penetrate a listener's head, to all manner of twitterings, chirrupings, squeakings, mumblings, chatterings and other sound combinations both regular and of an irregular kind that cannot be described in words. Some investigation of this "conversation" has been undertaken by means of sensitive modern recording equipment, and the results indicate most interesting possibilities. Not only are the various sounds obviously employed under special circumstances or for special purposes, but they seem definitely to be used for the communication of information. Further, considerable evidence has come to light indicating that the preciseness of this information is considerable: a distinctive call indicating thirst among all members of one species (*C. penicillata*) tested being, for instance, quite different from the call given by those individuals who customarily drank only milk. Thus the latter could be quieted by being given milk, but the others could not be, and the former could be so with water but not the latter. There appears also to be no limit to the variety of fear calls, many of which are produced only in response to particular objects such as black dogs or cats as opposed to those animals of any other color, or, as in a case that I personally observed, by any light-colored cake of soap or other globular object of some particular size and form, such as a smooth pebble. It is obvious that there is here a vast field for research that may produce most remarkable results, for it is certain that these tiny animals also carry on an apparently continuous flow of regulated sounds at supersonic levels.

The feeding habits of these and most other marmosets are also worthy of particular mention. Except from the examination of the contents of the stomachs of those freshly killed in their natural environment, we are able to learn of this aspect of their behavior only from the observation of specimens in the unnatural conditions of captivity. Little has been recorded on the former, but what has been is couched in the most general terms such as that they eat fruits, nuts and insects. In captivity, they certainly take a most varied diet and seem to require such for good health. However, they show the most remarkable individual proclivities, one animal drinking only milk and eating only certain fruits; another of the same species taking water, eggs and raw meat; still another a completely different combination; and so on. In fact, no two seem to select quite the same diet, and, what is more, they almost all seem to need a by no means infrequent change of diet, especially with the seasons or with changes in temperature or other aspects of their environment. None of this, however, is by any means unique to this group of marmosets, nor to marmosets or to the Hapaloids as a whole. This seems to be more or less the rule among most of the Primates, even those that are supposed to be pure vegetarians or even exclusively leaf-eaters, which we will discuss much later on. Their diet in the wild is probably just as varied, for different types of both vegetable and animal food become available in successive periods throughout the year in accordance with the seasons; and, as there is some noticeable seasonal alternation at the latitudes where the Tufted Marmosets live, they may normally undergo marked changes in diet.

The six longer-legged Tufted or, as they are now often called, Silky Marmosets are more than just various in coat color and pattern and have been assigned a very large number of specific designations. They are extremely numerous throughout an enormous territory, from north of the dry Caatinga (see map) on the eastern bulge of South America to the Amazon and thence west and south to the limits of the true equatorial forest. In structure and size they are throughout so similar as to be almost identical. They are larger than the species of the Tupi and much longer-legged, being leapers, and prodigious ones to boot. They are distinguished by having corollas of long stiff hairs, almost invariably either white or of a pale tint in contrast to the rest of the pelage, that stand out from all around the ears. The fingers are long, the limb bones exaggerated, the ankles drawn out and the feet and toes very long and slender. The tail is long but its fur is short, and there is a tendency for the fur over the shoulders and back to form a slight cape. They usually lack the triangular white blaze on the forehead that is so characteristic of the little Plumed Marmosets. They are inhabitants of the upper canopy of the forest and are reported often to be associated with troops of monkeys, with which they appear to travel and feed, only drawing somewhat apart to sleep.

These Marmosets come in an almost endless variety of colors and color combinations ranging from vividly contrasting patterns of dark rich brown and red-brown with white or cream to over-all buff-colored examples; buff, cream and white; or even pure glistening white. Although large numbers have been collected and examined from a wide range of localities, the greater part of their natural range is still referred to in the country of their origin as the *Terra Incognita* and simply has not been explored, let alone been investigated zoologically. Thus, no precise and final description of the numerous types of this group of marmosets can be given; but it has been observed that, while some color forms appear to be confined to specific territories, they may blend hither and yon peripherally into one or more other forms, while at the same time individuals within a most limited population may vary very widely. Further, there seems to be a tendency among these animals to throw out albinistic forms of various degrees of intensity, so that anything from a somewhat pale to a partially or purely white form may appear. Then again, there are cases on record of an individual changing color completely after illness or at one moult. Some form of skin disease has caused specimens in zoos to lose most of their fur and, presumably upon recovery, to grow back a new coat that is over-all white or pale cream. Still more confusingly, the same animal has then been known to change back at the next moult either to its original coloration or to another that is quite different. Considering the enormous area over which these kinds of marmosets are distributed, there must be a considerable number of valid species of them, but to what extent those forms that inhabit contiguous areas can interbreed is not at present known. This may add a further complication to their description and classification. Such a state of affairs is not, of course, unique to this group of marmosets any more than is the complexity of dietary preferences among the last group: it is a situation that is met with when studying almost any large group of Primates, as we shall see. It is not, therefore, within our province to attempt any specific descriptions of these animals. (For names of described species see the general list in the Appendix.) There is, however, one point of general interest anent the Tufted Marmosets that should be mentioned.

NORTH ATLANTIC OCEAN

ISTHMUS of DARIEN
COSTA RICA
C. CORRIENTES
BOGOTA
COLOMBIA
GUIANA MASSIF
Rio Br-ano
Rio Negro
Amazon
GUAYAQUIL
ECUADOR
Rio Madeira
Rio Tocantins
CAATINGA
PERNAMBUCO
PERU
BRASIL
BOLIVIA
TUPI FOREST
PACIFIC OCEAN
Rio de la Plata
SOUTH ATLANTIC OCEAN

FORESTS OF THE HAPALOIDS

The Marmosets and their allies are confined to the
tall equatorial forests of South America.
However, some forms—the Pinchés—are found in
the tall deciduous forests on and to either side
of the Isthmus of Darien. Two groups are also
indigenous to the tupi forests of southeastern
Brazil, which are somewhat widely separated
from the body of the Amazon selvas by the
uplands of the central Brazilian Massif.

There is today considerable confusion as to just what is meant by the "Common Marmoset," to which the Latin name *Hapale jacchus* is customarily attached. It appears that the animal first given this scientific name by Illiger in 1811 was a member of this Tufted group, or genus, and specifically one with a dark brown fur, the individual hairs of which were banded with cream-buff and were black at the base, giving the animal an over-all tashed or stippled effect with diffuse cross stripes and tail rings when the fur was brushed smoothly backwards, and having pronounced pure white corollas around the ears. This particular form has apparently had a rather curious history, in that it would seem to have been very common as a pet in the last century, then to have become progressively rarer in captivity and to have been gradually replaced, from the point of view of availability, by the little White-eared Marmoset (*Hapale aurita*). Then, about twenty years ago, if the limited records can now be interpreted at all, this latter animal in turn seems to have started to become scarce, whether by destruction of the forests in which it dwelt or because of economic or other causes is not known, and a number of the former animals began to appear for sale as pets. The name *Hapale jacchus* has been and still is often applied indiscriminately to both animals even in zoos, and both may be called Common or White-eared Marmosets. Finally, quite a number of the other tufted-eared, long-legged forms with pronounced corollas around their ears also began to appear on the commercial market, and these were called "Silky Marmosets." This purely popular name finally became applied to animals of the type described by Illiger as *Hapale jacchus*.

The name *Hapale* means the "Tender or Gentle Ones" and *jacchus* means the "Leaper." While the latter name is highly appropriate, the former is hardly so, since these marmosets are actually rather irascible, peevish and nervous creatures, quite unlike the little twittering *H. aurita,* which are notably of a gentle disposition. Further, they have long canine teeth and can give a bad bite, and this they will sometimes do without warning or immediate provocation but apparently deliberately, and especially when annoyed. They are more carnivorous than the small species from the Tupi and relish small live birds, which they tear apart and devour *in toto.* They also fight among themselves with a violence that may sometimes seem quite terrible to us. The causes of these fights are usually, and perhaps invariably, irregularities in etiquette on the part of some junior animal. On more than one occasion I have seen one of these animals catch the offending member of the group and deliberately break its arm or leg across a branch or a knee and then let it go. The wounded or punished animal then lurks for days in a corner and eats only the scraps left over by the others, while carrying its broken limb off the ground until healed; but, when this is achieved, it may in turn pursue its punisher and make his or her life intolerable for days.

The Naked-eared Marmosets (*Mico*) are altogether different animals. They appear to be confined to a swath of equatorial forest territory south of the Amazon River but extending from the Atlantic Coast about the mouth of that river to the foothills of the Bolivian Andes in the west, and thence south to the watershed between the Amazon and the La Plata river systems. These curious, rather evil-looking little animals stand somewhere between the marmosets that have so far been introduced and the longer-tusked, more carnivorous Tamarins that are to come. The typical species, which is called Silver Marmoset (*Mico argentata*), comes from the lower reaches of the Tocantins River, a southern tributary of the Amazon. It has become fairly well known to those specifically interested in these animals during the last few years, and especially in the United States, where quite a number have arrived for sale.

It is one of the most preposterously colored animal imaginable and is, by our standards at least, appallingly ugly. Its body is clothed in beautiful, pure white, long, silky fur; the tail, however, is jet-black, and the ears and face are naked and bright pink, the latter irregularly spotted with red blotches that look, at first sight, like sores. Worse still, the top of the head is bald, and this, combined with the somewhat flattened skull, gives the animal a glowering countenance that is more characteristic of the Tamarins than of the Marmosets. In captivity, this animal is by preference almost entirely carnivorous, relishing raw meat, birds, mice and frogs, and gorging itself on insects; but like almost all other animals, it also takes a modest quota of vegetable and mineral matter. Curiously, the people native to its country of origin contend that its bite is poisonous. The subspecies of the form are *melanurus* and *emiliae.*

Even more ugly from a human point of view are

the Bald-headed Tamarins (*Marikina*) that come from the northern side of the Amazon. These are obviously an extension or extreme form of the *Mico*, for their heads are completely bald and are black in color. However, there appears to be one species, called the Piebald Marmoset (*Marikina bicolor*), which comes from the Rio Negro Valley and precisely matches the Silver Marmoset, except that the naked ears and face are black and the tail is white on the underside and black with vague rings on the upper side. Another species, named Martin's Marmoset, from Brazilian Guiana, has a dark brown pelage but light limbs and underside. The bald face and head are, in life, a sickly puce color, but the ears are spotted with dark blue, and the hands and feet are pink and clothed with white fur above. There are literally dozens of stuffed skins of all manner of other animals in all the great museums of the world provisionally assigned to this group or labeled with all manner of names, but all obviously of this bald-headed group. It will thus probably be many years before we sort out the true relationships and affinities of these animals and ascertain exactly where each of them lives.

The remainder of the Tamarins fall into three quite distinct groups, the first of which is known as the Black-faced Tamarins (*Tamarin*). Of these there are three outstanding species-groups, all found north of the Amazon from the coastal plains of the Guianas to Amazonian Colombia, but only in the forested lowlands and in the valleys of the great upland masses that spread from east to west across this area. They do not extend over into the Orinoco Basin (see map).

The first and most common type is now known as the "Little Bearlike Tamarin" (*Tamarin tamarin*) but has had a variety of other scientific names in the past. This is jet black all over, except for a sort of saddle over its back—sometimes only between the limbs but in other specimens all over the upper and outer surfaces—of what is called "agouti" coloration. This means that the individual hairs are black at the base but banded black and yellow towards the tip. When brushed backwards, moreover, they give the animal a cross-striped appearance. The face is naked and jet black, as are the hands and feet. The Red-handed Tamarin (*T. midas*), found only on the northern or Atlantic seaboard of the Guiana Massif, is similar but has the most incongruous, bright orange hands and feet, this color being cut short just as if the animal were wearing gloves and "bobby socks." The third kind, from the areas west of the Rio Branco, is jet-black all over with only a slight brownish wash on the flanks, but has a naked, pale pink face and a white-haired "dart" on the nose. This species is known as *T. inustus*, meaning the "Charred," which is a quite appropriate title.

These Black-faced Tamarins form a very compact little unit of Hapaloids, and they appear to have rather special habits. For some extraordinary reason they constantly consort with other primates and notably with the Capuchin Monkeys. Troupes of these two kinds of animals travel about together and separate only when danger arises, whereupon the Tamarins give the alarm and then streak off through the treetops while the Monkeys swing and crash along behind them. They appear to be virtually untamable, can for their size give really terrible bites, and generally behave in a most unmonkey-like manner. I have kept many for months but have never been able to obtain the vaguest understandable reaction from any one of them, however gently and patiently handled.

The second and much greater group of Tamarins, conveniently but rather muddlingly called *Tamarinus*, are known popularly as the White-faced or Moustached Tamarins, and are altogether different animals. There are a dozen full species and no less than twenty-one named subspecies. They come from the vast upper Amazon Basin, which is to say from the lowlands below six hundred feet above sea level, ranging from west of the Rio Negro and north of the Rio Madeira to the foothill gorges of the Andes in Colombia, Ecuador, Perú, and Bolivia (see map).

It would be useless to try to give any specific or detailed descriptions of these varied animals, for they come in apparently endless color combinations and patterns. There is, however, at least one characteristic by which they may be readily identified. All have white hairs on their "muzzles" and on their upper lips. The feature reaches its ultimate in a species known as the Emperor Tamarin, or *Tamarinus imperator*, which is one of the most ridiculous-looking creatures in existence. It has a body only about eight inches long and is colored much like the Little-Bear Tamarin, but its upper lip is festooned with vast, pure white, Bismarckian moustachios that droop to its forearms. Although called "White-faced" Tamarins, they are actually black-faced but bear upon their visages

16. *Philippine Tarsier* (*Tarsius syrichta*)
One of a group of minuscule Primates of the
East Indies. It has finger pads like a tree frog,
and leaps about the forest undergrowth in pitch
darkness, catching insects in mid-air and drinking
dewdrops from leaf tips.

17. Pigmy Marmosets
(*Cebuella pygmaea*)
The sole contender with the Lesser
Mouse-Lemur for the distinction of
being the smallest Primate.

18. Black-plumed Marmoset (*Callithrix penicillata*)
A highly intelligent creature. It has claws like a
squirrel except on its great toe, which is thumblike
and bears a nail. Its eyesight is phenomenal.

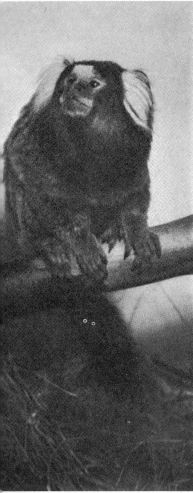

White-eared Marmoset
(Callithrix aurita)
Identical with the Black-plumed species but adorned with a corolla of stiff, pure white hairs that grow around each ear. It makes birdlike noises and has a large vocabulary, which the oldest male uses to enforce complex rules of behavior upon those whom he bosses.

20. Black-necked Moustached Tamarin
(Tamarinus nigricollis)
One of many highly colorful species of Hapaloids of the western Amazon Basin. All have some white hairs on the muzzle, and several have pronounced moustaches. They are bright and agile, and can make loving and reliable pets.

21. Golden Lion-Tamarin (*Leontocebus rosalia*)
Noted for the length and slenderness of their limbs
these Hapaloids are, when in good health, perhaps
the most vividly colored of all mammals. The hairs
are metallic in appearance and highly iridescent.

ST P. WALKER

23. Cottontop Pinché (*Oedipomidas oedipus*)
A relative of Spix's Pinché but from
northern Colombia. With needle-sharp
teeth and tusklike canines they can tear
apart birds and mice.

22. Spix's Pinché (*Oedipomidas spixi*)
Imported from Panama in fair numbers but under
the misleading name of "Geoffrey's Marmoset." It
is carnivorous, eating insects, snails, and birds.

24. Dusky Titi (*Callicebus cupreus ustofuscus*)
Although these large-sized Hapaloids are numerous in some Amazonian forests, very little is known of their habits and few are seen in captivity.

25. Goeldi's "Marmoset" (*Callimico goeldii*)
Until recently almost unknown, this animal is unique in many anatomical features and seems to stand somewhere between the Titis and other Hapaloids.

ERNEST P. WALKER

ERNEST P. WA

26. Douroucouli (*Aötus trivirgatus*)
The only nocturnal Primate of the New World, and a unique animal that has clawlike nails and falls somewhere between the Hapaloids and the Pithecoids. Although normally quiet and retiring, it can make a variety of loud noises.

ROY PINNEY

ERNEST P. WALKER

28. Silvered Sakiwinki
(Pithecia monachus)
One of the species that have the hair of
the head growing from a central whorl
and forming a bang over the forehead.
The rather coarse hair of all Sakiwinkis is long and scraggly. In disposition
they are, like their facial expressions,
"Sad Sacks."

27. White-faced Sakiwinki
(Pithecia pithecia)
The stiff, short, curved, carpet-like hairs
that cover the face are unique among
mammals. This seems to be a purely
sexual adornment, since the females have
naked black faces and yellow sideburns.

HEINZ RUHE

29. Red Uacaris (*Cacajao rubicundus*)
Shorn of their long, rather sparse hair, these in-
credible-looking creatures turn out to be immens
slender-bodied, with spidery limbs and enormous
hands and feet. This trio, photographed on arri
from the north Amazon Basin, is literally in
the pink of condition.

varying amounts of white hairs. They do not have the scowling expression nor the vicious mien of the Black-faced Tamarins and they are less carnivorous. They have much of the gentle expression of the smaller, trundling Tufted Marmosets, and, most significant of all, they make the same trilling noises and use just as great a variety of sounds.

In appearance they are enormously varied, and I have seen the preserved skins of some that are, in color and pattern, almost unbelievably vivid, with orange bodies, jet-black heads, white limbs and black-and-white-ringed tails; and others with black bodies, yellow heads, gray necks, red limbs and black tails with vivid yellow rings. They are, in fact, among the most colorful of all mammals. It appears that all of them change color from youth to adulthood, and in some cases the females may be totally different in appearance to the males. Little of a specific nature is known about their habits in the wild, and almost every year one or more new kinds are brought out of Amazonia.

The last group of the tamarins are animals so bizarre as to have been separated from all others over a century ago, and it is still doubtful whether they should be classed with these animals. They are known as the Lion-Marmosets, Leoncitas, Maned Tamarins or Golden Lions (*Leontocebus*). There are three distinct kinds, and they all come from the southeastern coastal forests of Brazil, east of the Caatinga, but there is still no precise information as to the extent of their distribution. The most perfect in color, and one of the most magic-looking of all animals, is the species known as *Leontocebus rosalia,* which means literally the "Lionlike Monkey of an Out-of-this-worldly Rose Color." There really is nothing else like it, as may be seen from the accompanying plate, which is not by any means a distortion of its coloration. The second species. *L. chrysomelas,* from the region of the Pardo River in the state of Bahia, has a black face, body and arms, reddish black hind legs, a golden yellow mane, hands and feet, and a black tail with a dirty yellow ray along its upper half. Recently, both intermediate and other color forms have been appearing, but we do not as yet know exactly where they come from or just what their relationships to the two typical forms may be. The third species (*L. chrysopygus*) is even more uniformly dark-colored, with a vividly contrasting golden tail, hands and forearms, and feet. Unlike the others it has brown instead of blue eyes.

Just why one small animal, with a body only about ten inches long when fully extended and with a tail only a little longer, that lives among the dark green foliage of tropical forests should be clothed in an incredible golden pelage that looks, even close up, like molten metal, is quite beyond our understanding. Further, this animal—as well as its close relatives—has limbs of the most exaggerated proportions, the fingers being held together and being almost as long as the forearms. Still again, these animals make noises that are even more varied and outlandish than those perpetrated by the talkative little Tufted Marmosets, and they have a high degree of intelligence and an uncanny "understanding" that in many respects transcends our normal logic. One that I had living with me for many years invariably started a high-pitched keening noise whenever I arrived at the place where it was resident, be it at a country house, a city apartment, or under the trees at our private zoo, and it just as invariably started this *before* I had even parked my car. Several dozen people can attest to this, but I have yet to find anybody who can suggest an explanation of how it could know, before it could see, smell, or hear me, that I was about to arrive.

A geographical feature accounts for the division of the tropical American equatorial forests into two parts, one, by far the greater, being that of Amazonia south and east of the mighty Andes Mountains, and the other, to the north and west of these mountains. In this latter area there are Hapaloids, but apparently of only one kind, and a very special kind at that, known as the Pinchés (*Oedipomidas*). There are three quite distinct species known as the White-handed, the Cottontop, and Geoffroy's or Spix's Pinché, found, respectively, on the Pacific lowlands from Guayaquil in Ecuador to Corrientes in Colombia; on the Caribbean watershed of Colombia; and from the lowlands of the Darien Isthmus north to the borders of Costa Rica. There is an unfortunate mix-up over the species from Darien because it has somehow acquired the popular name of Geoffroy's Marmoset (which should rightly belong to a subspecies of the Tufted Marmoset from southeastern Brazil, *H. petronius*), whereas its correct name is *Oedipomidas spixi,* or the "Swollen-footed Regal One of Mr. Spix,"—a rather remarkable title. This abstruse technical point is, moreover, of some account, for large quantities of these animals are imported yearly into the United States and are offered for sale as "Geoffroy's Marmosets."

Pinchés are long-legged, very long-tailed, leaping, arboreal creatures. They are bird-eaters and almost wholly carnivorous, a fact that is often not appreciated even by the more conscientious animal dealers. Numbers of Cottontops (*O. oedipus*) are also offered for sale in the United States every year, and recently some of the previously rare White-handed Pinchés have come in. People buy the poor little creatures, take them home, buy special cages for them, lavish care and affection on them, and then suffer profound frustration and distress when they die for no apparent reason. And die they almost invariably do. We had been through this routine time and time again and had just about decided that no amount of effort would succeed when we noticed that a friend managed to keep some indefinitely and apparently in perfect health. The friend was a pet-store owner in New York, well known to all in the fraternity in the United States and to many abroad, whose speciality is tropical birds. I don't think he realized quite what valuable information he imparted that day when he calmly stated in answer to my query as to how he did this, "I feed them all the cage birds and baby chicks that die." Since that time we have fed our specimens small dead birds and, failing these, mice, insects, chopped liver with raw eggs, dried Chinese shrimps, cheeses and black-peppercorns, and they have thrived and even bred.

The appearance of the Pinchés is almost indescribable but can be seen in the accompanying photographs. They are, on the one hand, alarmingly human in facial expression and in some other respects, but they are dreadfully bestial in habits. They have a set of teeth, and especially canines, that would, if enlarged, put any other mammal to shame, and they can wreak havoc on the corpse of a full-grown crow.

The remaining creatures that we class as Hapaloids have, until now, been grouped with the so-called South American Monkeys, but they have nothing in common even with the least monkey-like of these, which form the subject of the next chapter and which we call the Half-Monkeys. On the other hand, they have almost everything in common with the sundry animals described above, notably the possession of clawlike structures on fingers and toes, and the voices and mannerisms that seem to be unique to this group of animals.

The first is, to the science of zoology, an intensely rare creature called Goeldi's Marmoset, or *Callimico goeldii*, which means "Goeldi's Beautiful Monkey." However, this animal is apparently rather common in the area where it dwells—northwestern Amazonian Brazil—and has recently started appearing among shipments of wildstock from that country. They are very large tamarins shaped much like the Maned Lion-Tamarins but twice the size and jet-black in color. They have a mane on their crowns and a mantle over their shoulders, and the pelage is long, silky and very shiny. The young have black tails, but the adults develop three pale cream rings about the middle of the basal quarter of the tail, the ring nearest the body being the narrowest in width, that farthest from the body the widest. Nothing is known of the habits of this beautiful little creature, but the one I viewed in captivity behaved exactly like my Golden Lion-Tamarins, screaming and chittering as soon as I came within a certain range and swaying back and forth while it did so. Its voice also is closer to that of *Leontocebus* than to that of any of the other marmosets or tamarins.

The remaining Hapaloids are known as Titis and constitute the genus *Callicebus*. Until now they have been regarded as forming a separate subfamily of the South American Monkeys generally, and they are perhaps different enough from the Marmosets and Tamarins to warrant their remaining as such. There are a very large number of kinds of Titis, described under an assortment of names, and they have been known since the eighteenth century, but they are probably the least known of all the Primates. In fact, all but a handful of popular and even several technical works do not even mention them. To further confound the issue, English-speaking animal dealers have, unfortunately and sometimes not altogether honestly it seems, transferred the name Titi to the Squirrel-Monkeys, which are altogether different animals. All in all, it is an amazing fact that so little should have been done about these animals.

The Titis are all built upon a common and almost identical plan, but they vary fantastically in color and color pattern. Although seven species and twenty-four subspecies are now established, such vast tracts of Amazonia have never been explored that we still know practically nothing about the distribution of any one kind, or whether they intergrade, or to what extent they vary within the species. Many forms are known that appear to stand intermediate between others in coloration, but these do not always come from intermediate localities. One of the most colorful is known as *Callicebus torquatus*, which happens to be the first one described.

This animal has a body clothed in a brilliant shade somewhere between wine and copper, and of great lustre. The arms are black, the hands pure white, and the legs, feet, and tail jet-black. The face is white but with black skin and is surrounded by a dense, black fringe; the ears are black. The beard or throat ruff, which is common to all Titis, is white. Another form, *C. t. regulus*, is gray-brown with an orange throat ruff and undersides; its feet and hands are white. Others display almost every variation on this general plan, namely all manner of reddish browns, often with a wine-colored sheen, rusty browns and olive browns above, and orange, yellow, white or pure black below. There is something about the coloration of a Titi that is unmistakable and unique.

Titis are found in the Amazonian forests only, but all the way from the south bank of the Orinoco down to the divide between the Amazon and La Plata watersheds. There are, however, old records of specimens from "near Bogotá, Colombia," and the "Rio Pastasa, Ecuador," both of which localities are on the Pacific side of the Andes and thus in the Panamanian forest zone. However, animals obtained from local sellers may have been brought from great distances in the interior of South American countries, and, in the early days of scientific collecting, travelers were often careless in recording the true origin of specimens. None has been definitely recorded from the Pacific slopes.

Practically nothing is known of the habits of these very numerous animals in the wild except that they are arboreal, travel about in small parties, and sometimes come to the ground. In the absence of valid records of the contents of the stomachs of freshly killed wild specimens we do not know what they eat, but I have noted from captive specimens of mine that they seem to thrive best on an almost wholly carnivorous diet of insects, small birds, slugs, crabs, centipedes and fresh-water fish. They will eat fruit, but apart from green nuts a vegetarian diet appears to lead to chronic diarrhoea.

The Titis have four more teeth than the other Hapaloids, but in other respects they are very similar to them. Their every movement and vocal comment, their way of sitting, and their personalities are those of "marmosets," and indeed more those of marmosets *per se* than even of Tamarins. They are quite unlike any of the other New World Primates, as we shall now see, and in many respects they are not even quite halfway to monkeys.

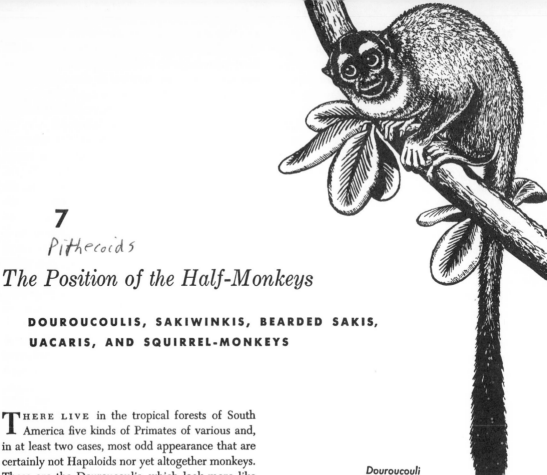

7

Pithecoids

The Position of the Half-Monkeys

DOUROUCOULIS, SAKIWINKIS, BEARDED SAKIS, UACARIS, AND SQUIRREL-MONKEYS

THERE LIVE in the tropical forests of South America five kinds of Primates of various and, in at least two cases, most odd appearance that are certainly not Hapaloids nor yet altogether monkeys. These are the Douroucoulis, which look more like certain lemurs; the Uacaris, which might qualify as bald monkeys but are of outrageous design; the Sakiwinkis and the Bearded Sakis, which really look like nothing else on earth and often bring a guffaw of laughter from those seeing them for the first time; and finally, the Squirrel-Monkeys. Contrarily, however, the last look so monkey-like as even to be called "Monkey-Monkey" Monkeys in the pidgin English used in the Guianas, but they are, anatomically, possibly the most specialized and unmonkey-like of all.

The Germans have a very serviceable and descriptive name for that great group of carnivorous beasts that we call the Civet Tribe, which contains a host of animals that are related to but are still not quite Cats—such as genets, rasses, mongooses, and so forth. They call them the "Half-Cats," meaning, of course, not that they are half cats and half something else, but that they stand halfway between the kind of animals we designate as true cats and those, whatever they may have been, from

Douroucouli

which both they and the cats were evolved. These five South American Primates hold just such a position vis-à-vis what we commonly call Monkeys, and so may be called Half-Monkeys. They may also be named collectively Pithecoids, after their most outstanding members, the Sakiwinkis (*Pithecia*). The creatures in question are all known by a number of different popular names, some of which are most misleading since they are more often applied to quite other animals. They go as follows:

	SP.	SUBSP.
A. **OWL-MONKEYS** (*Aötinae*)		
(1) Douroucoulis (*Aötus*)	1	10
B. **SAKIWINKIS** (*Pithecinae*)		
(1) Sakiwinkis (*Pithecia*)	2	6
(2) Uakaris (*Cacajao*)	3	4
(3) Bearded Sakis (*Chiropotes*)	3	3
C. **SQUIRREL-MONKEYS** (*Cebinae*)		
(1) Squirrel-Monkeys (*Saimiri*)	4	15

The current accepted taxonomic status of these animals is not so simply listed, and a word on this is desirable since it will further demonstrate the intermediate position of these animals in the general Primate genealogical tree, and especially on the branch that is exclusively of the New World.

The Douroucoulis are currently associated with the Titis to form a subfamily, as it is now called, of one of the two families of the New World Primates known as the *Cebidae*. (The other family is that of the marmosets or *Hapalidae*.) The Sakiwinkis, Uacaris, and Bearded Sakis are grouped together to form another subfamily of the *Cebidae*, and the Squirrel-Monkeys are linked with the Capuchin Monkeys (*Cebus*; to be discussed in the next chapter) to form a third. And until and unless further scientific studies show otherwise, these are the positions they must hold. Nevertheless, it is our firm opinion that such studies—which are known to be under way at the time of writing—will ultimately show that these five genera are more closely associated than at present believed, and that they may be set more widely apart from the Hapaloids on the one hand and from the remaining New World Primates (the Hand-tailed Monkeys, or Ceboids) on the other. They have several internal and external features in common; most notable to the casual observer being well-developed and fully opposed thumbs, pronounced terminal finger pads with linear whorls (fingerprints), and structures on all the digits that are halfway between claws and nails. Further, none of them has a prehensile tail—as do all of the Ceboids. Their habits vary greatly, but they all have certain mannerisms in common, and these are often more hapaloid than ceboid, and their voices and vocabularies are very extensive and altogether different from those of the Ceboid Monkeys. Twins have been reported fairly commonly among them, with the exception of the Bearded Sakis, which are very little known in any respect, and there are reports of their showing the otherwise typical Hapaloid habit of the father carrying the babies and weaning them.

Altogether, therefore, there are several valid grounds for bringing these curious, interesting, and in some respects odd primates together and for describing them as a unit, although they themselves obviously represent three and perhaps four separate little twigs of a side branch of the general genealogical tree. One of these is represented by the nocturnal Douroucoulis, but whether it is derived from an ancestor common to the other Pithecoids cannot yet be stated. The Sakiwinkis and the Uacaris show many traits in common, and there are grounds for associating the Bearded Sakis with these, though they are really very different animals both in form and in habits. The Squirrel-Monkeys are quite different again and certainly in many respects display more monkey-like qualities than any of the others, but they have some unique anatomical features and are in hardly any way like the Capuchins. In voice and behavior they stand far apart from all others.

Douroucoulis—also called Owl- or Night Monkeys, or Ei-A—are unmistakable once you have seen a live one or a good photograph of the face of one—see Plate 26. They are of moderate size, the body being about twice the bulk of that of a gray squirrel but the head being very large in proportion, and the limbs and tail very long. They are clothed in a wondrously soft fur that is neither exactly woolly nor silky but very fine and thick. On the face the hair is extremely short and sparse; on the tail it becomes harder and stiffer and forms a curious keel under the basal half of that organ. These animals, in common with the other Half-Monkeys be it noted, sit with their bodies hunched in a most distinctive manner, their hands tucked under the chest and resting on their feet, and they sleep thus but with the head sunk down on their forearms, so that they present a more or less spherical ball of fluff with only the tail trailing out of the back end. Since all Douroucoulis are colored a neutral brownish gray tinged with olive-green, they are perfectly camouflaged among tree branches and foliage. Their under and inner sides vary considerably in the different races or subspecies, from pure white through various gray tones to yellow and thence to a vivid orange, and this is in very marked contrast to the dorsal coloration. Their faces are really black, with sundry vivid and clearly defined white markings surrounding the enormous eyes and forming a slight beard. Sometimes this white forms two long wedges above the eyes and runs back into the black on the front of the head.

The outstanding feature of Douroucoulis is of course their enormous eyes, the irises of which are a rich reddish golden brown but which, unlike those of many animals so endowed, do not have a flat, glassy stare. On the contrary, they are always of a soft and gentle appearance and full of expression. The transparent cornea that forms the front of these huge orbs is so protuberant that, if you look across the face of a Douroucouli at a certain angle, you can see them actually sticking out from the plane of the face like two car headlights. They are light-collecting organs of an advanced construction and aid the little animals in finding their way about and catching insects—which they often do while the insects are on the wing or while they themselves are leaping through what appears to us to be total darkness. However, although these animals appear to be active throughout the night in the wild and certainly are so in captivity, there is considerable evidence to show that they do most of their feeding during those interperiods between sundown and total darkness and between the latter and dawn which appear as black night to us, but which astronomers have demonstrated are still not totally dark. No eye can see in the complete absence of light, but the eyes of these animals, like those of owls, can be used to see very small objects in darkness so intense that other nocturnal animals have to rely on their senses of smell or touch to detect them.

A Douroucouli sitting up looks like a rounded little animal, but if you straighten it out, as it were, or see the body of one divested of its furred skin, you will find that it is a very long, slender, streamlined affair, the body being shaped almost like that of a fish. The limbs too are exceptionally long, the ankle joints elongated, and the foot long and slender with a widely opposed great toe. The fingers have exactly the same relative proportions as our own but are very long and thin and terminate in distinctly swollen terminal pads that bear lines and whorls like those of our own fingerprints. All the Ceboids and also the true monkeys, the apes, and men display this character, and those of the Cynopithecoids, the Coloboids, and the apes are as individually distinct as those of men, so that no member of one species has whorls like those of any other, or, as far as is known, of any other species. Monkeys of various kinds have been identified by their fingerprints and thus returned to their owners or "convicted" of "crimes" as a result. The number of variations thus possible on a general theme, which would seem to be so simple, is actually so vast as to be really quite incomprehensible.

Another outstanding feature of Douroucoulis is their voices. These include not only twitterings, chirrups, and other tiny high-pitched sounds but booming and gonglike noises of almost incredible

volume and resonance. Moreover, no two individuals seem to have the same repertoire, and captive specimens may suddenly give out with an entirely new noise never heard during years of close contact and observation. One that we owned had a most particular call that we heard her employ—like our Pigmy Marmoset—only when a *black* cat appeared. This sounded something like "tckkk-tckkk 'er-(boom)," the last noise being gonglike and long-drawn-out. No cat of another color, or anything else we ever noted, called forth that particular sound.

In the wild they eat a mixed diet of fruits, some green nuts, insects, tree snails, tree frogs and other small animals, and apparently birds' eggs and honey. This last is unusual, but I have witnessed it myself in the jungle. In captivity they take a wide diet but have very individualistic preferences. One that I owned never once drank water in five years but sucked up bowls of milk. She ate only fruit and never touched nuts, roots or meat of any kind except for a few live grasshoppers and meal worms, both of which sometimes made her vomit. Her favorite food was white bread, which is supposed to be so devoid of real nourishment that it is hardly worth our eating. Another specimen ate raw meat and drank water, would pick over fruits and take out banana and apple, would not touch bread but would eat a whole large carrot or raw potato at one sitting. The latter's mate cracked and sucked hens' eggs, loved any form of candy, and, rather surprisingly for a New World Primate, took oranges and other citrus fruits. Citrus fruits are not indigenous to tropical America but have been imported from the Old World, and most animals from the former areas do not seem to understand them. Similarly, many Old World root-eating animals often spurn potatoes (an American plant) but eat carrots, parsnips and other vegetables indigenous to their territory.

Douroucoulis are found all over the Equatorial Rain-Forest and north tropical Tall-Deciduous Forest Belt of South America. Something over a dozen types, all probably subspecies of a single species, can be distinguished throughout this vast range, but nobody would probably dare identify any individual on appearance alone, for the types prove to be extremely variable within any one area and presumably within interrelated and inbreeding populations, and some color forms may turn up in widely separated localities. Several subspecies have been defined and their distribution outlined by Philip Hershkovitz (*Proceedings U.S. National Museum*, Vol. 98, 1949) in the northwest or Pacific forests, centered round Colombia, and he attributes all to but a single species. Those from the Amazon forests have from time to time received sundry specific names, but they have not been reviewed as a whole of late, and they may well prove to constitute but one additional species or even to be nothing more than another galaxy of subspecies and local varieties. Most notable among the varying external features marking these animals are the extent and arrangement of the black and white areas on the face and head, the tone of the upper surfaces, and the color of the lower. The last varies from pure white through gray to yellow or bright orange, but the young of the orange-fronted may have pale gray to white chests.

The purely nocturnal habit of the Douroucoulis is unique among all those Primates that we list in this book after the Lemuroids and serves to set them considerably apart from them, for it affects their entire make-up and must have a very ancient origin. Along with it, they have developed a number of behavior patterns that are more lemurine than monkey-like, notably nesting in holes in trees and apparently adhering to limited feeding territories around these permanent resting places rather than wandering, as do most other higher primates, over a much more extensive area and constantly shifting sleeping quarters within that area. They appear everywhere to live in pairs but to keep their twin offspring with them and to live all together in the same nest until the young are almost if not quite full grown.

Douroucoulis make extremely attractive, docile, and trustworthy pets if initially of a pleasant disposition, and particularly if raised from an early age after weaning. However, it must always be borne in mind that, like most if not all other kinds of living animals, they display a seemingly endless variation in disposition and character, and they are as a species high-strung and somewhat nervous, meaning highly sensitive to sudden movements, sounds or other novelties, and possessed of trigger-sprung reactions. Moreover, if suddenly and profoundly alarmed, especially when asleep or dozing, they may either instantaneously fly off in any direction regardless of obstacles or, if held, bite involuntarily, and they have a set of teeth that are amazingly sharp and marked by prominent canines.

Their hands are extremely dexterous, and they use them and especially the fully opposed thumb just as we do, selecting food morsels and other items with precision and bringing them up to the eyes for close inspection. Mothers make nests, selecting, twisting and bedding material just as we do with, say, wool or in stuffing a cushion. Most remarkable of all is probably their manipulation of a large live insect, for they will turn it about with both hands until the fluttering wings or any spiny legs or dangerous pincers can be bitten off, and then, holding it firmly in one hand, chop off the head and proceed to eat at leisure.

In captivity they become used to a belt and to having a chain attached to this when they are to be taken out. They will make a permanent retreat in a closet or settle down in a small cage with a sleeping box, but they cannot be housebroken and usually foul their sleeping quarters. They will become very much attached to humans known to them and will travel inside a coat or jacket all day, or night, clinging to the fold of the lapels with their hands and peering out above. At night they will travel contentedly on the back of a car seat but become much excited by red lights, to which color they, like the Hapaloids, seem to be most sensitive. It is advisable to debar them from bedrooms, since they customarily give vent to their terrific booming calls for about an hour before dawn and often uninterruptedly.

Perhaps nearest to the Douroucoulis in the scheme of life and on our family tree come the bizarre Sakiwinkis, though few people viewing examples of these two animals together would think that they had anything in common. The general outward appearance of the Sakiwinkis may be seen from the accompanying photographs, though not all of them look quite so utterly miserable. If, however, you were to shave both a Douroucouli and a Sakiwinki, you would find that you held two very similar creatures. Most notably alike are the hands and feet, the long, very slender bodies and limbs, and the broad, rather flat faces, though the eyes of the Sakiwinkis are as exceptionally small as those of the Douroucoulis are large. The unmonkey-like appearance of the Sakis is almost wholly the result of the long, rather coarse, scraggly fur in which they are clothed. It is notable that the first and second fingers of both these animals work together against the other three, but more noticeably so with the Sakiwinkis.

Sakis are denizens of the closed-canopy forest of Amazonia, that is to say south and east of the Andes, from the southern bank of the Orinoco to the watershed between the southern tributaries of the Amazon and the La Plata complex. They do not occur either in the Tupi forests of southeastern Brazil or in the Pacific forests of the northwest. They are wholly arboreal, though they sometimes descend to the lowest tree strata and even to bushes in search of certain particular berries. They travel about in large family parties, several of which may join forces when special foods are concentrated in a small area; such areas are often along the edges of the open, short-grass savannahs that are scattered throughout the vast blanket of Amazonia's forests. It must be realized that, although the whole of this territory is marked solid green on most general vegetation maps, the actual forest forms a vast and intricate latticework, almost all areas of any extent lying between rivers being open grass fields or savannahs. These not only look like but are in point of fact ecological "lakes," and they influence the surrounding vegetation just as if they were filled with another element. The foliage of the surrounding jungles comes tumbling down to ground level all around them, forming a dense mass about a hundred feet high and usually interwoven throughout its thirty feet of depth with all manner of climbing grasses and thin vines. All this is exposed to intense sunlight and heat, and in it grow plants that are not found elsewhere either on the ground or in the treetops. Among them are many that produce berries, as opposed to fruits and nuts, and the Sakiwinkis are predominantly berry-eaters, though they also nibble leaves and flowers and catch and tear apart small birds and mice and other little warm-blooded animals. An Amerindian tribesman in Guiana once showed me Sakis popping in and out of holes in hollow trees, catching sleeping bats, which they then tore apart, skinned and ate while sitting on branches outside the holes.

They are remarkably agile animals and can leap chasms among the treetops that would defy any Galago, Lemur, or even Pinché. They also have a most comical way of running along horizontal branches on their hind legs with their arms held wide above their heads and all the fingers extended. It is impossible to keep a straight face when you see a line of these glum-faced, shaggy-haired creatures performing thus, because one can-

not help but expect to see a diminutive G-man coming along behind them holding a minuscule rifle at the ready. Like lemurs they usually descend vertical branches backwards and with considerable caution, and they often hang upside down by their feet alone, like the Bushbabies, in order to grab or eat food.

Sakiwinkis have always been considered very difficult to keep in captivity, and it is true that they often refuse to eat or suddenly stop eating, or just die for no apparent reason though taking a well-balanced diet regularly. They are also sometimes prone to a most horrible performance only paralleled by a kind of hysteria occasionally displayed by the rodents known as Agoutis. This consists of a sort of emotional outburst that results in the animal giving every appearance of and sometimes succeeding in battering itself into insensibility and that often ends in death. It has been suggested that this is caused by brain tumors induced by certain parasitic worms that spend one phase of their life cycle encysted in the brain of a primate host; these are known to occur in Capuchins and other Ceboid monkeys and to produce in them a wide range of neurodynamic afflictions. Nevertheless, these animals have been kept for many years in both zoos and private homes and have even bred, or at least given birth in captivity, in Brazil. Possibly the reason for these contrary results is the incidence or absence of parasitic worms in the animals when caught. Another factor involved is, however, undoubtedly regulation of the humidity in the air, for Sakiwinkis live in very warm, extremely moist forests that often grow in water, and they spend most of their time at those levels in the foliage where the air is most heavily saturated. A dry atmosphere and especially steam heat produces inflammation of the respiratory passages and is otherwise apparently lethal to them.

As a whole, Sakis are very gentle creatures and make not only loving but tragically dependent pets that seem to ask only to be allowed to perch somewhere about their comparatively vast companion's person. Nevertheless, they are rather temperamental and if scared will, like Douroucoulis, bite involuntarily. Large males may have fangs over an inch long, and they all have extremely deep jaws which, although developed to house a noise-producing apparatus somewhat like that of the Howlers, give them added leverage in biting. Females particularly do not like anyone to touch their mates or their babies. In captivity they may eat well if they are given foods they like, but again this varies widely from individual to individual, and the things they select are often very odd. Raisin bread is usually a favorite, as are raisins, currants, strawberries, caterpillars and sour cream, but they sometimes will take only raw meat and fish, although they do not thrive on these. One I owned drank only milk, but had a craving for licorice in any, even the liquid form; on this he appeared to become highly intoxicated.

Altogether, Sakiwinkis are among the oddest of animals and certainly of Primates. They look like foxes with the faces of crochety old men, have sharper and more exaggerated teeth than most cats, make noises like birds, walk like men and jump like lemurs. Sometimes they may even carry their half-grown young at arm's length in one hand by grabbing the long fur of its back in a most inconsiderate manner.

The face, or that part of it surrounding the eyes and a small triangle on the mid-brow, and the inflated muzzle and chin, is naked save for a few tiny, sparse hairs; the skin may be jet-black, dark blue, or bright pink. The hair on top of the head is long and forms a sort of toque that in some races hangs down over the forehead in the form of a bang. There are a considerable number of recognizable forms, and at least two species, of Sakiwinkis. These may be divided into those that have bangs and those that do not. The former have either black, gray or brownish fur, the hairs tipped with silver, yellow or ochre; these may be subdivided between those that have pure white and those that have jet-black hairs on the hands. Then again, there is another "banged" form that is either silvery gray or pure glistening white all over except for a wedge-shaped, black area starting on the nape of the neck and expanding backwards to the base of the wholly black tail. This form may have a black or a pink face. Then there are also dark gray forms with a red-brown triangle of fur on the top of the head and a face clothed in pure white hairs; and still another kind that is jet-black all over and has a pink face. This may all sound rather precise, but unfortunately all manner of intergrades between many of these patterns are known, and what is more, no one color-form or pattern is necessarily typical of any one area, whereas, even if it predominates in one, the interforms between it and another distinct color phase may not come from an intermediate geographical position between the two. Descriptions of all these variations and their distribution would necessitate an excessive catalogue and would still not lead to sure identifications, for the over-all interrelationships of all of them have not yet been worked out or published as a whole, and there are still many large areas of unexplored territory in all the countries from which they hail. More varieties, or even full species, may thus still remain to be brought to light.

The Sakis without bangs (or with shorter hair on their heads) are distinguished by amazing structures surrounding the naked parts of their faces. These look just like the arrangement of tiny hard feathers on the faces of Barn Owls, and are composed of outwardly directed and backwardly curving (i.e., towards the skin) hard, bristly hairs that form a dense mat. In some forms this hair is pure white with a vivid daffodil-yellow "stain" all around the edges, where this structure meets abruptly with the long, shiny black hair of the rest of the head and body. In others, it is yellow, buff or brown. Meantime, the skin of the face in the brown form may be pink instead of black. But most confusingly, the females of the white-and-yellow-faced male form are, in at least one locality, black-faced, lack this mat, have bangs and a pair of long yellow whiskers of the "Dundreary" kind, and are otherwise almost exactly like some of the forms described above, with a coat of dark gray hairs tipped with yellow. Yet again, as one travels in one direction from the locality where this singular sexual dimorphism is found, the males become progressively more like the females, but in another direction, the females gradually get more and more like the males, the yellow whiskers even becoming short, stiff, and like a mat and the rest of the coat going black. The mat-faced, or nonbanged forms appear to be confined to the Guiana Massif.

Totally different in appearance though somewhat similar in manners are the Uacaris (*Cacajao*, which is, incidentally, pronounced *kassa-jow-oo*). If the Sakiwinkis are considered bizarre, Uacaris may be said to be positively grotesque. They have monkey-shaped faces, but they always look as if they are on the point of collapse from prolonged starvation. What is even worse to contemplate is the naked skin on the faces of two of the species; it is bright pink and turns to the livid red of a healing wound when the animals are excited. Most of them are naturally either partly or almost wholly bald, and the rest of the body is clothed in long, sparse hairs of uneven length that often lay bare their long, emaciated-looking limbs. Even adults that are in the pink of condition in their natural habitat and look plump, somewhat solid, and well clothed when sitting down, have a strangely bedraggled appearance when they stand up on all fours. They look even worse when they rise on their hind legs and run along with arms held on high like Sakiwinkis, for their long plumelike hair falls or blows away from their narrow, elongated bodies and slim limbs, and discloses the pink or almost white skin in which they are clothed. Belaboring a point is undesirable, but we cannot refrain from harping upon the altogether grotesque appearance of these animals when seen or handled —dead or alive—in toto, something that no photograph however good can show, for the creatures have a totally different appearance when sitting hunched up and when in motion or stretched out.

Uacaris have only half a tail, and this sticks straight out behind. Their hands and feet are rather large and bear very long, slender fingers and toes that are in form and arrangement much like those of the Sakiwinkis. In fact, if shaved and given longer tails, their bodies would appear much like those of Sakiwinkis. We normally associate short tails or lack of tails with life on the ground, but there are other monkeys—notably a Langur (Presbytis) found on certain Indonesian islands—that have half-tails like the Uacaris and are just as wholly arboreal. Although rather sluggish in captivity—which they appear to loathe on emotional if not on dietary grounds—they are fantastically agile among the trees of their homelands.

They also are highly susceptible to a dry atmosphere, their mouths and the mucous membranes of their throats and bronchial tubes becoming desiccated, cracked and irritated, bringing on coughs and all the symptoms of bronchitis and, latterly, of pneumonia and even tubercular-like hemorrhages. Kept in a very moist, hot atmosphere, they perk up and eat voraciously, being unusually fond of pablum, cereals, and other farinaceous foods. Altogether, we have found they do best on human baby foods, and a very large male *Red Uacari* we once had behaved like a baby in other respects, carrying around a doll with rolling eyes and sleeping with it in his arms. They are gregarious in the wild and seem to crave the companionship of their own kind.

The natural food of Uacaris is reported to be fruits, but the diet found necessary to keep them in good condition in captivity—something that is in any case rather difficult and has seldom been entirely successful until quite recently, and is now the result, in all probability, of our enhanced knowledge of vitamin requirements and the development of dietary boosters—indicates that they need either very special types of fruits or a much greater variety of foods. The term "fruits" is, however, a very wide one, and there is a world of difference between the fruits of plants such as we normally eat and the vast variety of nuts, beans, soft and hard fructifications, pits, seeds and whatnot that burgeon in the tropical forests. Besides, the buds, shoots and bark of plants, and multitudes of insects, arboreal snails and tree frogs are always available and may be taken in fair quantities. There is even evidence that these animals eat the bulbous roots and pithy stems of the numerous parasitic and epiphytic plants that festoon the branches of the trees in the forests where they live.

Uacaris can also make pleasant pets, though they seem really to be of a rather lugubrious nature, in keeping with their perpetually sad facial expressions. They are quiet for the most part but can give out with raucous yells and a variety of other indescribable noises. They are also usually rather passive, sitting quietly in a corner and huddled together if in company, but they can get about at unexpected speed and can jump remarkable distances. Males show marked protective attitudes and may leap at you to defend their females or young, and they have a habit of seizing the supposed attacker and drawing whatever part of him they can grab to their mouths and inflicting most unusual bites with a slashing motion of their upper canines, which are long and tusklike. In captivity they have motions reminiscent of small apes, walking short distances and then sitting, but in the wild they may actually gallivant about with apparent recklessness.

There are three well-defined types or species-groups, and these occupy different territories. The first has a pink skin and bright pink face, and is clothed in long, plumelike hairs, silvery gray or glistening white except on the head and back, which are light gray. It is known as *Cacajao calvus*, meaning the "Bald," and comes from a strip of territory in central Amazonia, lying between the Amazon and its northern tributary, the Japura.

The second is pink-faced and has flesh-colored skin but is clothed all over in reddish golden orange hair, is named *C. rubicundus,* and appears to be confined to the next wedge of territory to the north and east, lying between the Japura and the Rio Negro. The third species, known as *C. melanocephalus,* is very different from the others and comes from the opposite or northern side of the Rio Negro in the valley of the Rio Branco. It has black skin and black hair except on the thighs and tail, which are brown. However, the color of all these varies considerably, and it is by no means sure that any of them are exclusively confined to the territories described. The first two may only be color varieties of one type.

The so-called Bearded Sakis (*Chiropotes*) constitute a very distinct genus containing three recognized forms that may be varieties of a single species, valid subspecies, or even different species. They are the least known and rarest—at least in collections—of the Pithecoids, and like the other four types comprising this group of Primates, they have several unique aspects. The title Bearded Sakis is misleading in that, although they indeed have full beards, they look in no way like Sakiwinkis externally, differ from them considerably internally, and have different habits and altogether different mannerisms, voices and motions. How they originally acquired the title is not clear. The word *saki* appears to be an abbreviation of various names for various animals in sundry South American Amerindian tongues, such as *sakiwonka* and *sakimiri.*

The coloration of the three forms varies and to a considerable extent intergrades, but not to the extent that it does between the more numerous Sakiwinkis. The reason may simply be that they are much rarer animals, less numerous in forms, and confined to a more limited area, namely, south of the Orinoco but north of the Amazon, from the Guianas to Perú.

In the best-known form (*C. chiropotes*) the body is a deep reddish brown all around, but the head, beard, hands, legs and feet, and tail are black. The hair on top of the head grows outwards in all directions from a central point and forms a dense, doughnut-shaped mop. The tail is longer than the head and body and is carried straight except for a tight curl at the tip, is round in section (including the hair), and is of equal diameter throughout its length. These animals trundle rather

than run, and they cannot jump like the Sakiwinkis. They are rather dour in disposition, eat fruits as well as nuts, and take some insects but do not take meat or berries. Their voice and vocabulary are totally different from those of the Sakiwinkis, consisting of all manner of croakings more like those made by the Ceboids, a coughing call and, when alarmed or peeved, a sudden, long-drawn-out yell very like that of a Woolly Monkey. They drink by dipping a cupped hand into water and then sucking the liquid from its palm. Like several of the marmosets, either their urine or the secretion of some glands as yet unidentified gives them when healthy an almost overpowering effluvium resembling that of fresh tangerines. The belief that these animals are neither a kind of Sakiwinki nor even closely related to them is considerably strengthened by the fact that they often inhabit the same forests but keep altogether apart and appear to occupy an entirely different natural niche. They are treetop dwellers and move about in small family parties or little bands, but they are reported to have the habit of feeding alone, each individual far separated from all the others, and of coming together only when alarmed, about to travel to new feeding grounds, or preparing to bed down for the night. Their movements are deliberate, and although they will run along small branches, their passage from one to another is cautious in the extreme even in an emergency.

Their woolly coats are exceptionally dense and exceed in length of fur those of the Woolly Monkeys (see next chapter). This coat is somewhat "oily"—like the lanolin-saturated fleece of a sheep —so that even torrential rain fails to penetrate it, and it forms a sort of insulated blanket covering the entire body except for a small area around the eyes and mouth and the naked palms and soles. No suggestions have been put forward as to why this animal might need such a coat, but it leads to interesting speculations. An equatorial forest is not swelteringly hot as is often supposed; on the contrary, the temperature within it remains very constantly at a most agreeably moderate level. Hot air rises from its surface and is heated by the sun, but the cooler, moisture-laden air sinks to its floor and is seldom disturbed even by high winds, though it is slowly churned by gentle convection currents. For what purpose, then, does an animal need a thick insulating blanket?

The last of the Pithecoids are, at least in external

appearance, considerably more than halfway to the popular conception of a monkey. In fact, as was mentioned above, the observant inhabitants of the Guianas even call them, in their abbreviated but highly succinct form of pidgin English, the Monkey-Monkey Monkeys, meaning thereby that these animals seem to them to be more typically of that ilk than even the numerous Ceboids that also inhabit their country. They are commonly known in English as Squirrel-Monkeys, though they are in no way squirrel-shaped or -colored, are communal as opposed to family animals, and they don't even make the same noises as those rodents. In the countries of their origin they are called by a variety of names, but many of these have somewhat the sound of the scientific name of the animals, namely *Saimiri*.

If the skinned corpse of one of these animals is laid out alongside that of a Douroucouli and a Sakiwinki of similar over-all size, all will be seen to have remarkably like dimensions and proportions, apart from their heads. The skull of the *Saimiri* is of unique shape among primates. If viewed from the side, the brain case will be seen to bulge out backwards beyond the point where the vertebral column joins its base to almost as great an extent as does the face forwards of that point. The face itself is very small and the jaws short, so that the brain case is actually relatively very large for the size of the animal. The brain, although huge, is, however, simple, being comparatively smooth and not convoluted, and more like that of the Hapaloids than of the Ceboids and higher primates. Most of its development is seen in those portions that control the physical actions and movements of the animal. The teeth of Squirrel-Monkeys also resemble more those of the other Pithecoids than they do those of the Ceboids.

Squirrel-Monkeys are among the commonest, if not the commonest, of New World primates and occur in some areas in seemingly endless troupes containing often hundreds of members. Once, when tied up to a riverbank in a launch in Guiana, we counted up to 550 in one troupe leaping, in single file, a chasm in the trees over a little tributary stream, and as we moved up that river we passed troupe after troupe so that there were hardly ever less than two in sight. They are distributed from the San Juan Valley that separates Nicaragua from Costa Rica in Central America to the divide between the southern tributaries of the Amazon and the La Plata drainage basin to the south. They do not appear to inhabit the coastal swamp forest, but they range from its landward edge to considerable altitudes up mountain gorges—and this applies to almost the entire Amazonian and Pacific Forest belts—but these animals never wander more than a few hundred yards from a river or stream bank. They are in fact most specialized in their choice of habitat, adhering to the "edge" of the forest canopy. This needs explanation.

As was mentioned when speaking of the Sakiwinkis' preference for the edges of the savannahs, the equatorial forests form a vast latticework covering the major part of South America. The lattice itself is actually composed of the river systems, which are bordered by walls of vegetation. The forests beyond the riverbanks are actually hollow, the foliage being elevated on the vast boles of the countless trees to a height of from 80 to 150 feet above the comparatively clear floor below. The greenery forms a vast blanket held aloft on wooden pillars, but its edges descend to the ground all around, both at the margins of savannahs and along riverbanks. These edges, moreover, are thickened, almost as if they were folded or crumpled, by the growth therein of all manner of vines and bushes that require sunlight and cannot grow in the body of the forest. This whole mass is bathed in sunlight and is festooned with flowers, fruits and other edibles, and it is inhabited by an entirely different fauna from that of the forest canopy. Squirrel-Monkeys inhabit this tangle, through which they make regular aerial roadways, each troupe apparently patrolling a fixed length of riverbank, plus the "gorges" in the vegetation that run inland up its tributaries.

Although they are arboreal and spend most of their time crashing about the middle strata of these forest edges, they also ascend to the very tops of the nearest emergent giant trees, and there they may sometimes be seen leaping up into the air to catch insects. They likewise come down to earth not infrequently, and especially in the early morning, when the body of the forest is often filled with a dense ground mist. Their objectives in these movements, which are concerted and tend to follow a rhythm set by the time of day in combination with the prevailing weather, are primarily searches for different forms of food. Squirrel-Monkeys are considerably omnivorous but insects, snails, spiders, small tree frogs, land and tree crabs

—of which there are millions everywhere in the moist jungles—form a very large part of their diet. To obtain these, they go up to catch beetles, butterflies, katydids, and other diurnal denizens of the forest canopy, and down to grub for terrestrial types and especially those nocturnal and crepuscular kinds that are to be found wandering about on the dark forest floor for some time after sunrise. The Squirrel-Monkeys' descents upon the ground are in the nature of invasions pursued with a frightful urgency, the whole troupe coming down with a rush all together, as if they knew that great danger lurks at such levels. It was a very remarkable performance to observe when on one occasion some hundreds of these active, chattering, intelligent little elves swooped unexpectedly upon our camp, invading our tents, turning over everything and ripping boxes and other closed objects apart and even popping into the kitchen and snatching baking bread from an open but red-hot tin oven. Though five of us pursued them hither and yon with brooms and other "weapons," they almost wrecked our temporary home, stole nearly all our food, and appeared to be absolutely fearless, and quite indifferent to us.

The *Saimiri* is perhaps more truly communal than any other Primate; nay, rather, it is tribal, and to an extent that no Ceboid or Old World monkey so far observed is. The members of the troupe seldom scatter even if completely at peace and out of all danger. They stay within a few feet of as many others as possible; and they move, when feeding, by a wonderful method of partial and reciprocal drift, one part of the troupe slowly moving forward past the other parts, and then slowing down, to be followed by another section, like the crests of waves on the sea, so that there is constant movement but little progress of the whole. When alarmed, they set up the most unbelievable uproar in so many manners of speech that any description of the over-all result or of its component contributions is quite impossible. In fact, the vocalizations of Squirrel-Monkeys have to be heard to be recognized—though once they have been, they will never be forgotten or mistaken for any noises made by any other animals—and can only be described by recordings. Along with the vocal uproar, the troupe, as it rushes off through the foliage, sets up a racket that sounds like oceanic surf breaking on a beach. I have seen nearly a mile of the forest wall along a riverbank that had been lying perfectly still in the noonday sun break into billows of movement instantaneously as a result of a shot fired at quite another target. Once under way, the troupe may keep going for a mile or so and then "hole up" in a dense belt of growth, and stay absolutely quiet. I have been under such a hiding troupe quite unsuspected by them, and their behavior is very amusing, for the adults endeavor to keep the young ones absolutely quiet, which results in much astonishingly human-like behavior.

Squirrel-Monkeys occur in a considerable number of slightly different forms, but all are built upon a similar bodily plan and have a basic color scheme. One of the larger races—from inner Perú—is also the most colorful and one of the brightest colored of all mammals. It may be taken as a point of departure. The top of the head and the upper and outer parts of the body and the upper side of the basal half of the tail are a vivid green, with a pepper-and-salt effect of yellow and gray. The face is pure white except for black "spectacles," muzzle and chin; the throat, chest, underside, insides of the limbs, and the underside of the basal half of the tail are brilliant daffodil yellow. The terminal half of the tail is jet black and rather bushy. The flesh of the hands is pale pink. Other races vary in the intensity of the green and yellow, so that some may be olive-brown above and white below, and in the amount and arrangement of the black areas on the face and the tip of the tail. Some have almost naked ears, others have these organs clothed in short fur, and still others bear thereupon long tufts or fringes. All these variations seem to blend one into the other geographically, but four full species are now recognized (see Systematic List).

Again, some of these pure color variations may constitute valid regional subspecies or even species, but these animals represent a very good example of the kind of so-called classification to which Dr. Simpson refers in the statement quoted earlier in this book. Mere variations that can sometimes be matched within a single troupe have from time to time been given specific names, and at the same time the natural variations within any population have been sadly overlooked. And in this respect there is a really strange fact that calls for further investigation.

Most mammals—at least those that live on land—have an average maximum adult size. Among all species there are odd giants and dwarfs, but on the whole there is a recognized mean to which the individual progresses from birth. Among troupes of Squirrel-Monkeys, however, there appear to be two maximum sizes. While the average adult males and females are of one size, there are often a few, and apparently on an average of about 1 per cent, of about twice that size and four times that bulk. What is more, these individuals can be either males or females and need not even be fully adult.

Squirrel-Monkeys make rather pleasant and intelligent pets if they can be kept alive. They are not delicate, as several zoos have proved by keeping them for many years, but of the thousands that are exported from tropical America every year only a very few survive. That almost every individual is normally infested with considerable numbers of intestinal worms and other parasites cannot be denied, but deworming is apparently neither the answer to keeping them alive, nor even to keeping them healthy, and it may even in some cases be detrimental to their well-being. Parasites, however loathsome we may consider them, may in fact be beneficial to many wild animals, every member of whose ancestors may have been infested with them, and without them some animals may even be unable to digest or assimilate their natural foods. Squirrel-Monkeys are also susceptible to respiratory inflammations and infections if kept in too dry an atmosphere. They require a very mixed diet, including insects, meat, or their protein equivalents, but they are not so delicate in

these respects as other Pithecoids, possibly as a result of the greater amount of direct sunlight to which they normally subject themselves. They are very prone to develop sores on hands, feet, tails and rumps if the perches—which are essential in any case—and any platforms in their cages are not kept thoroughly cleaned and sterilized daily, for they are used to excreting off the edge of branches and their droppings appear to contain active fungoidal spores that are not destroyed during their very rapid rate of digestion. Their customary demise in captivity if wild-caught does not, however, appear to be the result principally of any of these causes, and it has been suggested that there is some entirely different factor involved. This cannot be lack of companionship, because they die more readily if kept in masses. It is not lack of sunlight. All we can say is that we have seen individuals survive when kept in the most abominable conditions, and others die like flies when provided with every advantage and given every care.

The five kinds of Pithecoids have a great deal in common, and the Squirrel-Monkeys for all their monkey-like appearance have more in common with the other four than they do with the Ceboids or New World Monkeys now to be described. There is a curious fragility about the Half-Monkeys that, of course, cannot be scientifically defined but that future anatomical studies may be able to explain. They are indeed a composite group, but, taken altogether, they display many unique features that cry out for further study.

8

Ceboids

The Monkeys of the New World

**THE PREHENSILE-TAILED MONKEYS
OF TROPICAL AMERICA**

Woolly Spider-Monkey

THE REMAINING primates found alive today in tropical America are in every way monkey-like. In fact, they are monkeys *par excellence,* since they, and they alone, fulfill all the requirements apparently demanded of this animal by the majority of people: and this because, in addition to their markedly simian appearance and behavior, they are all able to hang on to things by their tails. Just why this rather peculiar ability should have come to be considered so important or significant in the eyes of so many people and especially of youngsters is hard to say, though the idea is indeed a rather charming one, and its oddity was stressed in much delightful writing of the last century.

Actually, caudal prehensility, or the possession of a hand-tail, is rare not only among primates but among mammals as a whole. There are certain marsupials such as our own and some tropical American Opossums, and the Cuscuses and the Phalangers of the Australian Region, that have such organs; the scaly Pangolins of Africa and the Orient and two of the arboreal Anteaters of the New World are similarly equipped. Two odd Carnivores display this power too—the Kinkajou and the Binturong, which latter is a large arboreal

relative of the Civets, found in the Oriental Region. A few Rodents, such as the tiny Harvest Mouse and the tropical American Porcupines and certain rare relatives of theirs, the Hutias, from Cuba and Haiti, also have fully prehensile tails. Some other mammals, notably rodents but including even certain long-tailed bats, have partially prehensile tails, in that they can wrap them around a branch to steady themselves or to obtain a firmer purchase. What is more, not all these animals are exclusively arboreal, and not all of them can actually support the whole weight of the body suspended by the tail alone for any appreciable time. The little Capuchin Monkeys are of this ilk, but the other four related kinds of New World "Monkeys" have developed the technique of grasping and holding with the tail to a higher degree than any other mammals. They can, if they so desire, hang by it alone for considerable periods, use it for picking up and carrying things and even, it has been reported, for throwing objects. A hand-tail is one of the most notable evolutionary deviations from the basic mammalian bodily plan, and it is perhaps surprising that, once developed, it did not become universally adopted.

Despite their very considerable similarity to many of those animals of the Old World that are customarily referred to as monkeys, the members of this group of five genera of primates, which may be called the Ceboids, are really quite different both in origin and affinities, and in respect to general morphological and anatomical structure. All the living New World primates used to be called the Platyrrhines, or "Broad-nosed Ones," in opposition to the Old World monkeys and the apes, which were referred to as the Catarrhines, or "Narrow-nosed Ones." The distinction is still made but these terms are no longer used, and the *Hominoidea* (see Chapters 1 and 12) are now separated from the latter. On the whole, the American monkeys do have the nostrils much more widely separated than do any Old World forms, but they also differ in many other ways. The separation of the two on the primate family tree is a wide one—a chasm extending back to very ancient geological times when the ancestors of neither of them looked anything like what we call a monkey.

The Ceboids or Hand-tailed Monkeys consist of the following:

	SP.	SUBSP.
A. **CAPUCHINS** (*Cebinae*)		
(1) Capuchins (*Cebus*)	4	39
B. **SPIDER-MONKEYS** (*Atelinae*)		
(1) Spider-Monkeys (*Ateles*)	5	15
(2) Woolly Spider-Monkey (*Brachyteles*)	1	1
(3) Woolly Monkeys (*Lagothrix*)	6	11
C. **HOWLER MONKEYS** (*Alouattinae*)		
(1) Howler Monkeys (*Alouatta*)	6	26

The number of recognizable or recognized forms (*i.e.,* regional subspecies) varies from about two score in the case of the Capuchins to only a single one in the rare Woolly Spider-Monkey of the Tupi forests. Excluding the last, all vary greatly in color.

The little Capuchins are almost certainly the commonest New World primates, ranging from the southern borders of Mexico to the southern fringe of the forests far south of the Amazon–La Plata divide in the Argentine territory of Misiones between Paraguay and Brazil. They are also known as Sapajous, Macacos, Bondos, Machins, or in some cases quite erroneously as Ringtails. These monkeys travel about in troupes which, though never as numerous in individuals as may be those of the Squirrel-Monkeys, are far more widely distributed, for they are not confined to the borders of rivers but roam all over the closed-canopy forests. In fact, there can be hardly a square mile of territory throughout such forests in most of Central and much of South America that does not contain at least one troupe. Despite the necessity of closed-canopy forest for their well-being, there is still within the vast territory they inhabit room for a very wide range of environment as a result not only of altitude, which ranges from sea level to some thousands of feet in Andean mountain gorges, but also of the wide variations in moisture, amount of shade and other factors that occur therein, the extent of which has been fully realized only comparatively recently. Thus it is not surprising that a very wide and almost bewildering range of variation is found among Capuchins as a whole. Nevertheless, recent studies have made it possible to lay down a fairly simple basis of classification for them.

Basically, there appear to be two major kinds of Capuchins. First, there is a smaller, slender-bodied form from Central America, the Pacific forest area (see map) and certain regions east of the Andes, extending to include the Guiana Massif and south to about ten degrees below the Equator. These have light skins ranging from almost white through what is called "flesh color" to pink or light buff, and the hair on their little rounded heads usually forms a wedge-shaped central conformation on the crown—rather like that of a man whose hair has receded excessively at the temples—but which may sometimes have an upright fringe of stiffish hair running across the brow. The members of the second major division of Capuchins are much heavier in build and grow much larger in maturity. They have dark brown to black faces and thicker, denser, and sometimes even woolly coats that look as if they had been brushed every which way at once, and their heads are fully furred from the brows. Moreover, the hair on their heads may vary in length between the mid-line and the sides of the head, so that it forms either a central peak or two lateral tufts or "horns." There are further distinctions between the members of the two divisions. Those in the second group are distributed from the Guiana Massif to Amazonia, where they range across the continent to the eastern slopes of the Andes, mingling with, but neither breeding nor actually associating with, the southern forms of the narrow-nosed group; they extend south to the foothills of the central Brazilian Massif. In the

30. Black-bearded Sakis
(Chiropotes satanus)
Not really close relatives of the Sakiwinkis, despite their popular name, and
having very different habits, these
slow-moving, bearded Primates have
dense, soft, woolly fur of considerable
length. Even the babies have beards.
They are quiet, gentle, and apparently
very placid creatures that display great
affection for their own kind, but
great indifference toward humans.

31. Squirrel-Monkey *(Saimiri sciurea)*
Highly excitable, noisy, and rather
aggressive little monkey-like Primates
that live in huge tribal units along river
banks throughout an enormous area
of northern South America. There are
many subspecies differing in the intensity of their body coloration and the
arrangement of the black areas on their
faces. They have highly distinctive
vocabularies and make noises unlike
those of any other animals.

32. *Immature Black-capped Capuchin*
(Cebus apella)
Capuchins are the commonest of the New Wor
Primates and thus of the
American Monkeys, or C
boids. There are four g
groups but the young of
many of each are strikin
alike during the first year.
carry their tails curled
downward and can hang
this organ for limited peric

33. *Adult Male Black-capped Capuchin*
(Cebus apella)
When full grown, the capped, crested,
and "peaked" species of Capuchins that
inhabit the Guianas and the Amazon
Basin reach considerable size, are
powerful and aggressive, and are armed
with most formidable teeth. They travel
in troupes around limited tribal
territories but are often associated with
Tamarins and Spider-Monkeys.

34. *White-throated Capuchin* (*Cebus capucinus*)
The black-and-white species of Capuchins, with
a "widow's peak," inhabit Central America, and are
small and light-bodied. They are quick, inquisitive,
and mischievous, and make most hardy and engaging pets.

35. *Golden Spider-Monkey*
(Ateles geoffroyi subsp.*)*
One of a species from Central America.
This individual has not been overeating;
all of its kind are prodigious eaters
and usually have grossly distended mid-
riffs. Though they usually feign
timidity, they are actually very deter-
mined and have unpredictable tempers.

36. *Woolly Monkey* *(Lagothrix lagotricha)*
The gentlest and in many respects most "human"
of the Ceboids or Hand-tailed Monkeys of South
America. Their sad-looking faces belie their
meticulous but somewhat gay characters, on the one
hand, and their rare but terrible rages on the other.
They, too, are prodigious eaters; hence their
Brazilian name of "Bag-bellies."

37. Silky Howler Monkey
(Alouatta villosa)
A silky-haired species of Vera Cruz
and western Central America. Compared
to its South American relatives, it is
comparatively quiet. The largest New
World Primate, it eats fruit and leaves.
Appearing to become sad and morose
when caged, it is in its own world
an imperious creature.

38. Allen's Swamp Monkey
(Allenopithecus nigroviridis)
A small species of African long-tailed monkey, or
Guenon, that displays sufficient distinct features to
warrant placing it in a special genus. Discovered
in 1905 in the western Congo, the first live specimens reached this country in 1954. This is a
portrait of one of that group taken by Dr. Walker
in the National Zoo, Washington, D.C.

39. *De Brazza's Guenon*
(Cercopithecus neglectus)
One of the two most brightly
and precisely bedecked of
Primates, surpassed in brilliance
of coat and skin colors only by
the Oriental Doucs. This is a
large form of Guenon that is
strikingly dissimilar to all
other known species both in behavior and appearance. It is
a well-known member of the
fauna of Uganda in East Africa.

ERNEST P. WALKER

40. Roloway Monkey
(Cercopithecus diana roloway)
This is one of the largest and most unusually adorned of the several dozen forms of Guenons of tropical Africa. When young, it is gentle and readily accepts human companionship, but when full grown it is very strong and tends to assert itself and become antagonistic to men and to other animals. It comes from West Africa.

ERNEST P. WALKER

41. Diana Monkey
(Cercopithecus diana diana)
The typical form of the species, distinguished by the short black as opposed to the long white beard of the Roloway. Dianas are great jumpers.

42. Moustached Guenons
(*Cercopithecus cephus*)
Also known as Blue-faced
Monkeys; a small, active spec
from the Cameroons–Gabun
area. These are most typical
"monkeys," living in fair-
sized groups and traveling
the upper canopy of the gian
equatorial forests, feeding on
fruits, some leaves, insects, a
such small animals as
tree frogs and tree snails.

ERNEST P. WALKER

first group the nostrils are much closer together than they are in the latter: then, in the nonphysical sphere, the former are more active, agile, nervous and irascible, the latter more deliberate in all their movements, less vociferous and much more moody and morose, especially when old. While the last characteristics cannot be said to constitute scientific criteria, they are clearly manifest when examples of the two types are seen side by side.

The first of these major divisions of the Capuchins may then, in turn, be subdivided into three fairly well-defined types or species. Here, however, we run into the now almost age-old question as to just what constitutes a species; for while there are in both groups a few readily recognizable forms, in each case most notably distinct at the extreme opposite ends of their respective ranges, there are not only intermediate forms but whole series of types that, if laid out in sequence, seem to bridge the gap between these extremes by easy stages. Of the narrow-nosed, northwestern type there are, first, the Central American black-and-white forms —known as the White-fronted and the White-headed, that should be called *Cebus capucinus*— in which the dorsal and outer surfaces are pure, shiny black, and the face, chest, and under and inner sides are pure white in varying degrees. This type extends into the Pacific forest area of Colombia and Ecuador.

The second form of the narrow-nosed division comprises the so-called "Cinnamon Ringtails," which are named, rather muddlingly, *Cebus albifrons*, which actually means the "White-fronted." Their distribution is very wide and apparently (according to Philip Hershkovitz, *Proceedings U.S. National Museum*, Vol. 98, 1949) includes the coastal forest strip of Ecuador; the Caribbean drainage area of Colombia; the Maracaibo Basin in Venezuela; and a wide swath of Amazonia, from the southern confluents of the Orinoco east to the Rio Negro and the Rio Tapajos, west to the Andes, and south to about ten degrees below the equator. There is, however, considerable doubt about this tripartite distribution, and the forms in the Pacific forest region probably constitute one or two separate subdivisions or species-groups. There is still graver doubt about the status of a number of types that range from the island of Trinidad to northern Venezuela and throughout the Guianas. Though these have the nostrils close together, and often a central, wedge-shaped cap of fur on the crown, their skins

are dark, their bodies are thickly furred, and their limbs and tails are often dark brown almost to black. In behavior, also, they resemble the broad-nosed Capuchins, and in the fully developed examples from upland Guiana the crown of the head is flat and there are distinct tufts above the ears. They are known as *Cebus nigrivittatus*.

Capuchins of the second or broad-nosed group (*Cebus apella*) are often referred to by zoologists as the Tufted Capuchins, and are distributed throughout a wide crescent of territory from the inner or western side of the Pacaraima and Guiana Massifs south to the mouth of the Amazon and thence west throughout the southern half of the Amazon Basin and thence south again as far as the north Argentine. They are distinguished by having, in addition to the widely separated nostrils, heavy fur caps produced downwards into exaggerated sideburns that may, in old individuals and some races, form a fringe all around the face. Moreover, the hairs of the cap may be longer on the median line or on either side above the ears, so that they give the appearance of two horns. This group has not been critically reviewed within recent years, as have the "nontufted" species, so that it would be incautious to state categorically whether all the described types (subspecies) belong to one species or may be divided into two or more, distinguished by the form of their coiffure. It is possible that the "peaked" forms may constitute a separate species-group. The tufted Capuchins, however, are quite distinct from the nontufted and sometimes inhabit the same areas, keeping apart and behaving somewhat differently. They are, as we mentioned above, heavier bodied and somewhat more ponderous in their movements. Some collectors have said that the two may be readily distinguished by their voices, but sound recordings would be necessary to demonstrate the fact.

To this point, the division or classification of these monkeys may be said to be fairly simple, but when we come to try to identify more precisely any one individual or color type, we run into considerable difficulties. Merely as an example of the complexities with which the "more profound student" may be confronted, we cite a case with which we came in contact when collecting within the comparatively limited territory of Suriname (previously Dutch Guiana).

This small country—only some two hundred miles wide—is more or less square in shape and bounded on the north by the Atlantic, on the east and west by large rivers running due north, and on the south by modest uplands, almost entirely unexplored but clothed in montane as opposed to lowland forest. The country is cut from north to south into six subequal slices by seven rivers. Capuchins of the *nigrivittatus* group abounded throughout the territory but, we found, varied progressively from one side of the country to the other in an east-to-west direction by stages, each apparently bounded by two of the rivers. However, as one went southwards to the headwaters of the rivers, each type changed gradually until all came to look much alike. Taking an adult specimen from the two extreme edges of the country down near the coast and comparing them, one might well be entitled to refer them to distinct species, yet all appear to be but variations of a common stock residing farther inland. The various forms, between each two of these rivers, in fact, constituted what are called *clines*. This term connotes just such gradual and progressive changes, in space, that are brought about by all manner of causes, some of which may appear obvious, like changes in humidity, but many of which are as yet unknown to us. If so much variation can occur in so limited a territory, it is small wonder that the sorting out and identification of thousands of closely related forms from all over the enormous territories inhabited by these monkeys remain matters of the highest complexity, and this more especially when there are very considerable tracts where these animals have never yet been collected or studied in detail.

Capuchins are, as a whole, one of the commonest if not the commonest of all primates in captivity and more especially as pets, in zoos and as performers. Greater numbers of Rhesus Monkeys and other Macaques (see Chapter 10) are corralled and kept in confinement, but their primary use is for medical and other experimentation, and they have today been superseded as performers by Capuchins. Really very large numbers of these animals are exported from tropical American countries to all parts of the world every year. Since they are considerably tolerant of temperature changes and novel diets they may be said to be rather hardy, and they survive quite well in captivity in a wide variety of circumstances. They are also exceptionally intelligent in the human sense of that term, as many painstaking experiments appear to have demonstrated. If obtained when young and brought up as if they were precocious infants, they may become unusually gentle, loving and satisfying pets.

They always remain, however, "monkeys" in the widest, or should we perhaps say *wildest* sense. They cannot be fully house-trained like recognized domestic animals, and they always remain highly mischievous, so that, if left alone and free, they may wreck their owner's home. They are restless, enormously energetic, innately inquisitive and decidedly temperamental. Unlike the dignified and rather fastidious Guenons of Africa (see Chapter 9) they are hardly if at all responsive to disciplinary measures, but, unlike the Macaques and Baboons, they are not cowards. Although they make, in special cases, better and more reliable performers, sometimes going through the same routine without fault many times a day for years, they always retain a will of their own when "off duty," and no amount of scolding will make them desist from any action upon which they have embarked or upon which they have set their minds. They are all liable to sudden tantrums, and at such times they display qualities that can only be described as a combination of obstinacy and bravery. They do not seem to have quite the degree of guile displayed by, for instance, the Guenons, which may, by giving the appearance of docility in face of admonition, actually take over your household. Capuchins will never entirely submit, and they will defend themselves to the last. A fully grown individual, especially of the heavy-bodied, tufted species, can be a most formidable adversary for its size, having a gruesome set of teeth with very strong and large canines with which it can give a most severe bite. They are also a great deal stronger than the average person might suspect and when in a real temper can rip apart structures of enormous solidity. I have seen a crotchety old male completely demolish a cage that had housed, among other things, a half-grown Jaguar and a full-grown Giant Anteater —one which the latter animal had made considerable efforts to break open, using its immensely powerful forearms and four-inch claws. Once free of the cage, this particular Capuchin also deliberately sought out and attacked a man who had customarily fed but sometimes teased it, and bit him savagely and repeatedly until netted. It seems, in fact, that Capuchins have exceptional memories and other most human qualities.

It is interesting to note that Capuchins have highly convoluted brains rather like our own and that the total capacity of this organ is large in proportion to their over-all bulk. There really does seem to be some actual connection between the purely physical size and construction of a brain and the behavior of its possessor, and this may be at least a partial explanation of some of the quite remarkable, and in some instances almost unbelievable, performances by these monkeys when observed under experimental conditions. A great deal of such experimental work, extending over a number of years, was conducted by Dr. Heinreich Kluver, and was published by him in numerous works—the perusal of which is essential for students not only of the Primates but of animal behavior as a whole, and probably for psychologists too, and would also prove most rewarding to anybody interested in the world of nature generally. Dr. Kluver came to the conclusion that these little monkeys, in some respects, exceeded all others, even the apes, in certain abilities and notably in the use of tools.

One individual, for instance, used a hooked wire to unlatch from a wall a specially formed stick, which it then used, in turn, to get a larger stick that would reach food; and it accomplished the whole performance in a few minutes though all the tools were new to it. Even more astonishing was this monkey's use of a live rat on the end of a string to get food from a position far beyond its own reach outside a cage, and, although it achieved this objective by repeated trial and error, it did so in a matter of just over three minutes. Capuchins, in fact, appear to be able to concentrate on problems in an astonishing manner and to work at their solution with a persistence that is matched only by rats and surpassed only by men.

The same scientist also demonstrated that these animals could "draw"—that is to say, use various colored chalks on smooth surfaces in a manner that was not purely random, but involved grouping the colors together in sweeping curves or almost straight lines and then surrounding the results with regular configurations of other colors.

Even more startling were various other reactions of these animals. They watched movies with great intensity, and when certain animals were shown they appeared to become as oblivious of their surroundings as the veriest human addict. That they really "saw" and interpreted the movies seems to have been proved by their terror at the sight of large snakes in the pictures.

The outstanding aspect of Capuchins' behavior, however, is undoubtedly their "showmanship." Some Guenons and some Macaques appear to know when they are on exhibit and to deliberately "put on an act," the former usually becoming quiet and composed and generally acting in an amusingly coy manner, the latter performing the most outlandish antics in order to attract the utmost attention. The little Capuchins, however, seem actually to work at the job, to learn by patient trial and error, and then to perform—sometimes for years on end—with unerring precision. They are not so creative as the Macaques and Chimpanzees, preferring to develop a good routine and then stick to it. Some old troupers may give several performances an hour for several hours a day with only brief intervals for meals, and never miss a trick.

An example of patient training combined with what can only be described as uncanny intelligence on the part of a Capuchin was a common sight for several years recently at ocean resorts along the New England coast each summer. This was a Black-capped Guianese Capuchin that was about five years old in 1949. This small person traveled around these resorts during the summer season and went south or to California with her adoring master every winter. She put on the original and traditional act, but with subtle variations. Her master, born in Naples, played a hand organ that was not only a museum piece but a finely tuned instrument on which he rendered many unusual melodies. The little Capuchin wore a tiny jacket and three-quarter-length pants of medieval cut and a sort of *tarbush* for a hat, and carried a small change purse. She was not on a chain and sat on the curb with dignity and folded hands while the music jingled through three popular pieces. She then got up, curled her tail under her body like a spring and, walking on her hind feet, started round the circle of gawking human beings, holding out her hand for donations. If a dime or larger silver coin or a note of any denomination were offered, she took it politely and placed it in one of two appropriate compartments in the wallet and then doffed her little hat with great solemnity; if a nickel were proffered, she accepted it, put it away in another compartment in the wallet and then just touched her hat and gave a slight cough of acceptance. If pennies or any base metals such as "slugs" or transit tokens were offered, she held them up for close scrutiny and then hurled them to the ground and let out a chatter. But most unnerving of all, if she approached you and you offered her nothing, this diminutive individualist just stood there and screamed at you and, what is more, in a manner that appeared to be deliberately calculated to draw the attention of the assembled crowd to your non-performance.

This was an "act" that had been inculcated into the animal by a patient and kind human provider, and the little animal never faltered in her performance; but after working hours she relapsed, reverted, or relaxed—however you choose to express the action—into complete naturalness. She would gambol, refuse to come when called, play tricks, chatter, scream and scold, take things apart and generally behave like any other captive Capuchin with only a few months' experience of human life.

The habits and behavior of Capuchins in their natural environment vary considerably in details from place to place according to special circumstances, but they appear to be, on the whole, remarkably consistent. They travel about in gross family parties varying in numbers from less than a dozen to, according to some reports, as many as fifty or more individuals of all ages. Like so many other kinds of monkeys, the troupes appear to occupy, and to consider they have exclusive right to, territories of somewhat fixed limits. These may often march with the property of adjacent troupes, but may otherwise abut on belts of neutral territory or no man's land. Capuchins do not appear to maintain particular sleeping quarters for any length of time, but rather to bed down in appropriate trees as near as possible to wherever they happen to find themselves at sundown. There is some evidence that they follow set routes through the trees, and many troupes may follow the same route, especially if it leads to water; for these monkeys will descend to the ground or to branches overhanging rivers to drink. During the rainy season there is quite a lot of standing water in holes high up in the trees of the equatorial forests; but—and this is not widely appreciated—the lushest so-called jungle may be absolutely devoid of water or even obtainable moisture for months on end in the dry season, during which all but the largest streams and the rivers dry up, the arboreal water holes are empty and succulent fruits are scarce.

Capuchins become restive slightly before dawn and start to call and move about as soon as the sun is up. They then usually move slowly to feeding areas and make what may be called a breakfast, after which they have often been observed to spend two or more hours doing what can only be described as *nothing*. The older members sit about sunning themselves and croaking gently while the younger ones romp about and practise climbing and traveling techniques, only occasionally being admonished by their parents. They then appear to feed in a desultory manner for some time until the heat of the day, when the whole troupe may become silent and appear to take a siesta in fine weather. They feed again in the early afternoon and then seem to do their traveling in the late afternoon, sometimes covering considerable distances and with apparently predetermined purpose. Not all Capuchins behave precisely thus, and there is presumably much variation in daily routine according to the weather and other factors. But all observation seems to confirm that they all follow a somewhat orderly and regular pattern of behavior when unmolested and, like most other animals, are remarkably conservative and considerably confined by certain prescribed rules and within more or less set spatial limits despite what might appear to be the complete absence of any barriers to action or movement.

The close relatives of the Capuchins are considerably different animals, and each is in some respects most distinct. All have excessively long tails that are fully prehensile, taper towards the tip, and have on the undersides of their extremities curious naked strips of skin covered with cross-wrinkles like the undersides of our fingers. This constitutes a finger of a sort of fifth hand, and this not only is capable of supporting the whole weight of the animal but also is used to pick up objects.

While there is no really close relationship between any of the Ceboids—such as there may be said to be between, for instance, some of the Hapaloids—it would seem that the Woolly, the Woolly Spider, and the Spider-Monkeys form adjacent sprigs on a special branchlet of the primate tree. The Woollies are in many respects rather specialized, but they retain usable thumbs; the Woolly Spiders are an aberrant offshoot, and their thumbless hands and clawlike nails are obviously a specialization; the Spiders (*Ateles*) have developed in another direction equivalent in many respects to that of the little apes of the Orient that we call Gibbons. After the Capuchins, these last are the commonest and most widespread of the American

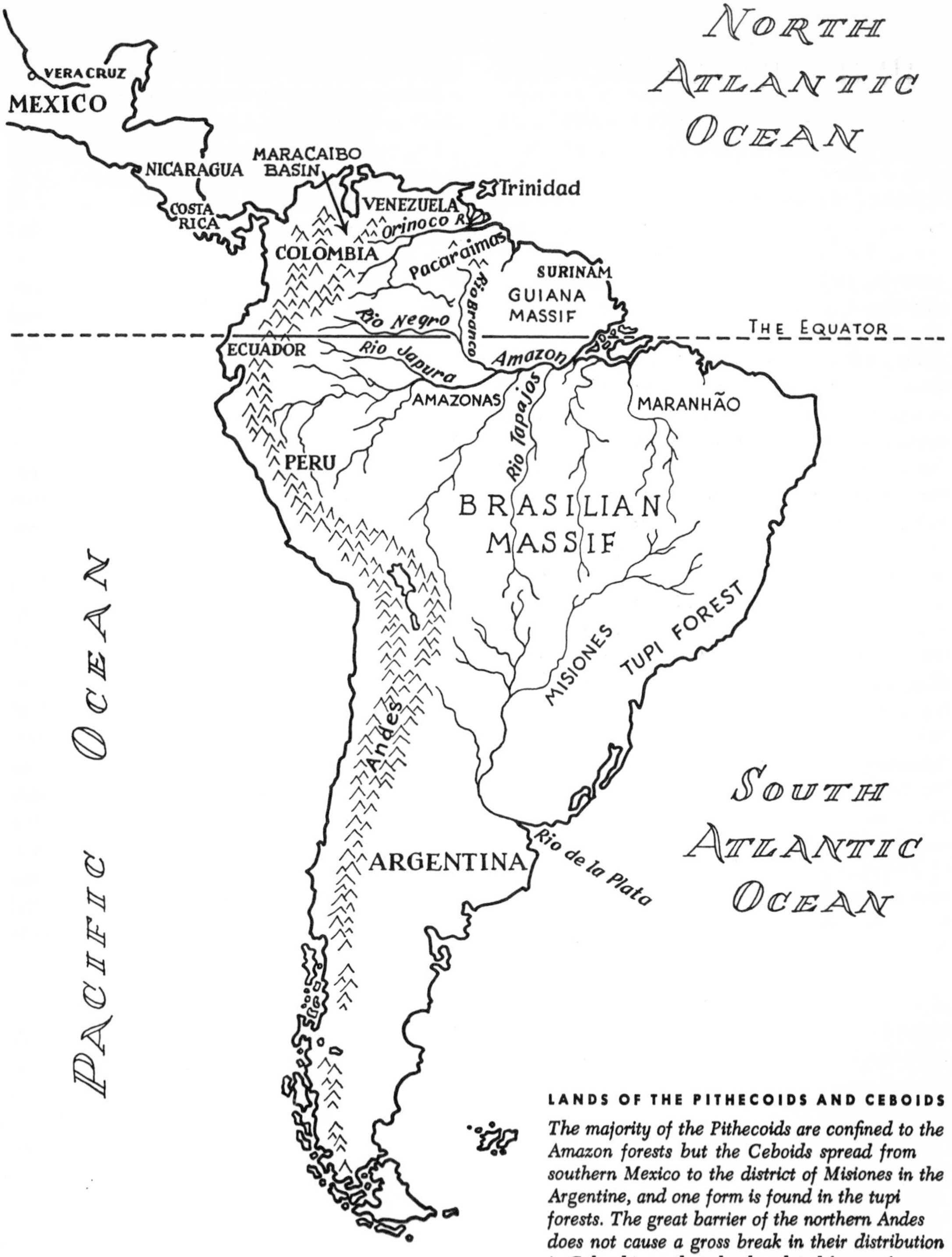

NORTH
ATLANTIC
OCEAN

VERA CRUZ
MEXICO

MARACAIBO
NICARAGUA BASIN

COSTA
RICA   VENEZUELA   Trinidad
Orinoco R.
COLOMBIA
Pacaraimas
SURINAM
GUIANA
MASSIF

THE EQUATOR

Rio Negro
ECUADOR   Rio Japura
Rio Branco
Amazon
AMAZONAS
MARANHÃO

PERU
Rio Tapajos

B R A S I L I A N
M A S S I F

PACIFIC OCEAN

MISIONES

TUPI FOREST

Andes

SOUTH
ATLANTIC
OCEAN

ARGENTINA   Rio de la Plata

LANDS OF THE PITHECOIDS AND CEBOIDS

*The majority of the Pithecoids are confined to the
Amazon forests but the Ceboids spread from
southern Mexico to the district of Misiones in the
Argentine, and one form is found in the tupi
forests. The great barrier of the northern Andes
does not cause a gross break in their distribution
in Colombia so that closely related forms of
three genera are found on either side thereof.
Both the Pithecoid Douroucoulis and Squirrel-
Monkeys are also found to west and east
of this break.*

primates, and they are now very common animals in zoos and as pets. In fact, it is quite surprising how many may nowadays be found in private homes in the United States.

These pot-bellied, spidery limbed, worried-faced creatures, with vicious tempers and unfathomable wills of their own, are distributed all over the equatorial and tall-deciduous forests of South and Central American tropics, apart from the Tupi forests of southeastern Brazil. They come in a bewildering variety of coat colors; and, although the majority of individuals in any one area may look very much alike or be virtually identical, there are always some in any troupe that differ markedly from the rest. They also vary remarkably in facial configuration and consequently in expression. About a dozen distinct color types, which may be called "nodal forms," have been given specific names, but there is now strong evidence that there are many intergrades between several of these and that these can on occasion be arranged in progressive series or clines; so that if one travels from an area where one form is typical to a distant territory where another prevails, those that one passes on the way will vary by degrees in the color of their coats and thus link the two extremes together. As with the Capuchins, our records and thus our knowledge of these variations and their relationships is not as yet sufficiently complete to warrant any over-all description, but a certain number of definable forms or species have now been recognized, and these supply a basis for identification of the majority.

Starting in Amazonia, we find what may be called a nodal stock represented by a pure black type (*Ateles paniscus*), with black face, hands and feet. Variations on this have been described as *Ateles variegatus*, which, though highly variable indeed, usually has a certain amount of white on the underside, and may also have pure white hands and hind legs, and a white strip along the underside of the tail. Another form called *A. marginatus* has a white brow and a bright red face that is hairless. Moving north to the Guiana Massif, pure black animals with naked, bright pink faces, once named *A. ater*, are found, but these change by progressive steps westward and may blend into the totally different-appearing form of the Orinoco Basin, named *A. belzebuth*. This is black with a golden rump, orange flanks and yellow undersides. The body is clothed in long, lanky hair in all these types, but there are forms that live at altitudes of

several thousand feet in the Andes, and some of these have much shorter, closer, more woolly coats, although never developing an underfur.

Stepping over the Andes into the western or Pacific-Caribbean forests (see map), we encounter a nodal type the members of which are basically brown-coated and have the naked skin of their faces varying from black to flesh pink, usually with lighter areas, and especially light "spectacles," around the eyes. Careful and all-embracing studies of the Spider-Monkeys of this area undertaken in recent years have led zoologists to believe that those of the Pacific slopes in Colombia are a separate species, called *A. fusciceps;* those in the Caribbean drainage area, a race of *A. belzebuth;* and those from the Panamanian isthmus, *A. geoffroyi*. Westward of Panama almost endless varieties of this last form are spread throughout all closed-forest areas of Central America to the lowlands of Vera Cruz State in Mexico. These are the types most often seen in captivity in the United States.

Spider-Monkeys, if shorn of their very long tails, have much the proportions of Apes, and in many respects they behave like them. Their thumbs are either reduced to mere stubs or are completely absent, and the four remaining fingers form a kind of hook. They travel through the trees by a method known as brachiation, that is to say, by timed swings resulting in leaps, like a man on a flying trapeze. Their tails are completely prehensile, and they can hang by them alone for long periods. They are very common animals, inhabiting some forests to the number of two hundred per square mile, each party having its own territory, traveling much the same tree routes daily, and sleeping in a special place. They can clear chasms about thirty feet wide by leaping and can move along through trees as fast as a man can walk over clear ground below. They are shy animals, but if you creep up on them they make a great display of ferocity, coming down to the lower limbs and shaking the branches, coughing, croaking and barking, and, according to Carpenter, who studied them intensively for many months, even lobbing dead branches at him with their hands or tails.

They eat primarily green nuts but nibble on leaves and buds and relish certain fruits. They also take insect larvae, tree snails and possibly small tree frogs, but they do not seem to understand the eggs of birds. In captivity they are basically vegetarians but, like all other monkeys, will take raw meat and chicken entrails—and sometimes with the greatest avidity, especially during the fall and throughout the winter. They have a fairly well-developed social system in the wild, there being gangs within the "tribes" which associate at night but split up by day. Some of these may be bachelor groups. They have no set breeding season, but the females have a definite oestrous period. The single young is first carried on the belly and then rides on it's mother's lower back with its tail twined around hers.

Being very common, these animals are offered for sale as pets at all times and in considerable quantities, and the price asked is often very moderate. Many people buy them, and, since they are rather hardy, they grow up in the household. When mature they are large animals and can become very difficult to handle. Normally rather cautious and gentle, they may nonetheless become extremely dangerous—and this without warning and after years of amicable placidity. To cite a typical case of such behavior, we may recount what once occurred when one of these animals, which had lived for four years in a small zoo and had been given absolute freedom with numbers of children, was taken to a studio to rehearse for a television performance. It was at first quiet, gentle, and loving to its handler, whom it had known for many months. However, a member of an orchestra present was sucking a lollipop, and this caught the monkey's eye. It started towards this man, leading its handler by the hand, but when the latter started to hold it back, it suddenly rounded on him without warning, seized him with both hands and both feet, and started to bite savagely. Shaken off, it bit two other men and then went straight for a woman sitting fifty feet away. It took over an hour to pacify the animal and catch it. Thereafter it became absolutely tame and gentle again, and remained so for a year. Then it erupted again, suddenly attacking a girl who refused it a piece of cake at the zoo.

The name Spider-Monkey is singularly appropriate, not only because these animals are slender-bodied and have exceptionally long, slim arms and legs, but also because of their peculiar gait when running along a branch or the ground on all fours, at which time the elbows and knees may actually angle upwards, giving a very spidery effect. Their movements are nonetheless very fluid, and, although they could hardly be called graceful, are so perfectly coordinated that the animal seems to flow along. This belies the true speed of their motions. If kept in a cage with other kinds of monkeys—and they are remarkably sociable in this respect, tolerating even Rhesus and other tough Old World monkeys—they almost invariably assume a kind of leadership over all, mostly by somehow getting everywhere first and notably to food. They just swing gently along, reach out with a long arm, and take the food from under the very noses of the other animals. Their agility in the forests is almost unbelievable.

A near relative of the Spider-Monkeys is a large but rare animal known as the Woolly Spider-Monkey (*Brachyteles arachnoides*), which comes from the southeastern Tupi forest region of Brazil, and is there the counterpart of both the Woolly and the Spider-Monkeys. Outstretched, its head, body, and tail measure up to five feet, and it is clothed in a dense woolly undercoat and a rather thick overcoat of long guard hairs. The tail is fully prehensile and has a naked finger-pad, and the thumb is either totally absent or is represented by a knob on one hand only. In color they vary from gray through various browns to yellowish; there is a slightly lighter cheek ruff, and the naked skin of the face is gray except for the muzzle and chin, which are flesh pink. They have very long, slender, thickened, clawlike nails. Nothing whatever seems to be known about their habits or even their food, and there are no records of their being kept alive and under observation. Despite their somewhat different appearance, these animals are very closely related to the Woolly Monkeys (*Lagothrix*), which we will now consider.

These have the reputation of being the ideal monkey pets, and they are indeed slow-moving, gentle, loving and very clean. Much of this reputation, however, is probably the result of the amazingly human conformity and expression of their faces, which have been described in such phrases as "a worried old man seen through the wrong end of a telescope," for while they are undoubtedly gentle in disposition and usually very reliable, untamed adults can be sullen, or even downright ferocious, if molested. They usually seem to have a terror of an open human hand, and if threatened with this, as if to be struck, their terror may turn to uncontrolled fury. They have extremely powerful jaws for cracking nuts and hard-shelled fruits, and exaggerated canine teeth, and if they do bite, their jaws sometimes have to be pried loose before they will let go.

They are heavy-bodied, with moderate limbs of about equal length, long tails that have the naked finger-pads under the extremities well developed, comparatively large thumbs and great toes, and thick, woolly coats with a dense underfur. They are normally obese simply through prodigious eating, so that their Brazilian name of *barrigudos* or "bag-bellies" is highly appropriate. Although half a dozen species have been described, it appears that most if not all of these are mere color types that blend geographically one into the other. They range in color from a uniform very dark gray that is almost black through silvery gray to nearly white, or through deep chocolate to pure brown and even to a creamy buff. Then again, individuals with lighter bodies and darker heads, limbs and/or tails are very common, but these individuals may sometimes change from this pattern to a smooth over-all dark gray in one season. They range all over the northern, and apparently throughout isolated tracts of the southern, half of Amazonia.

In the wild, Woolly Monkeys are found in small parties and very often, when feeding, intermingle with Capuchins, Spider-Monkeys and even Howlers, and these aggregations may also include bands of Tamarins. The Woollies seem to get along amicably with all others and are very sociable among themselves. At the approach of danger it is usually the Tamarins that give the alarm and then go streaking off first, straight throught the smaller branches, like squirrels; the next to scatter in flight are the Capuchins, which invariably set up a tremendous racket; the Spider-Monkeys often stop to shout and grimace, even descending to the lower branches to do so, and only leave at the last minute, swinging off in disorder; the imperial Howlers, on the other hand, usually assemble with much deep croaking and then start off all together with a great deal of crashing and set purpose, headed by the big females and chivvied by the males; but the Woolly Monkeys, as often as not, drop each into a crotch between branches and then remain absolutely silent, peering down with solemn expressions. Even rapping on the tree boles, which usually dislodges any stubborn arboreal animal, often fails to put them to flight, and they may then behave quite unlike any other monkeys, gathering slowly together into a single bunch, clinging to each other, and making a cooing noise. But when they do decide to retire, their going is so much less noisy and so much more rapid than one might expect that it is very often missed altogether. Travelers have told of being showered with fruit and twig fragments for upwards of an hour without being able to detect the perpetrators of the downpour in the foliage high above—and then, when all efforts to make them desist or to move had failed, of being amazed to see a fair-sized party of Woollies start meandering off, using hands, feet, and tails in methodical sequence, as if nothing were untoward.

In captivity they show much the same combination of caution and indifference. They move about with what appears to be the utmost care, accept food from the hand gently and take a long time breaking it apart and munching on it. Woollies are probably the only monkeys that, if used to humans, may be allowed freedom with some impunity. They are not nearly so destructive of our artifacts as others, and they will wander off to the nearest trees and climb about in them all day, usually without making any attempt to stray far from the place they have come to regard as their home. They display the normal curiosity of all monkey-like animals, and they likewise find the game of hide-and-seek highly entertaining, but they appear to have an innate trust in humans. Curiously, they have also been observed to show much affection for other animals both domestic and wild, and they will even adopt dolls, which they will carry about lovingly and take to bed with them if permitted and able to do so. They live rather well in captivity but are susceptible to cold and readily contract bronchial troubles, and are almost equally susceptible, like the Pithecoids, to respiratory troubles induced by too dry an atmosphere at high temperatures. However, it is the general opinion of zoo men that they are not easy to keep until maturity. They seem to need a great deal more exercise than their slow movements and rather lackadaisical habits might indicate, and their apparently normal habit of excessive eating seems often to be their undoing.

They are large monkeys when full grown, with head and body sometimes exceeding two feet and tails slightly longer. One young at a birth is apparently the rule, and the baby is nursed for over a year, but the period of gestation is not definitely known. They are slow growing and have a very long life span, if certain rather general records are to be believed. The intestinal tract does not appear to be in any way specially adapted to the vast amounts of food that these animals manifestly can eat, yet the volume they may consume in a day is prodigious. In captivity they will, with the usual individual preferences and dislikes, take almost anything edible, from leaves and green vegetables to raw liver, which they relish especially in the autumn, eggs, cooked meat, bread, jam, nuts, fruits, berries, root vegetables, rice, corn and other farinaceous foods, cheese, and all manner of candy, cakes and ice cream, which does not seem to harm them in the least even in huge quantities. In the wild they appear to take all manner of "fruits," with emphasis on green nuts, which they can readily obtain by splitting the hardest shells with their powerful jaws. They are also known to eat some leaves, buds and flowers, and they are reputed to take caterpillars, the grubs of beetles and the larvae of tree ants.

The last of the Ceboids or Hand-tailed Monkeys to be considered are known as Howlers or, most misleadingly in many parts of South America, as "Baboons." They are the largest of the Ceboids, and in one of their color forms the most magnificent of American Primates. In habits and character also they have a majesty that can hardly be matched. If the countries of South America ever decided to federate or wished to choose a common emblem, this might well be the best animal to select as typifying the continent, roaring his individualistic defiance at the world, emblazoned in red-gold on a green jungle treetop against an azure tropical sky. There is no other primate that approaches the Howlers in behavior, and there is none that so profoundly impresses human beings. If you have once been into the tropical forests of America beyond the tourist periphery and the secondary growth of farm and previously cleared land, and heard the Howlers, you will carry forever somewhere in the recesses of your brain a sort of sound recording that will never be equaled by anything else in nature.

These animals travel about the forest via the treetops but stay within recognized tribal territories. They are led by a large male who normally—and, it is often alleged, invariably—does all the roaring for the group. This is not always so, however, as the entire group have on occasion been observed indulging in a sort of ceremony, an old male leading off and the rest joining in for a brief period and then suddenly all falling silent at once. Not all Howlers call thus all the time, and in some Central American areas they may seldom utter a sound. Nonetheless, it is the leaders who will be heard making the forest ring with a long-drawn-out combination of sounds that starts with a sort of pumping growl, bursts into a series of booming howls, then converts to a single, double or triple roar, and finally trails off into an inconceivable complex of sounds that have sometimes convinced the uninitiated that at least four full-grown jaguars were fighting not more than a hundred yards away. Sometimes all the tribal leaders within hearing go off at very nearly the same time; and then, as each falls silent, you can hear more distant ones carrying on, so that the calls go rushing outwards in all directions like a wave. They often go on howling all day and all night in some areas. The activity does not seem to have any particular connection with changes in the amount of light, the incidence of rain or certain other such factors as have from time to time been suggested as its primary cause. Rather, it would seem, as suggested by Carpenter, that these roars are warnings to surrounding troupes to keep off feeding territories, and they thus become more frequent the denser the population and the closer the troupes are pressed together. The rowdiest are reported to be those inhabiting the Rio Branco Basin on the western slopes of the Guiana Massif; and these also are the largest and most magnificently colored, being all over a metallic reddish golden bronze, with huge pendent beards.

Howlers range from the southern Mexican border throughout the tall-deciduous and equatorial forests of Central America, south to the Amazon–La Plata watershed, and east to the island of Trinidad and the forests of Maranhão (see map). They come in almost all possible colors and color combinations, from pure black to pure metallic gold. There are at least six nodal types that are regarded as full species—a black form in Central America (*Alouatta villosa*), which has silky fur and ranges south and east to the Andes, where are found various closely related forms, named A. *palliata;* a red-gold type, A. *seniculus,* which is spread from the Caribbean watershed of Colombia to Brazilian Guiana; a variegated type, A. *belzebul,* which appears to blend into the southern form of A. *seniculus* and is either black with red hands, feet, and tail-tip, or brown with lighter hands, feet, and tail, and a yellow underside; and last, a rare form known as A. *carayensis.*

Apart from their various howling propensities,

the populations differ little in habits. Leaf- and fruit-eaters, they are immensely powerful animals with fully prehensile tails, thick coats and a positively frightening set of teeth. In disposition they are dour and grouchy, though they can be tamed—and are then silent, rather solemn and somehow pathetic. They do not do well in captivity, but shortly before writing this I met a collector from Brazil who asserted that a special selection of vitamins had now been devised which, when added to the diet of captive specimens, appeared to stimulate their appetites and keep them in good health, and even, he alleged, prompted them to howl. Until this is confirmed and such a formula becomes available, however, these animals should be regarded as being suitable only for larger zoos with specialized experience in such matters.

The disproportionate volume of sound made by Howlers is accomplished by special structures connected with their throats. These are extremely difficult to understand even with the aid of the clearest drawings made from a dissection, and are quite impossible to interpret without an illustration. At the risk of oversimplifying the matter, we may say that these structures consist—and most pronouncedly in large males—of two irregularly shaped, globular, bony boxes about the size of hen's eggs; these are formed from the hyoid bones and what are known as the thyroidal cartilages, placed one before the other in front of the throat and lying in the skin under the "beard" between the two sides of the lower jaw. They are connected at the back to the throat passage, and act as sound boxes, the actual roaring being made partly in the throat and partly at the back of the mouth.

The thumbs of Howlers are not opposed, and when climbing they use them held to the second or index finger, while the other three fingers are also held together and go around the other side of the branch. Their great toes are large and fully opposed. They move through the trees with a sort of trundling motion whereby four of their five grasping organs are if possible firmly anchored to something at all times. This curious method of progression, reminiscent of the deliberate motions of the Slow Lorises, nevertheless does not retard them at all, and Howlers can travel through the treetops faster than a man can run along the forest floor below them. They seldom leap unless very much alarmed. When feeding, they can hang for a very long time by their tails alone.

In their daily feeding routine Howlers seem to differ somewhat from country to country, though this may be the result of weather conditions rather than of set habit. They are about at dawn in most countries and feed until the sun gets hot, when they tend to rest while the young ones play. On overcast days they may feed on till dusk, and they are all active again from about five o'clock till dark. They may continue to feed for an hour after sundown. They stay within territories apparently regarded by themselves as belonging to their tribal group, and, if they wander off these, noise contests take place between them and the rightful owners of the adjacent territory. They are upper-canopy dwellers and travel by regular tree-roads.

Howlers have a number of habits that either parallel or are actually identical to those of some of the Old World monkeys we shall meet presently. Notable among these are blinking the eyelids and waggling their tongues with the mouths held open while facing each other—both actions, it has been suggested, being forms of communication. Further, they are more thoroughly tribalized than other American monkeys, and have clan rules of conduct more like Old World monkeys. Leader males have considerable authority, and direct communal activities vocally by a wide series of distinct sounds. The mothers have complete control of their own young, but if the latter get lost or fall, the whole tribe gather around and assist while the infant is retrieved—sometimes even when dead—the males watching out for intruders and roaring defiance at any who may approach.

9

The Multiplicity of Guenons

THE LONG-TAILED MONKEYS OF AFRICA

Crowned Guenon

W E N O W L E A V E the New World for good and return to the Old, where dwell all the living primates we have not yet discussed. These comprise all the *other* monkeys and the apes, but they also include ourselves, and this presents us with somewhat of a conundrum. Man has been indigenous to the New World since preglacial times, or at least since a time preceding some of the last advances of the northern ice caps, but he does not appear to be truly indigenous to these continents; for, according to all findings up to the present time, he came here from eastern Asia via what are now the island steppingstones of the Bering Straits or by a previous land bridge thereabout. However, at just what point in time we should draw the line between being indigenous and nonindigenous is still open to debate. It is common scientific practice today to use the somewhat arbitrary point in time called "the beginning of the Pleistocene Era"—which is to say an estimated one million years ago—and this is assumed to be the beginning of the onslaught of the first cold wave that produced the first southward advance of the northern ice caps in what is now called the (current) Ice Age. If we adopt this definition, Man is not indigenous to the New World

but is an immigrant thereto, and may be assumed not to have existed here before said Ice Age began. Certainly all that has been found of his ancestors to date is of the Old World, and he may therefore be treated as belonging to that area, exclusively and indigenously.

The *other* monkeys—which is to say all those animals that may qualify for such a designation in popular parlance, exclusive of the apes and men —are exceedingly numerous and may be divided into three major groups. From the point of view of current and precise zoological taxonomy, they all belong to a superfamily named the *Cercopithecoidea,* and indeed to a single family known as the *Cercopithecidae,* which in turn is subdivided into only two subfamilies called the *Cercopithecinae*

99

and the *Colobinae*. The reasons for this seemingly complex arrangement need not concern us, but their outcome must be given in order to obviate complaints that might be directed at the division of these creatures into *three* rather than two groups. This we do, moreover, by distinguishing the Guenons, together with the Talapoins, Swamp and Red Monkeys of Africa, from the rest of the *Cercopithecinae*—namely the macaques and baboons—and calling them the Cercopithecoids. There is, moreover, legitimate reason for doing so, because they may be clearly differentiated on dental characteristics, as we shall see when discussing the Mangabeys in the next chapter. The remaining *Cercopithecinae* are herewith designated the Cynopithecoids, meaning the "Dog-shaped Monkey-like Ones"—a general description which they have understandably often been given in the past. The third group, the leaf-eaters or *Colobinae*, are then designated the Coloboids.

The designation Cercopithecoids is given to these animals in deference to the Latin name of their principal genus, *Cercopithecus*, which means simply the "Monkeys" (*pithecus*) "with Tails" (*cercus*), but with the implication that these tails are exceptionally long and outstanding features of the animals. They are, of course, by no means the only monkeys with long tails, though one of them—a subspecies of the Montane group (see below)—may have the longest tail in proportion to its head and body length of any Primate. They form a closely knit group of species, found only in Africa south of the Sahara, and all but three of these are contained in one vast genus. Although certain species may grow to a considerable size in some instances and can give an extraordinary account of themselves if molested, they are on the whole rather gentle and composed creatures, with an enormous dignity, both in the wild and in captivity, and they are excessively clean and seem to take pride in their appearance and to delight in showing it off.

There are about one hundred subspecies of Cercopithecoids, but the number of Latinized names that have been applied to recognizable forms or simply to color variations of these animals far exceeds this quantity. Today, after prolonged study, this great host of closely related animals is divided into four genera, one of which contains but a single species, another four, and a third three subspecies. The fourth genus—that of the so-called

Guenons—is divisible into fifteen subgroups, but neither the exact number of valid and full species that each of these contains nor the total number of permissible species of Guenons is at present known. This may sound like a very odd and certainly an unscientific statement, and it therefore calls for some explanation. There are several factors involved, and an appreciation of these and some understanding of the problems they pose may go far towards explaining the basis of systematics, the work of taxonomists, and the frustrations experienced by nonspecialists who endeavor to obtain a clear statement of the facts of animal classification.

First, there are considerably over one hundred different kinds of Guenon Monkeys known to have come out of Africa, alive or preserved. Second, there are undoubtedly still more to be discovered. Third, many more than one hundred, and perhaps twice that number, of Latin names have been applied to these—the same specimens getting different names, different animals getting the same name, and specialists changing the names or replacing them with new ones. However, even more confusingly, most of these animals have been bandied about between the status of full species and subspecies. They have been differently grouped and sometimes regrouped by almost every specialist who has studied the Guenons. Some "complete surveys" or over-all reviews have also been undertaken from time to time, but not one of them has proved acceptable to all specialists, and all have, in time, been outmoded by new studies and by the acquisition of previously unknown kinds of monkeys. Agreement is no more in sight today than it was fifty or seventy-five years ago, and nobody can take the time or spend the money to travel all over equatorial Africa to collect all known kinds and map their distributions. Short of this, however, it is virtually impossible to sort them all out and attempt to get universal agreement on which types may be designated full species, which subspecies, and which of the latter belong to which of the former.

In the meantime, we have attempted to list and then discuss the Guenons in some semblance of order. To this end they are divided, as shown below, into fifteen "groups," each named after its best-known and outstanding species. We would like to be able to give the *names* (either specific or sub-specific) of all those creatures that we are assuming should be included in or subtended to each of these groups, but neither does space permit, nor does the current state of our knowledge make this possible. This list is the compounded residue from an elaborate distillation and filtration of all previous lists, and was submitted to Dr. W. C. Osman Hill, and subsequently finalized in accordance with suggestions made by him.

However, it must be understood that there is still no certainty as to the number of *species* that should be assigned to each group, but that there is, curiously, a little more assurance as to the number of subspecies. The exact designation of the latter is beyond the scope of this book.

		SP.	SUBSP.
A. SWAMP MONKEYS (*Allenopithecus*)			
(1) Allen's Guenon (*A. nigroviridis*)	1	1	
B. PIGMY GUENONS (*Miopithecus*)			
(1) Talapoins (*M. talapoin*)		1	4
C. GUENONS (*Cercopithecus*)			
(1) Spot-nosed (*C. nictitans*)		1	12
(2) Lesser Spot-nosed (*C. petaurista*)		1	3
(3) Black-cheeked (*C. ascanius*)		1	7
(4) Moustached (*C. cephus*)		1	1
(5) Red-eared (*C. erythrotis*)		1	3
(6) Red-bellied (*C. erythrogaster*)	1		2
(7) Diademed (*C. mitis*)		1	20
(8) Mountain (*C. l'hoesti*)		2	3
(9) Hamlyn's (*C. hamlyni*)		1	1
(10) De Brazza's (*C. neglectus*)		1	5
(11) Dianas (*C. diana*)		2	3
(12) Crowned (*C. pogonias*)		1	3
(13) Wolf's (*C. wolfi*)		1	4
(14) Monas (*C. mona*)		2	7
(15) Savannah (*C. aethiops*)		1	20
D. RED MONKEYS (*Erythrocebus*)			
(1) Patas Monkeys (*E. patas*)		1	3

That there are still as-yet-undescribed types to be found, some of which may even be valid species in the true sense of that word, is manifest to anyone involved in the international animal-trading business. For instance, in 1954 we received from a friend in Boston a *Cercopithecus* that had been bought from an importer two years previously as a semiadult of nondescript appearance but that had, in the meantime, grown to really remarkable dimensions. It had a dark greenish gray head and back, pale gray throat, chest and undersides, a tail jet-black above with a pure white belt to the tip below, and white hands and black feet. Its head and body, outstretched, measured just short of eighteen inches and its tail two feet nine inches, proportions that are simply not on record for any other monkey. What is more, it did not resemble any known description of any Guenon; and yet it was indubitably a *Cercopithecus*, had come out of an East African port (Mombasa), and was not a freak. Unfortunately it was killed in a fire before it had been properly examined and described.

The Guenons are arboreal, and most are predominantly denizens of the closed-canopy forests, but they are also distributed throughout the Montane, the lowland Tall Deciduous, and the Equatorial Rain and Swamp Forest zones. There are also certain species that have taken to living in Gallery Forest bordering rivers and streams on otherwise open savannahs, or in isolated copses on grass fields, and the members of the *aethiops* group are found all over the savannahs themselves. Apart from the diminutive Swamp Monkeys—which, of course, do not live in, but above, swamps—they are all very much of the same proportions. Some species, such as the Dianas, are on an average somewhat larger when adult, but there are indications of a moderate gigantism among some Guenons just as there are among Squirrel-Monkeys and some Capuchins, and individuals of almost all the well-known species with extreme dimensions have been recorded. To a certain extent, they are all omnivorous; but they seem to feed predominantly on green nuts and fruits, and have a tendency to take some leaves, shoots and flower buds, and also to eat insects, tree snails and other small animal items. It is often said that some of them eat birds' eggs, but I have not found a single authenticated account of their doing so in the wild, and captive individuals seem to take considerable alarm if presented with an egg—or, for that matter, with any rounded, smooth object resembling one, such as a pebble or a cake of soap. Why this should be, I cannot say, but it seems to be inherent in many arboreal primates, as noted among Ceboids and Hapaloids.

The arboreal Guenons are most delightful animals. In their own native haunts, they lead extraordinarily gay but constrained lives pervaded by a singular orderliness and decorum. They travel about in loose tribal groups but do not normally have designated leaders, and they seem to be free to do more or less what they want within limits, as in a true democracy. When undisturbed, they keep together by a regular system of complacent and contented croaks, but at the slightest sign of danger the spotter gives out with a coughing sound that is taken up by all the others. The whole troupe will then mill about until all or the majority have located and identified the danger; they then get under way but without any organization, though invariably all choosing the same direction for retreat. Unlike most other monkey-like creatures, they do not jump from branch to branch but go dashing along the most direct path available and then just sail out into the air and land upright, because of the weight of their long trailing tails, on the face of the densest mass of foliage available. This they grab with all four extremities; then they scramble upwards to the nearest branch and proceed *through* the next tree by the most direct route. A party of Guenons can cover space through a closed canopy as fast as a man can run on the ground along a forest path. It must not be thought, however, that they do not sometimes make mistakes or misjudge their leaps. I have seen many fall, including a whole line of hysterical Mona Monkeys that in their panic tried to leap a small river. One and all fell right into the middle of it, screaming loudly, but all quickly swam ashore without further mishap, using a dog-paddle stroke, and immediately clambered up into the trees again.

The young, which are born at any time of the year but which may appear seasonally in certain areas, are at first carried by the mothers in their arms but learn to follow along by themselves at a comparatively early age. They are extraordinarily fast-growing during their early lives and seem to be born with more competence than most other primates.

In captivity most Guenons are somewhat alike in temperament. They are fairly hardy and remarkably long-suffering. If introduced to human ways when young, they make extremely fine and understanding pets, but they tend to show personal preferences, and these may in some cases be based on the sex of the human being. Unlike the Ceboids, which are unpredictable and subject to tantrums, Cercopithecoids usually have established patterns of behavior, though these may be almost as inexplicable. Some things they will do readily, others they *may* do, still others they simply *will not* do. Then again, every new situation is assessed by them on their own terms and according to their own "philosophy." Just how they will judge it and what their reactions will be are usually beyond prediction. Old males of all kinds, and especially those of the more specialized types such as Dianas, tend

to be rather dour and dogmatic. They have a more set pattern of behavior than any other monkeys and often simply will not cope with novel situations at all, either ignoring them and going to sleep or making violent threatening gestures. If a Guenon ever really decides to bite you, whether out of spite, peeve or terror, you may well need prompt medical attention, for they can attack without prior warning and actually try to take a piece of flesh away with them, rather than give a warning nip or bite like almost all other animals. The little spot-nosed types, on the other hand, are almost as playful and mischievous as Capuchins.

The classification of the Cercopithecoids is not an easy matter. Setting aside for the moment the three forms that are sufficiently different from all others to warrant the creation of special genera for their reception—the little Swamp Monkeys (*Allenopithecus*), the Talapoins (*Miopithecus*), and the Red Monkeys (*Erythrocebus*)—we are confronted with some hundred distinct kinds of monkeys, all so similar in build as to be almost identical if shorn of their colorful pelts, but displaying a very wide range of coat color, pattern and adornment. Between a few of these there is some indication of gradation, but, unlike the Ceboids, the majority of forms constitute quite distinct and apparently "fixed" subspecies, each having a prescribed geographical range.

Then again, the young and immature of many of the Guenons are singularly nondescript in appearance and often are quite unlike their full-grown parents: the young of all subspecies of a group or even of sundry different species may look very much alike; and quite a number of subspecies and even some full species have been founded on the skins of single immature or subadult individuals, or even on such animals housed in zoos. Further complications have arisen through an overzealous desire to simplify the over-all picture, whereby whole groups of forms have been arbitrarily lumped with others of quite different appearance. A notable example is the association of those forms with pronounced peaks on their heads and very distinctive color pattern, known as *pogonias, grayi* and *nigripes,* with the Mona Monkeys, as mere subspecies thereof, when they are not only altogether different but even inhabit the same territory. The classic definition of a species was based on the assumption that all members of the population so defined could interbreed and produce fertile offspring but that none of them could do so with individuals of any other population. This neat formula has, however, had to be abandoned, for many animals that appear in every respect to be widely different have now been recorded as interbreeding, both in natural and artificial conditions—as, for example, in recent experiments carried out at Odessa in the U.S.S.R., whereby Rhesus Monkeys crossed with Hamadryas Baboons produced fertile offspring. We know little of the breeding habits of wild populations of monkeys and especially of the Guenons and so cannot say which forms can, may, or do interbreed. At the same time, we have in no case an over-all picture of the variation within any given population of these monkeys that look alike, and we also do not know to what extent whole populations may not be changing gradually in collective appearance, by natural selection, mutation or other causes. Thus the definition of species per se is not only extremely difficult but more or less arbitrary, and the best that we can attempt is to plot the distribution of all recognizably distinct forms. Doing this, it will be found that the subspecies of any one species or nodal type form a distributional checkerboard, or rather jigsaw puzzle, no two or more being found in the same area. The reason for this is obvious; for if two did so coexist, being but subspecies, they would interbreed, lose their individual identity, and thus become but a single intermediate form. The corollary to or extension of this is that, if two distinct kinds of monkeys are found in the same natural niche, and in the same vegetational zone in the same territory, they must not be interbreeding and may therefore be regarded as distinct species. Employing this formula, and at the same time taking into account the actual appearance of the animals concerned, scientists have now divided the Guenons into the above-named fifteen groups containing but one or two full species each.

But before going into this, we must introduce a rather exceptional kind of Guenon-like monkey of very small stature, unique appearance and somewhat marked anatomical distinction that came to light in 1907, and that inhabits the swamp forests of the southeastern Gabun and northwestern Congo Basin. It is considered to be sufficiently different from all other guenons to warrant the establishment of a special genus for its reception, and it is now known as *Allenopithecus nigroviridis*. The specific epithet is well chosen, since the pelage of the little

animal is basically black but the whole back, flanks and undersides are stippled with greenish yellow. The face is black with gray areas round the eyes, dark whiskers and a dark face fringe. The chin, throat, chest and inner sides of the limbs are bright yellow, and this color extends up the sides of the neck to behind the ears in the form of a long fluffy boa, the two tines of which almost meet over the back of the neck. These monkeys are very agile little animals, eat fruit, green nuts and leaves, consort in small family parties, and frequent the densest and dampest forests and particularly those that are seasonally flooded. At the time of writing, specimens are living in the National Zoo in Washington. They have very distinctive voices and make high-pitched noises unlike the calls of other Guenons.

There are those who contend that these so-called Swamp Monkeys are not sufficiently different from other guenons to warrant their separation in a special genus, and these specialists would place them close to the somewhat similar-appearing and also small species known as the Talapoins (now called *Miopithecus*)—of which there are four recognized subspecies, found in the western and central Congo Basin, northern Angola, and the Ruwenzori area of the Congo respectively. They are only a little bigger than large squirrels when full grown. In color they are a greenish black above, varying shades of gray below, and they have little yellow moustaches, short yellowish whiskers and orange spectacles around their eyes. These tiny monkeys have slightly different tooth construction from other guenons, and their hands and fingers are exceptionally short, with rather pronounced webbing between the digits. For this and some other even lesser reasons, they too have been separated as a distinct genus.

The Talapoins stand considerably apart from the rest of the Guenons, so that one might commence the description of the latter with any species. However, there is one large species-group that is both widespread—from Senegal to Uganda—and appears to be of a somewhat generalized nature, lacking exaggerations of coat pattern and adornment. This is known as the *nictitans* group or, colloquially, as the Spot-nosed or Putty-nosed Monkeys. There are about a dozen recognized subspecies that may represent one or two valid species and, taking distribution into account, these may be laid out in a series that shows certain progressive changes in coloration from one side of their range to the other. They are perhaps the commonest of the forest guenons, especially in West Africa, and are of most charmingly neat appearance. It has been suggested that, starting from them, one could develop almost all other extant guenons by exaggeration of certain features such as moustaches, whiskers, peaked topknots, beards, etc., and by multifarous developments of contrasting colors. They doubtless do not represent any such basic stock, but they are considerably less adorned than most if not all others.

Basically they are dark olive-green in color, the individual hairs clothing the body, limbs and tail being black, banded with various shades of yellowish olive. Their faces and extremities tend to be black, but there is always an inverted, heart-shaped white spot caused by a mat of extremely short, pure white hairs on the nose, in marked contrast to the rest of the face. In some forms the chin, throat, chest and under and inner sides may be gray or even white, and this may extend to the underside of the tail. Their eyes are a lustrous, rich, reddish brown and are extremely bright and intelligent looking. Most of them are small as guenons go, but there is a distinct trend to gigantism among them, or at least specimens of dimensions far exceeding the average are fairly frequently encountered. They are treetop dwellers and stay in closed-canopy forest, but in their various forms are found in coastal, swamp, palm, tall deciduous, and evergreen nondeciduous equatorial forests. They apparently eat a considerable quota of leaves, shoots, buds and even flowers in addition to some barks, green nuts, fruits and dry nuts, tree beans and such other items as remain in the pod on tall trees. Some of them—either individuals or whole populations—may display bright red coloration on chin and chest or about the anal region; but this may sometimes be washed out of their skins, while alive or after preservation, with soap and warm water, and it appears to be vegetable dyes derived from their food rather than true pigmentation of the pelt.

Distinct subspecies of Spot-nosed Guenons occur in the far western forest block (*C. n. stampflii*) west of the central Ivory Coast, in Ashanti (*C. n. petaurista*), in the Dahomey–Nigeria–British Cameroons and Fernando Po area (*C. n. martini*), in the north Cameroons Gabun area north of the Ogowe River (*C. n. nictitans*). The first two, together with a form called *buettikoferi*, are now regarded as a distinct group known as the Lesser

Spot-nosed Guenons. Then, in the Congo Basin, there are seven forms of the common Congo Monkey (*C. ascanius*). There is one form known as far east as Uganda (*C. a. schmidti*). When the known distribution of these is plotted on a map it may be seen at a glance that each occupies a different area which is either isolated from adjacent closed-canopy forest blocks by treeless or open forest belts, or is bounded by large rivers. In no known case do two forms occur in the same area.

The Moustached Guenons (*Cercopithecus cephus*) are found south and east of the Sanaga River in the French Cameroons to the southern limits of the great closed-canopy forest and to the Congo River. Allen and others placed two more, the Red-eared Guenon (*C. erythrotis*) from Fernando Po and its Nigerian ally (*C. sclateri*), in this group; and it may be that these monkeys, which are obviously closely related, should be so associated, for they have much the same coloring, occupy adjacent and contiguous areas to *cephus* and have much the same facial adornments. The true *cephus,* however, are smaller monkeys and, as can be seen from the photograph, have bright blue, naked faces and very exaggerated moustachios. Although appearing somewhat like the Monas, they inhabit the same territory but keep quite apart and distinct. They are neat little Guenons with short muzzles and rounded heads. They make most amiable pets and display a pronounced curiosity almost of the order of the Capuchins, and they are most adept at taking our artifacts apart. Almost all monkey-like primates for some reason appear to be fascinated by pills of all kinds, but every Moustached Monkey I have owned or known has had a positive passion for any such object, smashing bottles to get at them and, on one occasion, eating several dozen sleeping capsules without any apparent ill effects.

There are three forms of *erythrotis*—one on the island of Fernando Po, that is distinguishable from the common mainland form only by its smaller size. They are larger monkeys than *cephus* and are called the Red-eared Guenons. Unfortunately, the third form of this group (*C. e. sclateri*) does *not* have red ears, and in other respects is considerably different. The typical *erythrotis* from Fernando Po are of a greenish brown color and have darker to black hands and feet; the upperside of the tail is also dark throughout its terminal half. The back is suffused with rich brown that extends onto the upper half of the tail. The face is black,

43. Red-eared Guenon
(*Cercopithecus erythrotis*)
A rare species probably most closely related to the Moustached Guenons.
It is found on the island of Fernando Po and the adjacent parts of the mainland.
This form has an orange diamond of short hairs on the nose and a red fuzz on the ears.

ARTHUR W. AMBLER: NATIONAL AUDUBON

44. Green Monkey
(*Cercopithecus aethiops sabaeus*)
The typical West African form of the numerous Guenons of the orchard-bush and savannah belts of Africa, ranging from the Gambias to Somaliland and south to the Union. Always immaculate, they behave like pampered fashion models in captivity but make intelligent pets.

ROY PINNEY

45. Patas Monkey (*Erythrocebus patas*)
Also known as Hussar or Military
Monkeys, these ground-living, red-coated
animals have the habits, gait, and
personalities of dogs. They can be
broken to collar and leash, and may be
house-trained.

46. Black Mangabey
(*Cercocebus aterrimus*)
The crested or "peaked" species from
the southern Congo. These large, long-
tailed Monkeys of Africa are intermediate between the Guenons and their
allies of Africa, and the Dog-shaped
Monkeys of Asia.

ODD M. CHACE

47. Rhesus Monkey and Baby
(*Macaca* [*Rhesus*] *mulatta*)
The monkey *par excellence;* somewhat
sacred in India, its home country;
the classic escape artist; the "guinea pig"
of modern medical research; the pioneer
of space flight; delinquent of the Primate world; but tough, resilient, long-
suffering, and ingenious—in fact, the
mammal most likely to succeed.

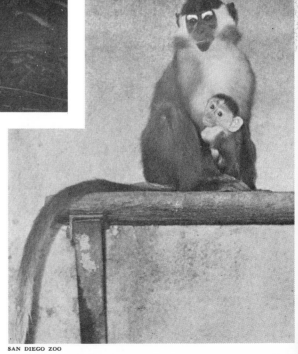

48. Red-capped Mangabey
(*Cercocebus torquatus torquatus*)
The largest of Mangabeys, from the
Nigeria–Cameroons area of West Africa.
The vivid white eyelids are believed
to be used as semaphoring devices for
communication. They are tall-forest
dwellers and prodigious jumpers.

SAN DIEGO ZOO

50. Pig-tailed Macaque (*Macaca nemestrina*)
One of the great Dog-Monkeys of the Indo-
Malayan region, often called the Giant Rhesu
shows special aptitudes as a performer both for
entertainment and for labor.

49. Lion-tailed Monkey
(*Silenus silenus*)
Oddest of the Macaques and
one of the few monkeys au-
thoritatively indicted of unpro-
voked attacks upon men.
Nonetheless, they have been
known to make reliable pets.

51. Crab-eating Macaque
(*Macaca [Cynamolgus] irus*)
A long-tailed species of Dog-Monkey that swarms
throughout the coastal areas of the Bay of
Bengal and parts of the Malayan region. They make
crustaceans their basic diet and are able swimmers.

ERNEST P. WALKER

52. Stump-tailed Macaque
(*Macaca* [*Lyssodes*] *speciosa*, subsp.)
One of the red-faced Dog-Monkeys of the Far
East, and specifically of the mainland group found
throughout the Indo-Chinese area. The famous
Japanese Ape is a close relative. They have tiny,
flattened, and curled tails upon which they sit;
huge cheek pouches; and engagingly comical
personalities. Old ones usually become highly
neurotic if confined.

53. The Black Ape (*Cynopithecus niger*)
A very odd and aberrant, baboon-like
Primate indigenous to the Celebes and a
few associated islands in the East
Indies. A quiet, retiring animal, it is so
highly regarded by the humans inhabiting its country that they claim it as
their original ancestor.

54. The Mandrill
(*Mandrillus sphinx*)
An extreme form of baboon
from the mountains and forests
of the Cameroons–Gabun area of
Africa. The grotesque facial
and rump coloration is
apparently of secondary sexual
significance. Rage can make
it brighter in tone, and it is used
to frighten attackers. A very
dangerous, powerful animal.

55. West African Baboons (*Papio papio*)
A family of the typical olive-green-
colored Baboons of the western group.
These strange-looking monkeys are intelligent, cooperative socialists and make
good mothers. They inhabit savannahs
and drier areas and are increasing
not only despite but because of the
advance of civilization.

56. Hamadryas Baboon
(Comopithecus hamadryas)
A tribal creature found in southern Arabia as well as in Abyssinia and the Sudan. In ancient Egypt it was trained to worship in the temples, wait at table, and weed crops. It was regarded as a messenger of certain gods and was mummified after death.

57. Mount Elgon Guerezas
(Colobus abyssinicus matschei)
A form of the great black-and-white leaf-eating Coloboids of East Africa, once the basis of the trade in "monkey fur." They are strangely aloof and have much of the majesty of the Howlers.

58. Hanuman Langur *(Semnopithecus entellus)*
The famous sacred monkey of the Hindoo faith, which roams unmolested through the villages and temples of India. A large, tough animal, it seems to understand its privileged status and vigorously fights its own kind as well as other animals.

59. Capped Lutong (*Trachypithecus pileatus*)
Probably the best known of the more than two dozen kinds of so-called Capped Langurs of the Assam, Burma, Indo-China, Malaya region. The newborn young are white. This species lives in Assam.

60. Douc (*Pygathrix nemaeus*)
A rare Coloboid monkey from Indo-China, it is the most curiously colored of all Primates, with garishly contrasting areas of the pelage and vivid skin hues. Almost nothing is known of its habits.

and there are vivid yellow cheek whiskers brushed back under the ears. There is a diamond-shaped, bright reddish orange patch on the nose, and the ears are fringed with long hairs of the same color. The upper lip, chin, throat, chest and undersides are pale gray; the underside of the tail is bright orange-red. The mainland form found in the northern Cameroons is identical but larger. Sclater's Guenon (*C. e. sclateri*) is known from only two or three specimens and comes from the delta of the Niger River. In this the naked areas of the face are blue, the nose spot is white, and the ears are also tipped with white. The terminal half of the tail is grizzled gray-green above but pure white below; the underside of the basal half is red. The whole muzzle, lips, chin, throat, chest and undersides are pale gray, and there are marked black plumes under the yellow facial whiskers; otherwise, it resembles the Red-eared Guenons.

Then, there is a large monkey, which has sometimes been erroneously designated as a subspecies of *nictitans,* that occurs throughout western Nigeria from the region of Lagos to the area of the Niger River in the east. This is named *erythrogaster*, which means the "Red-bellied." Actually, this occurs in two forms, one with a gray, the other a red underside, and both forms are on occasion to be found in the same troupe. The red color appears to be true pigmentation rather than staining. These monkeys keep apart from the other local monkeys, and almost certainly constitute a separate species.

One of the largest groups of Guenons is known as the *mitis* group or the Diademed Monkeys, of which there are twenty recognized forms including the well-known Blue Monkeys. These are southeastern forms, ranging from northwestern Angola (*C. mitis mitis*) along the south or eastern bank of the Congo River to Uganda (*C. m. doggetti*), and thence east and south wherever suitable territory occurs to the Indian Ocean seaboard and on to the islands that lie off that coast, from Kenya south to Mozambique. They are rather small, neat monkeys with blue skins and basically black pelage, but are variously adorned with white chin ruffs, collars, whiskers and, as their popular name implies, in some cases with regular diadems around their heads. Many of them have a prominent light brow line, and the back may be washed with gray, brown, yellowish or reddish brown.

These monkeys are not confined to the closed-canopy forest; in fact, few of them inhabit that vegetational zone. The majority are to be found in open forest, in gallery forest along stream and river banks, and in isolated copses on savannah country. They tend to descend to the ground to forage for berries and insects, and they inhabit scrub and low bushes in Mozambique. Though nervous and agile, they seem never to have learned about the dangers to be encountered on the ground, where they are the delight of prowling carnivores, including day-hunting leopards, which have a special predilection for monkeys in any case. They travel about in large gangs, numbering in some cases, it has been reported, over a hundred individuals, and eating a considerably mixed diet. Their vertical range is very extensive, being from sea level to, in many places, the upper tree-line and even up in the stunted growth above this on the great volcanic mountains of Kivu. They seem to be just as much at home in the dry areas of the Transvaal, Somaliland and Nyasaland as in these montane mist-forests. There is, however, still doubt as to whether some of the forms from high altitudes, at present assigned to this group, should not be transferred to the next to be described.

These are the somewhat similar, probably closely related, but truly montane forms known as *Cercopithecus l'hoesti* and *preussi*, the latter probably being only a subspecies of the former species. These are dark-skinned monkeys with black to dark gray pelage but with rich brown saddles on their backs and light gray whiskers brushed back over their ears, sometimes a white chin, throat and chest, and a white underside to the tail. They have a curious distribution. It is a discontinuous one and is confined to higher altitudes on various mountain ranges from the north Cameroons and the island of Fernando Po in the west, via the region of Ubangi-Shari, to the Ituri and Kivu in the east. Specialized faunas composed of readily distinguishable forms of many kinds of mammals, not only primates, have grown up on various of the higher mountain ranges of the central equatorial belt of Africa. Whether this be a case of parallel evolution, or of relics of a former lowland fauna that has been driven up into the mountains where the remnants have become isolated, is a moot point, but examples of sundry genera from very widely separated localities may often be surprisingly alike. These Guenons of the *l'hoesti* group offer a good example of this, specimens of *preussi* from Fernando Po and from the Bamenda Range in the north Cameroons for instance, being indistinguishable. They are leaf- and berry-eaters, and inhabit the dense, moss-festooned mountain forest; the latter is composed of gigantic bushes rather than trees, the branches springing from the trunks just above the ground, the limbs and branches being slender, and the twigs and foliage forming a dense mass down to the ground. The monkeys scramble through this endless entanglement with extraordinary agility, though they may also descend to the ground and scamper along through little natural tunnels under the tangle.

Standing somewhere near the mountain forms is a rather distinct species of Guenon known as Hamlyn's Monkey (*C. hamlyni*). Individuals of this type vary very considerably—almost like some of the Ceboids—and appear to constitute a distinct species with sundry clinal variations. However, the exact status and affiliations of this form have not yet been fully decided upon, and it, like the Red-bellied Guenon, must for the present be left, as it were, "floating" in the general scheme of things.

There is another Guenon of highly distinctive appearance that occurs in five distinct forms. This is called De Brazza's Monkey, or *Cercopithecus neglectus*. It is found in a central eastern area from extreme eastern Ubangi-Shari through the forested southern Bahr-el-Ghazal and the White Nile valley to Uganda and Kenya, inhabiting both closed and open forest, and particularly gallery forest, and large isolated copses where they are numerous and grow not too far apart on parklike savannah. It is an exceedingly beautiful large species with vivid coloration, as may be seen from the photograph. The variously colored areas of the coat pattern are clearly defined, and the animals when full grown and in good condition have an extremely neat appearance, just as if they were wearing well-tailored costumes. They also make attractive pets and are fairly hardy, especially if derived from wild populations living at higher altitudes. They need a mixed and well-balanced diet, including meat, and they relish insects, especially of the order that includes the grasshoppers and crickets. De Brazzas are tremendous jumpers and employ both the typical forest-guenon method of landing on massed foliage and the less typical means of leaping directly from branch to branch. They are also very fast on the ground, galloping like dogs with tails held high. It has been suggested that these animals are an offshoot of the *mitis* group, but there are no

intermediate forms nor any of the latter that give any indication of "leading" to the former, and the high-domed head and jowl adornments of *neglectus* are unique.

Far away in the western part of Africa lives another small and highly special group of Guenons known as the Diana Monkeys. Of these there are two outstanding forms called the Diana (*C. diana diana*) and the Roloway (*C. diana roloway*), which inhabit the farthest western or Gambia-Liberia forest block, and the next or Ivory Coast–Ashanti block respectively. Then there is a very rare, large Guenon of somewhat similar appearance that is named *Cercopithecus dryas* that was described in 1932 as coming from some part of the Belgian Congo. This the inimitable Dr. Ernest Schwarz, who has done so much to bring order out of chaos among the guenons as a whole, groups with the Dianas. There is some doubt, however, as to the status of this form, the place of whose origin is so widely separated from that of the others without there being any forms intermediate in either location or appearance.

The Dianas are the largest and most handsome of all Guenons. Although their general appearance may be seen in the photographs included here, neither of those depicted are full-grown males—and in any case their size, adornment and coloration must be seen in the flesh to be fully appreciated. The black-and-white areas of the coat are vivid and shiny and clearly defined; the white stripe on the outer side of the thigh is very striking. The pure white front of the Diana peters out on the lower chest and on the inside of the lower arm, but continues on to the belly in the Roloway. The front of the beard of the Diana is black from the lower lip; that of the Roloway is pure white. Full-furred male Roloways may have the periphery of the white front suffused with bright lemon yellow becoming most intense along the edge of the black upper sides, and the whiskers, which may form false ears fringed with black, arise on either side of the head and connect with the pronounced, upbrushed, horizontal brow fringe. The white front of both may form a wide shield effect, covering the whole chest and extending laterally beyond the upper arms and shoulders. Dianas have strangely catlike motions and carry their tails straight up, with only the tip curved slightly backwards, when stalking along branches. The muzzles of both these monkeys are quite prognathous when seen in profile, approaching in this respect the structure of the Mangabeys and some other dog-monkeys or Cynopithecoids. The head and body may measure up to two feet and the tail somewhat more. Dianas are exceptionally gentle and intelligent when young and show a remarkable variety of facial expression, but the adults become singularly aloof and even more than other guenons display wills of their own. They take most special care of their appearance, and unless in ill-health somehow always manage to keep every part of their coat in pristine condition. Their voice is also distinctive, and the noises they make include not only the usual croakings and chatter of all guenons—which cannot be described in words— but also long-drawn-out yells. Both Dianas and Roloways are fast becoming rare as a result, to some extent, of their continued slaughter for the pot, but much more because of the progressive elimination of the forests in which they live. Some degree of protection is being attempted in their native countries, and further relief may come to them from the rapid substitution of imported canned goods for monkey meat as an article of diet even in the remotest bush communities.

Leaving the gorgeous and rather "exaggerated" Dianas, we may next turn to a large complex of forms known as the *mona* group. Of these there are, according to Allen's *Checklist of African Mammals*, which constitutes the most recent over-all review of the Cercopithecoids, eleven subspecies. However, three of these that are of very similar appearance and have certain most exceptional features—notably a median fore-and-aft peak of backwardly directed hairs rising from the tops of their heads—undoubtedly constitute a quite separate group. They in no way resemble any of the Monas and appear to have different habits. Their names are *pogonias, grayi* and *nigripes,* and they may be said to compose the *pogonias* group.

Taking these last forms first, we find that the three types have much in common in addition to the median peak of backwardly directed hairs in the crown. All have green upper and outer surfaces and brilliant yellow under and inner sides. In *pogonias,* the face is black, with black tines running up the middle of the forehead and from the outer edge of the eyes to form fringes above the ears. Below this are yellow, upbrushed cheek fringes or whiskers. The muzzle is black, but the upper lip and chin are yellow. There is a black band down the mid-back extending on to the tail,

but the latter is yellow below. The hands and feet are black. *Pogonias* is found on the island of Fernando Po and throughout the north Cameroons to the west of the watershed that divides the British from the French Cameroons, but always at some altitude; *grayi* is distributed throughout the French Cameroons and the forested parts of French Equatorial Africa, east to the Congo; *nigripes,* which is in many respects intermediate in appearance between the other two, is found only in a strip of coastal territory between Cape Lopez and the mouth of the Congo in the Gabun. This country lies outside the closed-canopy forest, and these monkeys live in isolated copses and gallery forests and thus constitute an interesting example of the distribution of subspecies of mammals in accord with the incidence of different vegetational zones. *Pogonias* is one of the most vividly colored of all monkeys, and of all mammals for that matter, when seen in life and in its natural haunts. The general shade of the coat is not just the dull olive-green so often encountered among mammals, but is a bright leaf green more like the colors seen in birds, though whether this is caused by pigment, refraction, the incidence of algae or a combination of these is not known. Also, the yellow of the throat, chest and undersides is a most vivid golden buttercup tone in life, though this loses much of its brilliance when the pelt is dried and preserved. The stomachs of freshly killed members of this species that I have examined have been crammed with insect remains. They appear to be treetop dwellers, and they make curious twittering and whistling noises more like birds than monkeys.

The eleventh form of guenon listed by Allen as belonging in the *mona* group must, it now appears, be extracted therefrom, and associated with three other types, to which the names *denti, elegans* and *pyrogaster* have in the past been given. These together constitute the *wolfi* group. The typical form is distinguished by having reddish limbs, unlike all other guenons, and by light to white underparts and patches inside the arms and legs. They have long ear tufts, and all the members come from the Congo Basin and east thereof.

The Mona Monkeys are represented by seven subspecies which range from the extreme western forest block (*C. mona campbelli*) through the Ashanti block (*C. mona lowei*) to the Nigerian-North Cameroons block (*C. mona mona*) and thence right across the central forest belt of Africa to the western banks of the Congo. There are Monas throughout the French Cameroons and Equatorial Africa that appear to be of the typical subspecies; but east of the Congo they appear to be replaced by *wolfi*, of which there are other subspecies from the Kwangi and Stanley Falls areas. Monas are, collectively, as common as the members of the *nictitans* group, and in some places are much more numerous. They have greenish brown upper and outer sides washed with rich brown on the lower back, and gray undersides, but the skin is bluish and the fur below is very sparse. The face is black or bluish with pronounced yellow tufts over the ears, a light yellowish brow line, an almost naked muzzle, and, in fully adult males, a chest shield almost as pronounced as that of the Dianas. They are mixed feeders, taking insects and some other animal food—notably tree snails—and all sorts of fruits and some leaves. Once again, the emphasis seems to be on green nuts—which, when identified and tasted, usually prove to have the most violently astringent juices.

These monkeys travel about in considerable gangs, and are rowdy and altogether behave in the manner expected of monkeys. They are slightly hysterical compared to other Guenons and, as I have mentioned, I have seen them on several occasions misjudge their distance when leaping and fall to the ground as well as into water. Since the canopy where they dwell is often eighty feet above ground, it is somewhat mystifying to find that they do not seem to be either killed or seriously incapacitated by such falls, but scamper up the nearest vine to rejoin their companions. The name *Mona* is said to be derived from the Moorish name for all monkeys and to have been borrowed or adopted by the Spaniards in early days and then transferred to the New World, where it is often used alternately with the true Spanish name, *mico*, for any long-tailed monkey.

Finally, standing halfway between the arboreal Guenons and the terrestrial, cursorial Military Monkeys are a large assemblage of closely related Cercopithecoids with limbs of subequal length, which carry their tails held either in an upwardly arched curve so that their tips are just off the ground, or high in the air. To these a positively excessive number of Latinized names have been given—*Cercopithecus aethiops, tantalus, sabaeus, pygerythus, lalandi, rufoviridis* and so forth—but, although they certainly differ somewhat in color

and color arrangement, the whole lot appear to form only a single vast species-group which may be known as the Savannah Monkeys or the *aethiops* group. There are now some twenty subspecies of this group recognized, but the differences between many of them are very slight. They are spread all around Africa throughout the savannah belt, from Senegambia to Abyssinia and thence south to the Cape and west again into Angola (see map). If the Military Monkeys are to be separated from the arboreal guenons as a genus, there is really no reason why this subgroup should not also be so, for they are quite distinct in appearance from the arboreal species but are much less so from the Military Monkeys, and their habits and general behavior are more like the latter. In popular parlance, they are known as Vervets in South Africa, as Grivets in northern areas, and as Green Monkeys in West Africa. For purposes of simplicity, we will call them all collectively Savannah Monkeys. They are semiterrestrial animals, and are equally at home on the ground, among rocks or in trees. They stalk about, trot, run and gallop like dogs, and they are also great jumpers. They have rather short, sleek hair, long tails, small hands, naked black skin on their faces, prominent ears and neatly brushed whiskers that diverge from the cheeks over the ears and neck (see photograph). In color, all of them are an agouti shade of greenish to yellowish gray-brown from the tops of their heads over their backs and all their outer surfaces, including the tail, but all have lighter to white undersides, and some are dark green above. The light areas extend down the inner side of the limbs, and the short hairs covering the hands and feet are usually of the same color, but the naked skin of both is black. Their eyes are usually an extremely rich, almost luminous brown, but individuals with blue, green or yellow eyes occur in some races or species.

One can learn a great deal about animals by living with them, though not necessarily about their normal behavior in the wild. Almost any animal—even a wild-caught example of our dull-witted North American Opossum—often will not only let itself be handled but will actually show signs of "joining the human race." Guenons of all kinds often appear to do so with enthusiasm, but they always preserve an essential aloofness and dignity that is sometimes hard to tolerate. Nevertheless, you simply cannot *force* one of these monkeys to do anything. You can readily interest it in a wide variety

SAHARA DESERT

SENEGAL
GAMBIA

Niger R.

LIBERIA
IVORY
COAST
ASHANTI
DAHOMEY
NIGERIA
LAGOS
BAMENDA
Sanaga R.
FERNANDO PO
CAMEROON
Ogowe R.
CAPE LOPEZ
GABOON

Sanga R.
UBANGI
SHARI
Ubangi R.
Congo R.
CONGO
BASIN

BAHR
EL
GHAZAL
ITURI
STANLEY
FALLS
Ruwenzori
KIVU

White Nile

ABYSSINIA

SOMALILAND

UGANDA
KENYA

TANGANYIKA

NYASALAND

MOZAMBIQUE

MADAGASCAR

S o u t h
A t l a n t i c
O c e a n

ANGOLA

TRANSVAAL

SOUTH AFRICA

CAPE
PROVINCE

CONFINES OF THE CERCOPITHECOIDS

*All the Guenons and their close allies are confined
to the forested parts of Africa—most of them
to the tall equatorial and deciduous, closed-
canopy forests therein, except the members of the
savannah or aethiops group of the Guenons,
the Nisnas or Red Monkeys, and a few other
Guenons, such as the Mitred Monkeys and
Gray's Monkey, which have taken to living in
isolated copses in orchard bush.*

of activities, show it how they are performed, and cajole it into first imitating and then doing these things itself; and, what is more, you do not have to demonstrate repeatedly for them as you do for a Capuchin. These monkeys, if intelligent in the first place—and there are idiots among them too—pick up all manner of unexpected "tricks," seemingly without anything more than a single demonstration. Yet, tame or not, trained or untrained, they always retain an independence of character that is awe-inspiring. The most docile and dignified may round on you and give a slashing gouge with its formidable canines if you insist, by action or even by word of mouth, that they do something that happens to be distasteful to them.

In the wild, Savannah Monkeys travel in large tribal units of mixed sexes and of all ages. The males appear to be polygamous and the older females polyandrous. They have an oestrous cycle exactly equivalent to humans, and the young are born at all times of the year. They are great travelers, and although the same tribe may reappear in an area time after time, they may not do so for months, during which period they may have moved over an enormous circuit. They are pronouncedly carnivorous, and much of their food consists of insects, scorpions, centipedes, lizards and other such small fry, but they also eat a lot of bulbs and roots, and will take both fallen and growing nuts and fruits and some leaves. They are, in fact, completely omnivorous, but they must have a quota of animal food in their diet. In captivity they, like almost all other monkeys, should be given raw meat and especially the uncooked internal organs of birds or mammals, particularly when they are kept indoors during the winter in colder climates. They not only love bright sunlight but need it, and a sun lamp is a very good adjunct to their cages in winter. It is not necessary to bother about their being exposed too long to these rays, for they will turn their backs to the light before it can have deleterious effects on their eyes and will get out of its beams altogether when they have "had enough," as long as a box is provided for them to shelter in.

The three closely related forms of terrestrial Cercopithecoids known as the Patas and the Nisnas Monkeys (*Erythrocebus*) are sufficiently different from the Guenons to be given separate generic status. They also are known as Red Monkeys, Ground Monkeys, Military Monkeys, or Hussar Monkeys—the last in reference not only to their color, which vaguely resembles that of the red coats once worn by those regiments, but also because they have a habit of marching about on open places in what sometimes appears to be alarmingly military precision. From this evolved their still better known name of Military Monkeys.

Although these monkeys can and often do climb trees and rocks, they are essentially terrestrial. They have front and hind limbs of about the same length, are fully plantigrade—which is to say they walk on the flats of their hands and feet—and carry their tails arched upward and above the line of the back. They are found only on open savannahs and grass fields, never entering any kind of forest—not even isolated copses of closed trees. They apparently seldom drink. They run, walk, trot and gallop with the gait of dogs, and move about in large packs bossed by old females. They are large animals, up to two feet in body length, with slender torsos and long, well-furred limbs. Their faces are markedly prognathous, and their canine teeth are fanglike.

They are found all across central Africa from Senegambia to Abyssinia and thence down the east side of the continent to Tanganyika, but always adhere to the drier, more open belts bordering the true savannahs, which in turn ring the forests. To understand the distribution of these or almost any other African monkeys it is, as has several times been said, essential to have some over-all appreciation of the distribution of vegetation on that continent. All animals are absolutely and without exception confined to one or more vegetational zones at all times. On the other hand, each vegetational zone has its own fauna, and wherever that zone is found, the same animals will be found upon it. In Africa, all the zones run from west to east above the equator and then turn abruptly south down the east side of the continent and finally, in some cases, again west. A glance at a vegetation map will show exactly why and where the Military Monkeys are to be found. There are two outstanding forms of these animals, the Patas Monkey of the west and the Nisnas of the east.

Both are basically of a typical "desert" coloration and are lighter below, often having light tails, limbs and faces, including the cheeks and brows. The normal color is a rich brick red above, cream white below, but both vary from a very light buff to almost black on the back and from pure glistening white to dull red on the underside. The Patas have light faces and dark gray, naked noses; the Nisnas, a dark brow line and black-skinned faces with a cream ruff on the hinder cheeks and a light nose.

These monkeys would, according to their habits and behavior, better belong with the Cynopithecoids, but their internal anatomy and particularly their skulls and teeth, although rather exaggerated, are nonetheless typical of the Cercopithecoids. They go about in large parties, grubbing among the grass tussocks for small animal food, scatter when approached, and run off like dogs or any other cursorial animals but often leave sentries in trees or on elevated rocks. They make extremely cooperative pets, and if attached to a chain by a belt will soon learn to walk to heel or in front of you and generally behave like the best of domestic dogs. They are much less destructive of property than other monkeys and can be trained to use their own outhouse for sleeping and toilet purposes. They are very rugged and tough in the better sense and will order even the largest dogs off their, and thus your, domain with unexpected and sometimes alarming peremptoriness. Although having decided wills of their own, they appear to be astonishingly even-tempered and reliable.

10

The Tribes of Ruffians

THE MANGABEYS, MACAQUES, AND BABOONS

Gelada

S O   E V E N T U A L L Y, we come to the division of the Primates that contains what are, to most of the world, the most typical of all monkeys. We often forget, here in North America, that our indigenous fauna and even more so that of our sister continent, South America, is highly exotic to the majority of human beings who live and have for countless centuries lived on the other continents. Although Capuchins and Spider-Monkeys are fairly common in European and Asiatic zoos, they are still regarded as peculiar monkeys compared to such as the Rhesus and other Macaques that have been known in those parts since time immemorial. The monkeys that are depicted in Ancient Egyptian wall-paintings, in early Indian and Javanese bas-reliefs, in the most primitive Chinese paintings, and in some very early European coats-of-arms are almost without exception Dog-Monkeys, or what we herein call Cynopithecoids. What is more, apart from the sacred Langurs, which have held a very special and privileged position in India for centuries, almost all monkeys known to civilized man since earliest times have been members of this great group of Primates.

The Cynopithecoids are certainly the most diverse, and probably by actual count of living individuals the most numerous, of the twelve branches of existing primates. In numbers of individuals they undoubtedly surpass all others, and they possibly exceed the total of two and a half billion or so human beings that now crowd the earth. Their numbers throughout the Oriental Region could not be computed: vast hordes of Rhesus still roam large parts of India, and beaches in Burma and Malaya may at times be literally covered for miles on end with other forms of macaques. They swarm, in one form or another, throughout coastal mangrove swamps, in all types of forest, on farmed land, on rocky open places, on mountains and in montane forest, and even in towns. They inhabit islands great and small, and they even tramp about in snow fields, swim in the sea and jabber at you from caves. Their geographical distribution is, moreover, far more extensive than that of any other group of primates with the exception of Man. If you draw a line from a point near Dakar on the westernmost bulge of Africa, at 15° W. and 15° N., to a point at the northern end of the Japanese island of Honshu, at 140° E. and 40° N., Dog-Monkeys may be found almost everywhere on land surfaces to the south thereof, excluding Madagascar, North China, and Australia (see map.) They also occur in North Africa, and in the Celebes east of Wallace's Line.

There are about twenty-five full species of Cynopithecoids extant today, but a much greater number have been described and given names during the two centuries since the establishment of the Latinized binomial form of nomenclature for animals, initiated by Linnaeus, and the actual number of distinct forms—now mostly accepted as regional subspecies—is, at this writing, eighty-three. The words of Dr. Simpson quoted in our first chapter indeed assume special significance at this point, for there can hardly be a Cynopithecoid that has not been assigned at least two names at one time or another, or been switched at least once from one genus to another. There may, in time, prove to be as many actual species of Guenons or of all Cercopithecoids as there are of Cynopithecoids, but the vast majority of the former belong to one great genus and are most closely related. The Dog-Monkeys are almost endlessly diverse in size, form, structure and habits. They may be listed as follows:

		SP.	SUBSP.
A. MANGABEYS (*Cercocebus*)			
(1) Peaked (*C. aterrimus*)		1	1
(2) Crested (*C. albigena*)		1	3
(3) Capped (*C. torquatus*)		1	3
(4) Plain-headed (*C. galeritus*)		1	3
B. MACAQUES (*Macaca*)			
(1) Lion-tailed (*Silenus*)		1	1
(2) Bonneted (*Zati*)		2	5
(3) Crab-eating (*Cynamolgus*)		1	21
(4) Rhesus (*Rhesus*)		3	7
(5) Pig-tailed (*Macaca*)		1	5
(6) Stump-tailed (*Lyssodes*)		2	7
(7) Moor (*Magus*)		1	3
(8) Barbary Ape (*Simia*)		1	1
C. BABOONS			
(1) Black Ape (*Cynopithecus*)		1	1
(2) Drills (*Mandrillus*)		2	2
(3) Baboons (*Papio*)		4	18
(4) Hamadryas (*Comopithecus*)		1	1
(5) Gelada (*Theropithecus*)		1	1

Various attempts have been made to classify these animals according to the length of their tails, but the results have neither genetic nor distributional significance or validity; and what is more, the development of this organ proves to have no relationship to the habitat of the animal either, for some of those with the longest tails are predominantly or wholly terrestrial, while some with the shortest tails are arboreal. In fact, these animals appear to constitute two related but divergent branches of a major limb of the primate tree; one is the "monkey-like," the other is the "baboon-like," and members of each are found in both Africa and Asia and may have either long, medium or short tails.

A notable feature of the Cynopithecoids is that the adult males and sometimes also the females display outstanding sexual adornment and other physical exaggerations; so that, on the one hand, they often show marked sexual dimorphism— meaning that the males are strikingly unlike the females—and on the other hand, the young look quite unlike their parents. Extreme examples are the Drill and Mandrill, and more especially the Gelada, the young of which nobody would ever imagine could grow into the adult form or bear any relationship to such a creature. Young dog-monkeys are almost without exception either rather pretty or pathetic little scrawny things, with somehow tragic eyes, soft voices and most gentle ways. They are usually very trusting of humans and quickly come to regard them, if the latter are kind and gentle, as their rightful parents. As they grow up, however, their temperaments tend to change with their appearance, and they normally become first distant, then grouchy, ill-tempered and aggressive, and finally downright unfriendly and dangerous. In bodily form, many of them develop into creatures that appear to us to be both grotesque and appallingly hideous, often with a dental armature that is positively terrifying to behold and that, in the case of some baboons such as the Gelada, actually surpasses in size of the canines the largest living cats. The baboons, in fact, develop in maturity into creatures that, if discovered on another planet, would probably not be considered "monkeys" at all. Nonetheless, there are many authentic records of fully adult tame macaques of the larger species, and of baboons of various kinds, and some of these include accounts of the most marvelous reliability, faithfulness and intelligence being manifested by these animals. Also, long ago, baboons were trained by the Egyptians to weed gardens, harvest fruit, carry water and even wait at table, and macaques are still used today to gather coconuts and even to collect botanical specimens from jungle treetops. Despite their prognathous, dog-like faces, the Cynopithecoids still harbor active and well-developed brains in their heads.

The temperament of the Dog-Monkeys as a whole is rather unexpectedly uniform, and it differs markedly from that of any of the other groups of primates. While the Cercopithecoids are marked by a considerable fastidiousness, and the Coloboids, as we shall see, by a strange aloofness, the Dog-Monkeys can best be described as "incorrigible slobs." All are tribal in habit, but instead of the precise formality noted among the Hapaloids, the considerable orderliness seen among Ceboids, or the amiable democracy to be observed among the Guenons, they behave—as that perspicacious anthropologist Dr. Earnest Hooton once succinctly wrote —like totalitarians. Despite all their gestures, dashing about, grimaces, rude noises, hideous teeth and threatening attitudes, they are basically cowards, and if confronted with anything of real consequence, from a small stick to a lid of a garbage pail, the average individual will retreat precipitately, and if cornered cower with hands held over its head, whimpering. However, when in company, they tramp about destroying things as if they owned the earth and adopt a wholly insufferable attitude to every living thing that is, in the aggregate, smaller or less numerous than their own host. At such times they may become not merely aggressive but definitely dangerous to lone animals or even to small parties of human beings. The boldest are baboons; these have recently become a real pest in certain parts of Africa, where they have increased in numbers so greatly that they not only cause serious damage to growing crops but have even invaded city suburbs. In 1953 a horde descended upon a hotel in Durban and eliminated all confections prepared for a large luncheon party, cleared the establishment of its residents and wrecked the entire place. Such mischievous activities are not unique to baboons or even to Cynopithecoids, but records of mortal attacks upon armed men are authenticated only in the case of this group. There are instances of Drills, Mandrills, several kinds of Baboons including the Hamadryas, and Rhesus monkeys ganging up on lone hunters or small parties of travelers and pressing home a concerted attack. The circumstances are exceptional, for it is a very rare thing for animals to attack humans or other living creatures deliberately. Fights, in nature, are actually exceedingly rare between different species—ten thousand fictional or allegedly factual stories, films and sagas notwithstanding; planned attacks are even rarer and possibly never have occurred unless provoked, and by man at that. The Dog-Monkeys, acting in unison, can, however, become most fearsome adversaries— and this not only in the wild, as any zoo keeper can affirm. Even the cowardly Rhesus can launch a sneak attack, usually on the back of the neck of an unsuspecting or preoccupied man, that can have the most serious results.

We call these primates collectively the Tribes of Ruffians advisedly, for they are just that. Nevertheless, it has to be admitted that in their behavior, both socially and generally, they more closely resemble us than do any of the other primates. There are those among them, like the ubiquitous Rhesus, that behave distressingly like gangs of delinquent humans, imbued as they are with considerable intrinsic intelligence but bent, it seems, upon activities of a highly destructive nature. They plunder the food supplies of men and other animals, brawl among themselves and threaten others. At the same time, they are sturdy and tough and amazingly resilient in face of adversity; they can apparently breed in almost any circumstances, can maintain life on almost any diet, and generally display a remarkable fortitude. And it is for these reasons that the Rhesus has become such an important figure today as a sort of official "taster" for humanity, all manner of things being tried out on it before they are upon man. These creatures have already reached the upper atmosphere in experimental rockets, and they will probably land on the moon far ahead of any man.

The Mangabeys of Africa display little of the hooliganism and practically none of the aggressiveness of the Macaques and Baboons. In general appearance they are much like the larger Guenons, but they may be distinguished from them by certain slight but persistent and significant features of their teeth. Their popular name, for some reason, constantly calls for explanation, and it appears that it was originally bestowed upon them without logical reason and completely by chance, the first to be described having been stated to have come from a place called Mangabé in Madagascar— which, of course, was completely inaccurate since there are no monkeys on that island. Actually, the Mangabeys comprise four quite different groups of monkeys, each of which might well be assigned generic status. All are, however, at present included in the genus *Cercocebus*. There are ten recognizable forms or subspecies, comprising four well-marked species, which in turn may be clearly separated into the four groups called the Peaked Mangabeys (*Cercocebus aterrimus*), the Crested (*C. albigena*), the Capped (*C. torquatus*) and the Plain-headed (*C. galeritus*). They are spread right across the forest belt of Africa, from Gambia in the west to the Tana River in Kenya in the east, and south to Lake Mweru on the borders of Northern Rhodesia.

The Peaked Mangabey, of which there is but a single known form, has, as its name implies, a tall median fore-and-aft peak of hair rising from the top of its head. It is a rather scrawny-looking monkey; the fur is long and loose, and in color mainly black without any speckling such as is seen in the Capped forms. The face is naked and somewhat prognathous, and the eyelids are light. Its hands and feet appear to be oversized, and it is a somewhat ungainly animal though agile enough in the trees. Peaked Mangabeys inhabit the whole forest area south of the Congo and are found in many territories that are inhabited also by both Crested and Capped Mangabeys. They are closed-canopy dwellers but will descend to the ground to forage, especially along stream and river banks. They are said to travel in small family parties or in pairs.

The Crested Mangabeys are represented by three forms of *C. albigena,* known as *C. a. albigena,* from the southwest Cameroons, Gabun and lower Congo area; *C. a. zenkeri,* from the Sanaga River area of the Cameroons; and *C. a. johnstoni,* from a wide swath of territory to the east, stretching from the Ituri in the north to the forests of Lake Mweru in the south (see map). They also have loose, soft and rather long hair, devoid of speckling or banding, and of a general smoky gray or black color. Their distinguishing feature is an erect crest of long hair that rises from the back of the head and spreads out like a cossack hat. This gives them a most bizarre appearance which, combined with the light areas of skin around their eyes, makes them look perpetually frightened, like a character in a cartoon.

The Mangabeys without crests, which could be collectively called the Capped forms, are six in number, divided between two well-marked species and spread from the extreme western forests in Gambia to the Tana River region in Kenya in the east. They do not occur south of the Congo River. The first three are subspecies of *Cercocebus*

torquatus, known as *C. t. atys,* from the Liberia area; *C. t. lunulatus,* from the Gold Coast; and *C. t. torquatus* from the Nigeria-Cameroons-Gabun areas. These animals are of a general gray to black color, lighter below, with the naked parts of the face ranging from pink to black through various degrees of gray or pink with gray blotches. The areas around the eyes are lighter and the eyelids usually vivid white, in contrast to the rest of the face. In *atys* the top of the head is of an olive shade, that of *lunulatus* blackish brown, of true *torquatus* a bright brick to wine red with a somewhat speckled effect. The cap of these monkeys is defined by a contrasting black or white band or collar at the back of the head, and there is also a black or light line down the spine. There is a considerable amount of variation in color in all forms, both between the young and adults and between local or regional races. At one end of the scale are almost pure dark gray animals with darker caps; at the other are forms with vivid red caps, white throats, chests and collars, and white tips to their tails, jet-black faces and glaring white eyelids. All have pronounced whiskers brushed back and slightly downwards from the side of the face to the ears, and another ruff, below this, brushed back and slightly upwards, so that the hairs of the two sets of plumes form outwardly-projecting flanges or "crests" on either side of the face. The hair on the top of the head of these forms is parted in the middle.

The remaining three forms are subspecies of *Cercocebus galeritus,* known now as *C. g. agilis,* which ranges from the southern Cameroons to the Ituri, north of the Congo; *C. g. chrysogaster,* found in the central and southeastern Congo; and *C. g. galeritus,* found in the Tana River valley in Kenya. They are only an eastern extension of the previous species, but they show some marked differences. As in *torquatus,* the hair is short and fairly dense and firm, but the facial whiskers are much shorter. The hair on the head of *agilis* grows in a whorl on the forehead; that of *chrysogaster* is "brushed" straight back; in typical *galeritus* it grows in a whorl and forms a pronounced bang or toupé on the forehead. The coloration of the crown does not, however, contrast with the rest of the body. The upper sides of these animals are pronouncedly speckled with golden brown, giving (in *chrysogaster*) a sort of greenish agouti effect, while the undersides are bright yellow. In *agilis* the whole head and body are speckled with yellow and the underside is white, and some specimens are so light that they were once given a special name—*C. hagenbecki*.

Mangabeys have pronounced, naked, hard callosities under their tails and on either side of their rumps capping the prominences upon which they sit and formed by the articulation of the thigh with the pelvis. These are firm, thickened pads with roughened surfaces, and are so large in the adult males that they grow together to form a kind of built-in seat-pad. Mangabeys are very large monkeys, some with head and body measuring as much as three feet and with tails of equal length. The Red-capped species has an exceptionally long tail. One specimen, measuring seventeen inches, had a tail twenty inches long, and another with head and body of only fifteen inches carried a tail slightly over twenty inches long. They are also long-legged creatures and great jumpers. All Mangabeys have large cheek pouches, like the Macaques, in which they temporarily store food for later mastication. As a result they have no need for the complex stomachs of the leaf-eaters. They also lack laryngeal pouches such as are specially developed in the throats of many other monkeys to aid in noise-making, and they are unusually quiet animals. To compensate for the lack of vocalization they appear to have developed other rather exceptional methods of communication. Almost all Managabeys have either pure white eyelids or light naked skin areas around their eyes, in vivid contrast to the dark skin of their faces. Even in deep gloom, these white marks stand out like small beacons. It has been observed that when one Mangabey appears to wish to communicate with another, it stares at its companion's face and then starts blinking its eyelids rapidly and irregularly. They may also flutter their lips at each other or open their mouths slightly and waggle their protruding tongues up and down or from side to side at great speed. It is believed that the eyebrow patches are in fact sort of beacons to attract the attention of communicants, and that the flicking of the eyelids is then a sort of semaphoring—not, of course, based on the transmission of letters or words, but rather of general concepts or emotions, as in drum telegraphy. Mangabeys are tribalized, and they certainly seem to be able to organize their actions in an emergency without making a sound—a rather uncanny performance, and one unique among monkeys, which are notoriously rowdy creatures.

Stepping from Africa to Asia, we choose for description first a unique animal now often known as the Wanderoo but which would better be called the Lion-tailed Monkey (*Silenus*). This should not be regarded as in any way implying that this animal is the closest relative, among the Cynopithecoids of Asia, of the foregoing Mangabeys of Africa. The choice is, rather, one of convenience. These animals inhabit the forested western Ghats of southern India, from Goa south to Cape Comorin. They travel about in small tribal units of up to some score of individuals, and they stay among the hills and strictly off the lowland coastal plains. The name Wanderoo is an unfortunate one, as it correctly applies to certain Langurs of Ceylon—a local word that has also been inaccurately transposed from the Singhalese into English as "Wanderer." Somehow, it became attached to this quite different animal of the mainland.

The Lion-tailed Monkey has from time to time been regarded either as a species of the great composite genus *Macaca*, or as constituting a separate genus of its own called *Silenus*. We prefer to follow the latter course in view of the animal's many unique features. There is no other primate, or other mammal for that matter, that in any way resembles it in general appearance or special adornment, as may be seen from the accompanying photograph. It is black in color except for the "judicial-looking" ruff, which is a beautiful smooth gray. The tail, which has a dumbbell-shaped club of fur towards the tip, is usually about three-quarters the length of the head and body—which may reach over thirty inches—but specimens in which it is almost as long are recorded. Old males are magnificent in appearance, very strong for their size and rather dangerous in disposition.

There are several accounts in official British-Indian reports of people being attacked by these monkeys and of children who had been left unattended near the forest being killed by them. Although they show a certain baboon-like militancy and are usually untamable if caught and confined when full grown, they still can make extremely gentle and engaging pets if taken young, hand-raised and kept away from their own kind and from other monkeys. I once had a nearly full-grown male that was as gentle as a spaniel, as polite as a well-brought-up human child and as intelligent as a three-year-old Chimp, though it had fangs like a small leopard. It lived in a spacious cagelike structure built from floor to ceiling. This contained a sleeping box, and the animal scraped this out systematically every morning. It could also open the door to its "cage" and often roamed about the house but never broke anything. Its particular joy was the kitchen, where it sat by the hour on its own stool watching every move in the preparation of meals. It would answer only to the complicated name of "Ootacamoond," which is that of a range of hills where its parents were found. Such forms of address as "Hi, you!" and other vulgarities it ignored with obvious and pointed distaste.

It is distressing that, as with so many other outstanding types of monkeys that have been known for centuries, we cannot give any but a most general account of the behavior, habits or even food preferences of this species in the wild. Prolonged observation of, presumably, any specific form of animal will bring to light a seemingly endless parade of new, unexpected and exceptional facts peculiar to that animal, and the studies of such painstaking investigators as Dr. Carpenter, both in the Orient and South America, certainly confirm the remarkable dissimilarities in the behavior of even the most closely related forms of primates. Casual observation, however, tends to obscure these differences and even to foster ignorance, for all monkeys and particularly the forest dwellers appear, at first sight, to lead much the same lives, crashing about in troupes with apparently but one objective, namely to obtain food. Since the majority of monkey species still await an observer such as Dr. Carpenter, regrettably little can be said about most of them, but it should be recognized that there are worlds of fascinating fact waiting to be recorded about each. All too little is known about the Lion-tailed Monkey in its native environment: but almost too much has been recorded about some of its relatives, the other Macaques, under unnatural conditions. Nonetheless, even these most anciently known, commonly recognized and universally publicized creatures are still, in many respects, extraordinarily obscure.

There are now at least sixty kinds of Macaques recognized by zoologists as constituting valid subspecies. These are divided between eight species-groups, all of which have at one time been raised to generic rank and given generic names. The members of each are indeed, in all cases, much alike but considerably different from all others, so that these species-groups may be regarded as sub-

genera, and it is for this reason that their assigned technical names are given in the list on page 121. They vary greatly in size, outward form and habits. The order in which we introduce them is purely arbitrary, since they do not display any recognizable succession or progression either from the Mangabeys of Africa or from the Lion-tailed Monkey to the other extreme of the Cynopithecoid type, which is to say the Baboons.

The Macaques known as Bonnet and Toque Monkeys, which form the subgenus *Zati* and are now customarily classed as the *sinica* group, come from the southern part of India and Ceylon respectively. There are two forms of the former and three of the latter (see Systematic List) but the differences between these subspecies are slight. The Bonnet Monkey (*Macaca*, or *Zati radiata*) is found throughout peninsular India from Cape Comorin in the south to Bombay in the west and almost to the mouth of the Ganges in the east. It ranges from the coastal lowlands to a considerable height in the mountains on the central plateau and is a very common animal. It is a small monkey, of various dull shades of brown, with a long tail, naked face and forehead that can be thrown into horizontal wrinkles like the brow of a worried human being—and apparently for the same reasons and by the same method as in men—and a ridiculous topknot of long, darker hair that grows outwards all around a central point. This falls down over the brow and ears like the tousled mop of the traditional maestro. The fur is close and short, the face pale, the eyes bright and alert, the hands and feet large but neat, and the tail rather "ratty," slender and tapering, with very short hairs. They are agile little animals that travel about in large consorts and are a great nuisance to farmers and other local citizenry. They eat a very varied diet but relish man's most cherished crops of fruits, vegetables and cereals, and they are not averse to pilfering chicken's eggs, stored provisions or anything else they can lay their hands on. They are adept escapists and have an uncanny knack of keeping just out of harm's way though waiting till the very last minute to retreat, even from gunfire.

Their relatives on the island of Ceylon are known as the Toque Monkeys (*Macaca*, or *Zati sinica*). Three forms, distinguished by differences of coat color, are found on the lowlands, in the foothills and in the highlands respectively. They are rather scrawny-looking little monkeys with most bizarre

125

expressions, having naked faces and tall foreheads crowned with an upright fuzz of hair like an overgrown crew-cut, so that they look perpetually startled. They are ingenious creatures imbued with enormous curiosity, but are of a rather retiring nature and are easily alarmed, when they will, if cornered, huddle together in masses screaming and chattering in terror.

Not too far removed from the *sinica* group come a vast host of closely related, small- to medium-sized macaques of various brown, yellowish brown, fawn, grayish brown colors, with long tails. The hair on the top of the head is brushed straight back, though in some types it grows from small whorls on the forehead and in others it may form a slight peak. The naked face and the callosities on the buttocks are pale pink in most forms, but the eyelids and/or areas around the eyes are usually lighter. There are twenty-one subspecies now recognized, but all are associated in one species known as *Macaca ira* or, if this be considered a subgenus, as *Cynamolgus irus*. This species has an enormous range, extending from Upper Burma through Siam to Indo-China, and thence south throughout the Malay Peninsula and all its offshore islands to the Nicobar Islands, Sumatra, Java and Bali and many of the smaller islands lying around these, Borneo, Palawan and the Philippine Islands, and innumerable small islands between them; in fact, they are almost everywhere in the Indies on the Asiatic side of Wallace's Line. The great majority of the subspecies are island forms, but the distribution of these is in many cases most odd, identical examples being found in limited areas on the coast of one of the great islands and on but one group of small islands lying off that coast, or on one far away from it.

The real status of many of the described subspecies of this monkey, which is popularly and widely known as the Crab-eating Macaque, is actually very uncertain, for the differences between all of them are slight, and there may be many cases of the parallel development of similar or identical features by different populations on two or more widely separated islands. Also, there is no real point of departure for the description of them, for the typical form (*Macaca*, or *Cynamolgus irus irus*) itself has an enormous range and varies considerably in appearance, while the original description of the first specimen to be given (by F. Cuvier, in 1818) is vague as to detail, to say

the least, and its place of origin is given simply as Sumatra. The same subspecies is, however, said by Chasen (*A Handlist of Malaysian Mammals*, 1940) to be spread all over the Malay Peninsula, Penang and Singapore, the Rhio and Lingga Archipelagos, Banka, Billiton and Banjak, large parts of Borneo and its coastal islands, the Karimata Archipelago and other islands off the north coast of Borneo.

Crab-eating Macaques are inhabitants of the lowlands and are never far from the sea or fresh water. The majority are truly littoral, inhabiting coastal mangrove swamps, swimming and fishing in creeks, and subsisting for the most part, as their popular name implies, on crabs and other crustaceans. Why these monkeys should have taken to this odd diet cannot of course be stated, but it is interesting to observe how the sundry groups of Macaques form, in their over-all distribution, a more or less continuous web covering the whole of India and southeast Asia, but one that is constructed like a giant jigsaw puzzle. In this, all the odd bits meandering between the areas inhabited by other species are filled with Crab-eating forms, so that it almost looks as if they were the late-comers or have been pushed out to the coasts and islands everywhere by other forms. Most of these coasts, moreover, are fringed by a wide belt of mangrove swamps. In such growth there is really nothing to eat of a vegetable nature apart from the mangroves themselves, and there are comparatively few insects apart from mosquitoes, but there are everlasting supplies of crabs and other crustaceans and some shellfish. Any monkeys living therein would almost be obliged to take to such a diet.

This is not to say that members of this group of Macaques, despite their popular name, live exclusively on crustaceans or even solely in coastal swamps and on seashores. They will readily munch on fruits and they relish grain. In many islands they scamper about in droves all over the place, invading gardens and plantations and generally behaving like other Macaques. In Bali they are treated with great reverence. They are no more molested in that country than are the sacred Langurs in India, and they have for centuries been allocated property of their own.

I had the good fortune to visit Bali before tourism took it over. Outside the town of Klungkung on the south coast there was then a large wood of vast trees, completely clear of any vegetation below, but instead carpeted with vivid green moss. Upon this, bright orange flowers rained from above to lie glistening in the gloom, for daylight could only just be discerned as pinpoints of light in the far distance between the tree boles. The wood was the property of the monkeys, and they swarmed therein, subsisting, it seemed, for the most part on bowls of rice and other comestibles placed just under the edge of the tree canopy by the local residents. I took to wandering in this wood daily and communing with the monkeys, which crowded around me in hundreds for tidbits or just to stare and comment—at least, I did so until a Balinese friend with whom I was traveling found out about my activities. I was then hauled off before the equivalent of the local Chamber of Commerce and peremptorily told either to desist or to leave town. I subsequently learned that what had alarmed the elders was not so much my impertinence in holding commune with creatures regarded as sacred and superior, but my stupidity in exposing myself to the very likely possibility of being attacked and seriously injured by these enlightened ones.

The third great group of Macaques comprises seven forms divided among three well-marked species, one of which contains the most widely known and recognized of all primates—the inimitable Rhesus Monkey, or Bandar, as it is known in its native India. The three species concerned—all of which have tails of medium length, somewhat shorter than the head and body—form the *mulatta* group of the general genus *Macaca*, or a subgenus named *Rhesus*. They are, respectively, four forms of the typical species (*M. mulatta*), two of the Assam Monkey (*M. assamensis*), and a very curious species that lives on the beaches of the island of Formosa, swims in the sea and eats shellfish, known as *M. cyclopsis*. Combined, these animals have an enormous range from the borders of Afghanistan in the west, along the Himalayas and parts of Tibet to Sze-Chwan and to the Pacific coast of southern China in the east, and thence south to central peninsular India on the one hand, and throughout Burma, Siam and Indo-China on the other. They are rather large monkeys, the adult males being very sturdy and heavy set.

In color, all the Rhesus, in the wider sense of that title, are some shade of yellowish brown, lighter below and sometimes considerably darker on the crown and lower back, which may be washed with rich brown or gray, or have the hairs lightly tipped with black. Their faces are naked and somewhat doglike, and are very pale pink, flesh-colored, light gray, yellowish or rosy. The naked areas of the buttocks are also pinkish but the pads are dark. The young are scrawny and rather pathetic looking, with oversized, naked ears and almost naked chest and belly, the skin of which has a bluish tinge. They change very considerably in shape, comparative bulk and general appearance with growth, and old males become almost baboon-like, with heavy shoulders, prognathous jaws and a very alarming set of teeth. The various forms or subspecies differ considerably in the density and length of their coats according, for the most part, to the altitude at which they live. Those from Nepal, Tibet and other high places are clothed in thick, almost woolly coats, those from the hot plains of India have very light, sparse, silky fur over the back and outer sides of the limbs and practically no fur at all on the lower flanks and undersides. Rhesus can, however, change their coats to a considerable extent if moved from one climate to another, and, if kept out of doors where the seasonal temperatures vary widely, will put on fur in winter and lose it in summer.

The Assam Rhesus (*Macaca*, or *Rhesus assamensis*) occurs in the typical subspecific form in the mountains of Assam, the Mishmi Hills, the Naga Mountains and throughout the mountains of northern Burma, Tonkin and Annam. A distinct subspecies (*pelops*) is found between the two- and six-thousand-foot levels in Nepal, Sikkim and Bhutan. They are sturdy, heavily furred monkeys with rather square faces, go about in large troupes and tend to inhabit particular hills or mountain sides permanently. Travelers have often asserted that they not only loose rocks on people passing below them, but actually pick up such rocks and bowl them down the slopes. Throwing is a purely human action, but the behavior of these and other Rhesus on occasion often comes very close to it. Very similar to these are the Tibetan form of the true Rhesus, *M. mulatta vestita*, and two other mountain subspecies, known as *villosa*, from Kashmir, the upper Punjab and Kumaon, and *mcmahoni* from Kafiristan and Chitral. The Formosan animal (*M. cyclopsis*) is a distinct and full species, with a shorter tail, that has taken to dwelling in coastal caves and become a beachcomber.

The typical form of Rhesus (*M. mulatta mulatta*) has a very wide range extending from the lower Punjab all across lowland north and central penin-

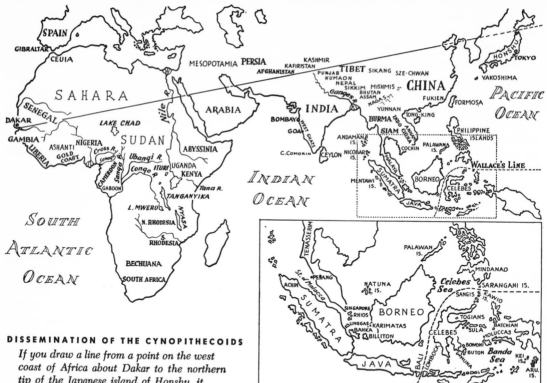

DISSEMINATION OF THE CYNOPITHECOIDS

If you draw a line from a point on the west coast of Africa about Dakar to the northern tip of the Japanese island of Honshu, it will be found that almost all Dog-Monkeys— and, for that matter, almost all other Primates in the Old World—dwell to the south and east of that line. They range south to the tip of Africa and, in Asia, not only to Wallace's Line but even beyond on to the Celebes and certain other islands to the east thereof. There are also the famous Barbary Apes of North Africa and Spain, and certain forms that extend north to Kashmir.

sular India to Assam, Burma, Siam and Indo-China and thence northeast through Yunnan and Tonkin to central China from Sze-Chwan to Fukien on the coast. The Chinese animals were once thought to be quite different, and to have very short, stublike tails or none at all, but it was slowly realized that the Chinese were in the habit of docking the tails of young ones kept as pets.

It was Rudyard Kipling who immortalized the Bandar, and nobody except perhaps the remarkable Brahmin who wrote in English, Dhan Gopal Mukerji, has ever surpassed him in the understanding of this incredible nation of almost human beings. That these animals have an understanding among themselves and are able to communicate like us has been fully accepted for centuries by the human inhabitants of India, who have clothed the Bandar with a certain sanctity and the immunity that goes with it, though of an order more lowly than that bestowed upon the sacred Langurs. In fact, the Bandars maraud unmolested in the temples of India, but their social relations with the laity of that country are a curious mixture. There is a close economic interreliance between the two, combined with a deep-seated mutual respect, and though both parties growl at each other "officially," they nonetheless manage to get along with the essential business of living together. The Bandars are alleged to be "inferior" and to be incorrigibly antisocial, but they are not only tolerated—they are given enormous latitude.

Bandars tramp about in large tribal units consisting of both sexes and all ages. The males are considerably larger than the females, and become very heavy set with almost baboon-like faces, prognathous jaws, and fanglike teeth. In color they are a gingery brown tending to grayish on the back and yellowish on flanks, chest and underside. The naked face is pink, the flesh of hands and feet gray; but the naked rump is a bright rose color. There are pronounced naked, hardened seat-pads, most evident in the old males. The hair is straight, soft and almost silky in the common lowlands form, but may be wavy and almost woolly among those who dwell in mountains; and these animals range to altitudes of six thousand feet just like the other subspecies already mentioned.

The troupes stay, as far as possible, in wooded areas, thickly grown cultivated land or vegetation bordering streams, but they may inhabit rocky areas and enter villages and towns. They prefer to stay near water and do much swimming voluntarily. They eat all manner of grains, fruits, seeds, berries and roots, for which they grub industriously, and they take all the insects, spiders, snails, frogs, lizards and other small animal life they can find and catch. On the whole, they stay pretty much to themselves, but the males will sometimes attack in consort if their females or young are in danger. In captivity a male will often jump you if you try to handle or molest any of the females.

For almost a century now the Rhesus has played an important part in medical and certain other researches. In many anatomical and physiological as well as in some psychological respects they resemble ourselves sufficiently to be able to "stand in" for us during the testing of chemicals, vaccines and such, that are believed to be possible deterrents to human disease. There can hardly be a product, in fact, that has not first been tried out on Rhesus Monkeys, and in this respect these animals have rendered mankind an incalculable service. They have also been employed to test many mechanical devices, and among such the most exciting are undoubtedly rockets. A deeply moving series of photographs was published a few years ago of a group of them cowering in a rocket, both before a flight up into what is virtually space and upon their return. The expressions on their faces before take-off displayed extreme anguish; on their safe return the utmost relief.

Psychologically, Rhesus are almost alarmingly human in many respects. They have proved their considerable intelligence in innumerable most ingeniously devised tests, and they appear to rate a generally high I.Q. as compared to other mammals, but no artificial investigation is needed to demonstrate these facts. Anybody who has kept these monkeys as pets or worked with them—and despite their croaking protests, they may actually be said to work diligently on occasion—will attest to their

remarkable understanding of complex situations and of human emotions. If we were writing in another context, we could give examples of behavior by Rhesus Monkeys that would doubtless not be believed. Their understanding sometimes appears quite uncanny and in every way belies the old adage that "monkey see, monkey do." Rhesus have done many things under experimental conditions that they had certainly never seen done before.

Of somewhat similar general appearance to the Rhesus Monkeys are a group of five closely related forms constituting a single species known as *Macaca nemestrina*. This would appear to be the true or typical Macaque, for no other generic name has ever been bestowed upon it, and it is regarded as a sort of central point from which all the other species-groups may be envisaged as radiating outwards towards their particular specializations. These monkeys are known popularly as Pig-tailed Macaques, but although their tails are very short, being only about as long as their heads, they are, in fact, not nearly so piglike as the tiny, naked, twisted things borne posteriorly by the next group, the Stump-tailed Macaques. They are large monkeys but considerably longer-legged and somewhat heavier than the Rhesus. The typical form (*M. nemestrina nemestrina*) inhabits Sumatra, sundry islands in the Straits of Malacca, and the mainland of the Malay Peninsula, north to lower Siam. In the rest of Siam, Tenasserim and Burma, this is replaced by *M. n. leonina,* which is also found on the Mergui Archipelago. There are other forms in outlying areas—one in the Naga Hills in Northern Burma (*M. n. blythi*); another on the Andaman Islands (*M. n. andamanensis*), which is said to be found also in peninsular Siam; and finally one on the Mentawi Islands off the west coast of Sumatra (*M. n. pagensis*). The Burmese forms have much longer fur, shorter faces and limbs, and very small hands; the tail is furred and usually bears a terminal tuft. The island forms have naked tails.

These monkeys have, since time immemorial, been trained—and especially in Achin and other parts of Sumatra—to harvest coconuts and other fruits from palms and tall trees. This curious custom was noted by early Chinese chroniclers, who were delighted by it and advocated, though apparently without effect, the introduction of the practice, if not the exponents of the art, into their own country. Very much later, the Forestry Department of the British Federated Malay States employed these animals to collect shoots, flowers, leaves and fruits from the tops of the forest canopy for identification purposes, the constitution of tropical forests being almost endless and practically nothing being known of it from a botanical point of view, since the essential parts of the trees are some hundred feet out of reach above. The monkeys so employed were either young males or females, because the males are just too strong to be tractable, being as big as a two-year-old boy and with limbs of almost equal girth but being as strong as a full-grown man. Chains or strong ropes were attached to belts around the "waists" of these monkey-workers, and they were taught to go aloft and "unscrew" the coconuts and then let them drop. I have seen such a trained Pigtail and the amazing thing was that, however it got its rope looped around limbs, it invariably unraveled itself by following the rope backwards and weaving under and over limbs until it was free to descend, and then often holding the slack in its left hand, away from snags, as it did so.

Pigtails are the monkeys often referred to as Giant Rhesus, and they have earned both an enviable and at the same time sanguinary reputation in show business. Adult males of the Sumatran form are enormously powerful creatures, and are clothed in a rather beautiful, silky, slightly greenish yellow, glossy fur that lies smoothly over the body. The face and ears are naked and there are prominent brow ridges; the top of the head appears to be slightly concave or dish-shaped, and the hair that clothes it is usually darker than that on the body and forms a mat like a crew-cut. In the Burmese type it forms a horseshoe-shaped dark cap of upright hairs. These animals show very marked intelligence and have been trained to do the most amazing tricks and to learn whole acts or series of acts. A specimen owned by the extremely versatile French comedian, Gil Maison, not only dressed itself but conducted an orchestra while imitating a soloist on a diminutive piano and then proceeded to dance with its master, specializing in the impersonation of extreme types of jitter-bugging. The animal was, however, dangerous to all strangers and had to be kept chained when off the stage.

Even heavier of body are the Stump-tailed Macaques, sometimes also known as the Red-faced Monkeys, and called scientifically the *speciosa* group; they also bear the subgeneric title of *Lyssodes*. There are two full and distinct species, namely, *M. speciosa*, of which there are five distinct subspecies, and *M. fuscata*, of which there may be two separate forms. The former are often also called Bear-Monkeys; the latter are universally known as Japanese Apes. They are all distinguished by having tiny tails, only an inch or two long in the largest forms, that are curled to one side—usually the right when viewed from behind—are somewhat flattened and may be naked. The animals have only a very limited power of movement of these ridiculous appendages, and they sit on them irreverently. If one of them waltzes about, presents its backside, and then twitches this little tail at you, you should be neither shocked nor distressed for it is the animal's most correct form of address, and you should therefore be considerably honored.

The five subspecies of *speciosa* are found respectively in peninsular Siam (*rufescens*), in Tenasserim and Siam (*melanota*), in the mountains of Cochin (*arctoides*), throughout Annam, Tonkin, Yunnan, upper Burma and Assam (the typical *speciosa*), and in Sikang and Sze-Chwan in western central China (*thibetanus*). These forms increase in size in that order, becoming ever heavier of body and more thickly clothed in increasingly dense fur. The Tibetan form is a colossal animal that walks with the strange pacing gait of the Japanese Ape, head thrust forward, shoulders and rump held high, and the spine apparently sagging in between.

Very little is known of the habits of these animals and particularly of the Tibetan form, but a close friend of mine who made two expeditions into the far inner recesses of western China tells me that in places they are to be met with in enormous droves at certain times of the year, when they appear to be migrating from one mountain range to another. At these times they will descend into the cultivated valleys and play havoc with crops and even invade small villages and isolated peasant houses. The natives, he says, just have to clear out at their approach, and even the availability of firearms does little to halt their progress, for they seem to take umbrage rather than fright at gunfire. They do a lot of digging, like baboons, and carry their youngsters till they are of considerable size suspended from their bellies and partly concealed in their long capelike fur. They have large, bunshaped plumes of hair on their heads and sort of capes over their shoulders.

All these monkeys walk on the palms of their hands and flats of their feet, with a sort of stumping motion but with a gait that is a true *pace*. They have the equivalent of a "high gear" which is really a gallop. In color, they are of various shades of rich reddish brown to golden brown or gray-brown, and their faces are bright red but go brighter with rage or heat and bluish with cold or fatigue. They are mountain animals and very rugged, those of the more northern areas being active in the snow and apparently impervious to cold. The young of all of them—and this goes for the Japanese Ape as well—are extremely attractive and intelligent little creatures with most engaging ways, endlessly active, and are born comics. Unlike their parents, which grunt, croak and sometimes roar, they make all manner of scratchy little noises, greet you by showing their teeth in a primitive smile, chattering and smacking their lips at you. They also indulge in sundry strange little dances, presumably for exercise, bouncing up and down on all fours like diminutive mechanical dolls for minutes or hours on end in the same spot, and they put on various displays that are hilarious to watch. Sudden sounds make them jump like a ham comedian feigning surprise, and they may go into a series of violent twitchings if they are shown something inexplicable, such as waves breaking on a beach. They make wonderful and most loving pets when young, completely adopting their human owners as parents, and they can be readily trained to perform a wide range of actions at almost any age. In fact, despite the positively terrifying appearance of the adults, these monkeys seem to be exceptionally amenable to human understanding and reason, once they have overcome their native distrust.

These monkeys are seldom seen in captivity, especially as adults, but the Japanese Ape has become fairly common in collections since World War II. These are also heavy-shouldered, muscular animals, measuring from about twenty to twenty-four inches from crown to rump when adult, and, when standing on all fours, about eighteen inches high, but they appear much larger because of their profuse long fur. Their faces are a brilliant pink, which gets even more livid with rage, excitement or heat, but which also goes blue with cold or fear. They are delightful little clowns when young and give the appearance of understanding just about everything one does or says. They are also almost inconceivably mischievous and tremendously destructive, but are usually consummate "artists," putting on an "act" as soon as they are in company,

before a camera or otherwise the center of attention, and sometimes continuing to do so for hours.

As they get older they usually become increasingly crochety, morose and dangerous; but there are exceptions, and even those caught when full grown, which at first give every appearance of hostility, may suddenly decide to join the human race, settle down and become the most friendly and reliable companions. I was once given a neurotic old female that had bitten several people and ripped one man's arm from elbow to wrist. She at first gave every indication of being incorrigible and very dangerous, but suddenly became not only friendly but pathetically loving and a most reliable performer. I have never known a primate—and human beings are not excluded—that was such a shrewd and correct judge of character.

Japanese Apes are still common on the island of Yakushima off the southern tip of the main Japanese islands, and at sundry points on those islands, notably around Kyoto. They are exceptionally rugged beasts, romping about in and digging under the winter snows for food, and sometimes swimming in the sea along the shores in summer. They play a great part in the mythology, history and folklore of Japan, for it was three of them that were the original "See no Evil, Hear no Evil, and Speak no Evil" of Buddhistic teaching, and it is these animals that have become known to the whole civilized world from the innumerable statues and small replicas showing them holding their hands to their eyes, ears and mouth respectively. Curiously, the representation of mammals in any graphic form was for long prohibited to Japanese artists, while that of birds, flowers and so forth was encouraged; thus paintings of this monkey are rare. Those that do exist were mostly made in Korea and usually lack the perfection of the rest of Japanese animal art. Monkeys have played an equally important part in Chinese art since the dawn of history. The species represented therein are mostly Macaques but are occasionally a small species of true ape, obviously a Gibbon. There are also a few representations of the great Red-faced Monkeys of Sze-Chwan.

There are said to be two distinguishable forms of Japanese Macaques, the typical *fuscata fuscata* of the main islands, and *fuscata yakui* of the Island of Yakushima, where it is fully protected.

There remain two peculiar macaques to be described. They are in no way related, and constitute individual little subgenera of their own. These may be named *Magus* and *Simia,* but both are currently included in the over-all genus *Macaca* as the *maurus* group and the *sylvana* group, respectively. Both animals inhabit areas outside the general range of the Macaques. The first, which is known as the Moor Macaque, is an inhabitant of the Celebes on the Australian side of Wallace's Line, a locality which it shares with only two other primates—namely, the Tarsier and a most curious baboon-like animal that we will describe presently, called the Black Ape. The second is the well-known Barbary Ape of North Africa and southern Spain.

According to Elliot (*A Review of the Primates,* 1913) there are three distinguishable forms of the Moor Macaque, namely, *Macaca* or *Magus maurus ochreatus,* from the southeastern peninsula of the Celebes and the adjacent islands of Bowoni, Muna and Buton, which is black, with the hair of the legs streaked with white, giving a silvered effect; *M. m. tonkeanus,* from the Togian Islands in the northern Gulf of Tomini; and the typical form (*M. m. maurus*), from the southwest peninsula and the Aru Islands, which have the forearms, inner side of the thighs, and the hind feet pale gray. There is, however, considerable doubt about this breakdown, and for several reasons. First, there are Moor Macaques on the northern peninsula of the Celebes that do not look any different from those on the eastern, southeastern and southwestern peninsulas. Second, they occur also on the west coast, and, although all are essentially black animals, there is a considerable amount of dull or light gray displayed on the limbs of many of them in any one group. Then again, the same monkeys inhabit a lot of other small island groups off the coast, but none has ever, as far as I can ascertain, been definitely recorded from the Aru Islands, which are over nine hundred miles to the east on the other side of the Banda Sea, have a wholly Australoid fauna, and are separated from the Celebes by the Kei Islands and the whole stretch of the Moluccas and Sulas (on which such animals are not found). In fact, the gloomy-faced Moor Macaques probably have either but one subspecific form or several dozen, including one on each of the four great peninsulas of Celebes and possibly another on its west coast, and numerous other races on sundry islands.

The name "Moor" has nothing to do with either the human nation of that name dwelling in Morocco or open, grassy uplands. It appears to have been taken from the scientific name for these animals, *maurus,* which means dark or obscure. The animals are both, for they are black in color and obscure in habits. There happen to be true upland moors in the Celebes, but these monkeys are not found upon them, dwelling rather in the lowland forests. They go about in large troupes sometimes reported to number some hundreds, and they like to comb beaches. They apparently take a mixed diet but are reputed by the native peoples of the Celebes to be distinctly carnivorous. Similar if not identical macaques are constantly reported as coming from the eastern side of Borneo, but no authenticated records have yet come to light. How this macaque happens to be residing on the Australian side of Wallace's Line presents an interesting puzzle to zoologists, for nothing like it or from which it might have been evolved is known in the Philippines, the only direction from which it might have island-hopped. Fully grown males are huge, beetle-browed ruffians with grouchy temperaments and enormously powerful forebodies. They have the look of, and may possibly be a form of baboon.

The last of the Macaques is the famous Barbary Ape of northwest Africa and Gibraltar. Zoologists do not know exactly what to do with this animal; for, although the fossilized remains of monkeys, and even of those of the Cynopithecoid type, have been unearthed all over southern Europe and even as far north as England, there is no evidence of this particular animal or any other typical macaque being found in either Europe or Africa, nor anywhere west of Mesopotamia, at this latitude. The question immediately arises as to whether this animal is a relic of a previously indigenous population of macaques or is an introduction of fairly recent date, perhaps brought by the Arabs in their great westerly conquests of the sixth century. Although they are in some ways closest to the Stump-tailed Macaques, nothing exactly like them is known anywhere in Asia; and thus, if they were brought by the Arabs, their ancestors must have become extinct in the meantime. Perhaps they were the inhabitants of Persia when that country was greener and was the granary of the world. They are now known as *Macaca sylvana* but have been given the subgeneric name of *Simia* and the specific epithets *magus* and *inuus.*

There is a fantastic belief that there is either a natural or artificial submarine passageway that leads from Gibraltar under the Straits of Gibraltar to Punta de la Almina at Ceuta in North Africa, and that the "apes" know of this and pass back and forth by it from one continent to another. Of this there are some very interesting things to be said. First, the Rock of Gibraltar, which is a vast pile of agate, is riddled with caves, the extent of which is either not known or is kept a close secret by the British military authorities, for they are used for the storage of ammunition and other important materials and as a water reserve for the town and garrison. In these caves have been found some of the most famous of all fossils. The second odd fact is that, despite the monkeys being official charges of the government for almost a century, and an individual tally being kept of them in sickness and in health, their numbers have fluctuated in an inexplicable manner. The Rock is not a large thing from a topographical point of view, but much of it is virtually inaccessible, and it is pockmarked with little natural shelters and thick bushes, so that the monkeys could hide out for long periods; but they spent most of their time around the human habitations and could be counted daily. The number of expecting mothers was known and all the births noted; when bad weather threatened the whole lot often changed locale, and deaths were always recorded, but still the total population would apparently from time to time increase suddenly or decline drastically. The famous Sergeant Brown, who was for so many years "in charge" of the apes, pooh-poohed the idea of a secret passageway to Africa but never ceased to wonder at these sudden changes in the number of his charges.

The Barbary Ape, or Magot, as it is known in French—a term of opprobrium for all ugly Primates, including ourselves—is a beetle-browed, grumpy, grayish brown animal with rather long, thick, slightly wavy fur, expressive eyes and a wide vocabulary. It is a typical "slob" and aggressively obnoxious rather than just mischievous. Given an inch, it will take an ell; offered a home, it will take over the household. Nonetheless, it has repeatedly been reported, and by totally unrelated sources, that these animals suffer loneliness acutely and will adopt all manner of small animals of other kinds and carry them about with them, stroking, caressing and even feeding them. Strangely, it has also been observed that the males often carry and care for their own babies. They are still fairly common in North Africa, where they travel about the coniferous forests in large gangs, feeding upon the kernels of pine cones and all manner of fruits,

nuts, vegetables and young grass shoots. They raid the farmsteads of the Moors and are generally a considerable nuisance. Also, they are hard to combat, since they post sentries like baboons and have incredibly acute eyesight.

The Magot has many baboon-like qualities, but it is definitely to be classed in the Macaque tribe of Dog-Monkeys. This is not so definitely the case with the animal we place next on our list—the so-called Black or Celebesean Ape (*Cynopithecus niger*). This also is virtually tailless but has the proportions, stance and gait of a true baboon and, like the baboon, heavy and prominent bony brow ridges and a very long, doglike face with a slender, raised nasal ridge and a curious elongated swelling of naked black skin on either side of this, below the eyes. It is jet-black in color, well clothed in fairly thick fur, and has an extraordinary topknot of long stiff hairs that can be erected at will, giving the animal a most bizarre expression. This strange animal is found at various points all around the great island of Celebes and on Batchian in the Moluccas Group. It has been rumored to be found also on some of the southernmost Philippine Islands, and it is certainly found on the Sangi Archipelago, but whether it has been introduced there by human agency is unknown.

These monkey-like animals are held in great reverence by the indigenous coastal peoples of the Celebes, both of Malayan and Papuasian origin, who insist upon tracing their tribal lineage back to them and who consider them considerably superior to all humans and notably to "white men." In this they may have a point, for the animal is not only altogether odd among primates but appears to regard our species in a particularly friendly light. These curious creatures are predominantly coast-dwellers and never stray far from water. From what source they were evolved we do not know, but they are unique, though they are usually associated with the macaques because of the location of their home territory.

The first of the baboons that demand our attention are two somewhat monstrous creatures found in West Africa and known to us as the Drill (*Mandrillus leucophaeus*) and the Mandrill (*M. sphinx*). These are found in two rather limited areas, the former in the northern Cameroons forest area between the Cross River on the eastern border of Nigeria in the west and the Sanaga River in the south, and the latter from the Sanaga south throughout the southern Cameroons and Gabun to the Congo and east to the Ubangi. Neither are, as commonly reported, found anywhere west of the Cross River, and certainly not in the Ashanti and Gambian forest blocks.

They are very heavy-bodied but compact and immensely muscled animals that pace along on all fours, with the backbone sagging somewhat and the shoulders a little higher than the rump. They both have small, thick and well-furred tails that they hold erect and that appear to stick out of the upper side of the hinder end of their backs because they have immensely developed buttocks, devoid of hair, bright rugose pink in color, that protrude far out behind the end of the spine. They are clothed in thick, straight, rather fine but long fur, the individual hairs of which are banded black, yellow and olive. The hands and feet are plantigrade. The young of both are fairly normal looking and rather resemble certain small short-tailed macaques; they have light pinkish faces, short muzzles, intelligent brown eyes, and slight backwardly directed cheek ruffs but very bony, naked faces. Adult females are heavy set, and have immensely prognathous, doglike muzzles, heavy cheek ruffs and slight beards. Drills are a dull olive-brown; Mandrills are charcoal gray with an overwash of greenish brown; the difference between the two is that the bases of the hairs of the former are light ochre, those of the latter black. Up to this point the two animals are fairly similar, but the adult males differ in every other respect. The Drill has a shiny, jet-black face with hugely raised "cheekbones" that form a "V" bisected by the long, thin nose ridge. The nostrils are large and terminal and point forwards. The face is surrounded by a deep fringe of fur going outwards in all directions, and there is a wedge-shaped central black topknot that extends forward to just above the brows. The adult male Mandrill is altogether different; it is, in fact, the most astonishing looking of all primates.

The general appearance is well shown in the accompanying color plate, in which the colors are, if anything, underplayed. The skin is bright blue, that on the swollen and voluted areas of the face being a vivid sky blue. The nose ridge and nostrils are lacquer red, and this color may extend to the lips. The whiskers are pure white, but the beard and the parts of the ruff behind the angles of the jaws are orange. The fur on the top of the head and of the main body is brownish, but the under-

mane, chest and limbs are jet-black; the naked tail and the monstrous buttocks are purplish blue surrounded by brilliant scarlet.

The males of both the Drill and the Mandrill are very much larger than the full-grown females. The young of the two species are often extraordinarily alike; in fact, the only way that young males of the two may be differentiated is by the creases on their noses which, even at the earliest age, resemble those of their parents. Young Drills have one large ridge or crease on either side of the median line running down the muzzle from between the eyes to between the nostrils; baby Mandrills have several small ridges on either side.

Drills are forest-dwellers and travel about in large family or tribal parties of modest numbers. They are sometimes aggressive towards man and other animals, though they will normally move away from danger. They have a terror of metal, which they can apparently detect—probably by smell, since metal is unknown in nature—at a considerable distance. They are completely omnivorous and gain a living by turning over logs and grubbing over the forest floor, eating fallen fruits, insects, large quantities of tree and ground snails, lizards, worms, frogs, snakes, rats and other small animals, uprooting water plants, digging for roots and bulbs, and taking a lot of funguses. They also eat sundry barks and the tiny primitive plants known as Selaginellas that carpet the floor of the forest where the light is dimmest. They have a regular vocabulary and are constantly talking to one another; they also bark like big dogs, growl, and roar with a kind of pumping action—very like the sound made by lions when they are rounding up prey. The mothers are very solicitous of their offspring, and the large males stalk around the group with eyes constantly alert for any interlopers. If approached they may make a frontal attack and lob stones and sticks at you with their hands, or waltz about and project material with their feet in a movement like a dog digging.

Mandrills are also basically inhabitants of the forests, but they spend much time outside its confines on open and particularly on hilly and rocky places, where they turn over stones in a constant search for insect food. They are meticulous and almost dainty in their habits, picking up tiny food items and examining them with the utmost care at the ends of their long noses before rejecting or eating them. Mandrills usually travel in small family parties, and the males spend most of their time some distance away from their charges; but they are always alert and instantly place themselves between them and any aggressor, planting their forefeet wide apart, lowering their heads, growling and occasionally opening their mouths in fake yawns that display their enormous battery of yellowed, fanglike teeth. This is usually enough to discourage even a leopard, but if it does not, they jump up and down and seem to work themselves into a kind of fighting frenzy wherein the color of their skin becomes more brilliant and patches of bright red appear on wrists and ankles and the chest goes vivid blue. They are immensely powerful brutes at any time, and when in a defensive mood or a rage they can do almost as much destruction as a gorilla, and are much swifter. A large adult male can top thirty-two inches sitting up, and their jaws match those of a large leopard. The Drill and Mandrill are manifestly specialized forest forms of baboons. It may therefore seem strange that they have only apologies for tails, while the true baboons have comparatively long tails.

The true Baboons live outside the closed-canopy forests of Africa and are cursorial animals that usually dwell in mountainous and rocky places but may climb any available trees for use as lookout points. There are vast numbers of Baboons in Africa, and it is a somewhat difficult task to reduce their numerous forms to any semblance of order.

Reference to a vegetation map will show the distribution of the closed-canopy forests in Africa. Excluding from the remaining areas the real deserts of the Sahara and the Mediterranean zone, we may then see at a glance where baboons are found. This vast tract, formed like a backwards "ɔ," stretches from Senegambia to Abyssinia, thence south down the east side of the continent, and then back west again to the Atlantic coast and finally north to the Congo. To this must be added the valley of the upper Nile and a patch in southwestern Arabia in order to complete the territory of the Baboons. Throughout this whole sprawling subcontinent of open forest, orchard bush, savannah, grass land, scrub land and semidesert, covering both lowlands and the bare escarpments of mountains, innumerable gangs of these hideous, industrious and audacious animals roam. They are one of the few forms of life on this planet that are not much unsettled by our activities and that neither retreat before them nor make any attempt to comply with them. Baboons just carry on as if we were not around, making what use they choose of our agricultural and other efforts, and often feeding and multiplying at our expense. In some parts of Africa, and notably in the Union, they have become not only a pest but a menace.

There are now eighteen kinds or subspecies of true baboons recognized. These are divided among four species; four to the first, the Chacma (*Papio comatus*—for which *P. ursinus* may have to be substituted); five to the second, the Yellow Baboon (*Papio cynocephalus*); seven to the third, the Anubis (*Papio doguera*); and two to the fourth, the Western or Olive Baboon (*Papio papio*). The Chacma is a large form with black face, hands and feet, and the usual brindled olive-greenish-yellow coat, that inhabits the open, dry and upland areas of South Africa, Bechuanaland and parts of Rhodesia. It used to be known as *Papio porcarius*. The Yellow Baboon is smaller and an inhabitant of savannahs and open forest throughout a belt of territory north of the Chacma, ranging from Nyasaland and central Rhodesia to Tanganyika and the southern Congo. It has been variously called *Papio sphinx, babuin* and *thoth* in the past. The Anubis —previously known as *Papio anubis*—ranges from the northern limits of the previous species in Tanganyika all the way up the eastern half of the continent to Abyssinia and thence north via Uganda and the eastern Congo to the Sudan and west along the northern edge of the forests almost to Lake Chad. It has a pink face and varies considerably in color. The Western species, which is really olive in color and used to be known as *Papio olivaceus,* spreads from Lake Chad west to the Atlantic coast in Senegambia, between the Sahara on the north and the equatorial forest belt on the south.

The general form of all baboons is much the same. The body is doglike, the arms being slightly longer than the legs, so that when walking on all fours, as they invariably do, the back slopes from crown to tail base. The tail is carried curved slightly upwards and then does not reach the ground. The head is very large and the shoulders are heavy. The face is produced forwards into an exaggerated doglike muzzle with the nostrils at the extreme tip, and is naked. The eyes are small and very close together, and they are sunk beneath a straight brow ridge. There are ruffs of long hairs brushed back from the angles of the jaw, and the larger species have slight crests down the neck and small manes or capes over their shoulders. Baboons are all of a dull brownish color, either olive-agouti, yellowed, or having a reddish tinge. The hands and feet are gray or black, and the face may be black or pink. They have large callosities on the buttocks.

In habits also they are much alike, in that they are gregarious, and, although usually going about in parties of from thirty to a hundred, they may in times of drought or food shortage join in regular armies of hundreds and then proceed to emigrate. At such times they are absolutely fearless and may do enormous damage to crops and other property. The current theory is that they do *not* post sentries; but, although this may be so in some localities, I can vouch for the fact that they certainly do so in others. The life of baboons is a hard one, for they live in territory that, although often rich in food for ungulates, great cats and carrion feeders, is poor in smaller fare such as that which suits omnivorous primates, like bulbs and succulent roots, insects, fallen fruits and so forth. They spend their lives turning over stones and grubbing under grass tussocks, and they work at this most assiduously. They are all born water-diviners and can in some mysterious way locate it, if it is not at too great a depth, in a vast area of apparent dryness, and then dig for it. Captive baboons have often been used for this purpose. Being thus preoccupied more or less whole time, they are very vulnerable to surprise attack by leopards and other marauders, and so it is that one or two always sit up on a high place facing away from the tribe and scanning the approaches, turning their heads constantly, like radar antennae. They have special calls to attract the attention of the other watchers and other noises to bring the tribe to the alert.

On the whole they are tolerant of other animals and are often indifferent to the ungulates, ostriches and other browsers and grazers, but they are perpetually at war with the carnivores. They dote upon ostrich eggs, which they carefully crack at one end, then, lifting off a piece of shell, upend and suck. Other favorite foods are honey and the larvae of wasps, both of which they gather by dragging and rolling the combs about in the grass or other rough herbage to free them of the adult stinging insects. They collect minute beetles and ant lions by patiently sifting sand through their fingers, and they have a most ingenious way of collecting insects that lurk on grass and bushes. To obtain these they uproot the herbage and flay it on open ground or rock, and a group will often gather around and grab for both seeds, berries and insects as they are knocked out. They are, in fact, extremely cooperative among themselves, though they are constantly fighting and bickering.

Despite their inherent ferocity they can make remarkable pets, and individuals have been trained to do all manner of manual tasks such as pumping water, sweeping, picking fruit and sorting produce in bulk with a precision that is seldom matched by human labor. They have also been taught to do much more complex things on a daily routine, like ringing a bell at a certain time. In the entertainment world they are, however, not so reliable, apparently becoming excited and confused by crowds. This may be the result of their gregariousness in nature. If a baboon presents his naked, glowing posterior to you, he, like the Red-faced Macaques, is not being rude but is greeting you in the most friendly and courteous manner he knows.

When we speak of Baboons, the average person will probably envision one particular kind known as the Hamadryad. This is, however, so different from the foregoing True Baboons that it has to be treated separately and has been given its own name of *Comopithecus*. This animal, which is pale gray, has a pink face and a large cape (as shown in the photograph in these pages), and inhabits Abyssinia, southwestern Arabia and parts of the eastern Sudan. In ancient times it appears to have been indigenous also to the whole Nile valley down to and including the Delta, and it was one of the commonest animals in Ancient Egyptian civilization, having therein a very particular and honored place of its own. Hamadryads were regarded as the companions, servitors and mouthpieces of Thoth, the god who had the head of an Ibis, was the giver of knowledge and was himself the mouthpiece of the Creator of all things. Thus the Hamadryads were regarded as entities somewhat superior to mere man and with a direct line to the gods—a sort of nonhuman priest class. In accord with this status they were allowed many privileges during life and the honor of mummification upon death. Tens of thousands of these mummies were laid to rest in special tombs throughout the ages. The animals were preserved in their usual seated position with hands on knees, and their individual names were written in ink on the outside of the bands of cloth that were wound round the corpse. There were three degrees of mummification according to class among humans, and the same distinctions were applied to the Hamadryads. The most important even had their internal organs removed and put in what are called canopic jars—four in number, and each of a different color—which were placed around the mummy at the cardinal points of the compass, just as with royalty and priests among men.

Despite their holiness, the Hamadryads were put to work by the Egyptians. First, they had certain religious duties, which included morning prayers, to perform, and there are many drawings of them seated facing the rising sun with hands raised on high. It appears that they were trained to do this daily at the temples. However, more menial tasks followed, such as sweeping out said temples, fetching and carrying for priests, and even serving at table. These activities may sound far-fetched, but the Egyptians had a remarkable way with animals. Lower-class Hamadryads had to slave for lay aristocrats, and they are represented in tomb paintings as picking fruit, stacking cordwood, apparently weeding gardens, turning irrigation treadmills, helping to dock river boats and sorting trays of unidentified small objects. The Hamadryad was thus perhaps more closely integrated into the life of our kind than any other animal in history, the dog not excluded.

In their own natural habitat, these animals are quite different, being ruffians of the first order. They are rock-dwellers, fully tribalized, and aggressive, and they display forcible proprietary feelings. In several areas they share territory with the Gelada, to be mentioned in a moment, and regular warfare conducted upon almost technically perfect military principles takes place between the two species. There are some hardly credible accounts, withal from the pens of the most respected travelers, many of whom were themselves military men, that describe scouting, manoeuvring, defense in depth, outflanking and all manner of other refinements in the art of warfare as employed by these animals.

Their adversaries, the Geladas (*Theropithecus gelada*), are totally different creatures and are among the most extraordinary in existence, in both appearance and temperament. They are the most exaggerated of all primates in bodily form, and are so extreme that they no longer resemble a monkey in any sense. They are huge creatures clothed in long, black, plumelike hair that forms a great mane over the neck and a cape over the shoulders that may, in large males, reach almost to the ground when they sit up on their haunches. They have long, thick tails ending in a dumbbell-shaped club of longer hairs. Their heads are rounded but the muzzle is prognathous; however, it is not pointed and shaped like that of a collie dog as is that of the other baboons, but globular, with upturned nostrils placed well above and behind the bulbous "lips." The face is bright red and naked, and there are large ridges running from below the outer side of the eyes to a point on either side of the nostrils. They have vivid white eyelids. Most extraordinary are their chests, which are naked and bright red in color, and form a prominent, heart-shaped, eye-catching adornment. The males are twice the size of the females, and when a fully adult male, who may measure thirty inches sitting up, opens his mouth to yawn, you will recoil in horror even if the animal is behind sturdy bars, for its teeth and particularly the canines surpass in length and sharpness even those of the great cats. The females, in the intramenstrual period, develop the most extraordinary "necklaces" composed of strings of little globular swellings in loops around their necks and across their chests. These look like the more exaggerated forms of tattooing indulged in by some primitive human tribesmen.

Despite their terrifying appearance, Geladas are no more aggressive than the ordinary baboons; in fact, most travelers who have encountered them in their own habitat say that they prefer to move out of the way of men. However, they will attack the marauding Hamadryads if territorial rights are infringed, and they will put up a stubborn defense against interfering men. Their habits otherwise are said to be those of typical baboons. I have never heard of a pet Gelada, but they seem to show considerable affection for each other in captivity, and have also been known to adopt other small animals as pets of their own. A friend of mine who has observed them in Abyssinia offered the suggestion that they, like the lion, are so overwhelmingly powerful in their own sphere, that they seem, again like that animal, to have developed a certain aloofness to all lesser breeds, and are consequently rather indifferent to their activities unless they interrupt the even tenor of their own lordly lives.

They inhabit rocky, mountainous regions in southern Abyssinia, and travel about in large troupes.

Golden Snub-nosed M

11

The Aloofness of the Leaf-Eaters

**GUEREZAS, LANGURS, AND LEAF-MONKEYS,
AND THE SNUB-NOSED AND PROBOSCIS MONKEYS**

THE REMAINING monkeys, in the restricted sense of that term, comprise a single and distinct family named the *Colobidae,* Coloboids, or Leaf-eating Monkeys. This is a very considerable family, spread in a wide belt across Africa, and in Asia from western Pakistan to Tibet and China and thence south to Ceylon, Java and Borneo. Its members can be clearly divided into three major groups, the Guerezas of Africa, and the Langurs or True Leaf-Monkeys and the "Funny" or Odd-nosed Monkeys of Asia. There are about forty-three distinct species in all, distributed among no less than eleven genera. The actual number of forms, however, greatly exceeds four dozen, for many of the species occur in a wide variety of regional color types which are designated as subspecies. Over forty such of Guerezas alone have been described and named at one time or another—often, moreover, as full species.

Although differing very widely in form and to a somewhat lesser extent in size, all these animals are fairly closely related, and they are all constructed on a plan that differs markedly from those of both the Cercopithecoids on the one hand and the Cynopithecoids on the other. They are, on the average, large monkeys, and all but one kind—the Mentawi Island Snub-nosed Monkey—have very long tails. The shape and arrangement of their teeth are distinctive, but the strange construction of their stomachs is even more unusual. Instead of being a simple sac as in other monkeys and most other mammals, this organ is prolonged into a curved succession of dual lobes or pouches partially separated from each other by constrictions, and thus in some ways it resembles the multiple stomach of those hoofed animals that chew the cud, or ruminate. The Coloboids are for the most part leaf-eaters—some appear to be exclusively so—and all are predominantly vegetarians, though insect remains have been found in some abundance in the stomachs of several species. The sacculated stomach construction is especially suitable to the digestion of leaves and other coarse green matter, and it has even been suggested by one observer that the Proboscis Monkeys may to a certain extent ruminate by belching up semidigested food into their mouths and then rechewing it.

The family is named after one of its outstanding genera, that of the Guerezas or *Colobus* Monkeys of Africa. The name *Colobus* is of interest, having been given to the first one described—and called "Pennant's Full-bottom Monkey," incidentally—on account of an apparent mutilation of its hands, the Greek word for "mutilated" being *kolobos*. The supposed mutilation, however, is a natural development of the hand, wherein the thumbs are either reduced to tiny knobs or entirely absent. The group may be listed as follows:

	SP.	SUBSP.
A. GUEREZAS		
(1) Olive (*Procolobus*)	1	1
(2) Brown (*Colobus badius*)	3	18
(3) Black (*Colobus polykomos*)	4	19
B. LANGURS		
(1) Typical (*Semnopithecus*)	5	14
(2) Purple-faced (*Kasi*)	2	5
(3) Lutongs (*Trachypithecus*)	12	27
(4) Banded (*Presbytis*)	9	19
(5) Doucs (*Pygathrix*)	2	2
C. ODD-NOSED MONKEYS		
(1) Tonkin Snub-nosed (*Presbytiscus*)	1	1
(2) Mentawi Snub-nosed (*Simias*)	1	2
(3) Great Snub-nosed (*Rhinopithecus*)	3	3
(4) Proboscis (*Nasalis*)	1	1

This family includes many of the most surprising-looking of all primates and some of the most colorful of all mammals; in fact, there are probably no more brilliantly or ornately bedecked fur-bearing animals than the Doucs or Painted Monkeys of the Indo-Chinese region.

While the behavior and habits of the Coloboids are as varied as their appearances, there is a certain quality about all of them whereby they stand apart from all other monkeys. This is hard to define and may indeed be more a product of our reactions to the animals than of theirs to us, but it results in a strange form of aloofness on the part of all of them. Guerezas on an African treetop, Langurs in a Hindu temple, and, I am assured, Proboscis Monkeys on a river bank in Borneo will often just sit and regard a man with a steady stare but seemingly with complete indifference, quite contrary to the attitudes adopted by other monkeys or the deeply enquiring contemplation of the apes. They seem also to go about their business with singularly little if any regard for other creatures, including man. Possibly for this reason, alone or

in conjunction with other of their strange traits, many of the Coloboids are regarded as sacred or holy in various parts of the world.

In parts of West Africa the Guerezas are looked upon as symbolizing or as actually being the messengers of God—in many respects the counterpart of Mercury, the go-between of Heaven and Earth—and their habit of ascending to the tops of the tallest trees at dawn and sunset and sitting quietly facing the sun is considered to be indulgence in prayer on the part of the monkeys. In India, the Langurs are regarded as sacred and holy, and are allowed absolutely free run of the country, the towns and the temples. In early accounts, the Golden Snub-nosed Monkeys of China are remarked to be treated with considerable reverence by the human inhabitants of the mountain fastnesses where they roam; and the Hill Batuks of Sumatra attribute strange traits to the Lutongs.

Many Coloboids are either rare or confined to limited and seldom visited areas. Most of them are not only aloof but shy and retiring, and none of them does well in captivity. In fact, very few are seen in zoos outside of the countries of their origin, and they are rather hard to keep even in those countries. As a result, they are perhaps the least popularly known of the monkeys as a whole, despite the fact that the "monkey fur" of commerce was derived from them and the sacred Langurs of India have been prominent in that country for centuries. The behavior of none of them has been exhaustively studied or made the subject of prolonged observations in the wild, and what we know of their habits is for the most part pieced together from numerous incidental observations and references. The taxonomy of the group has received considerable attention, and much has been written on some of the Guerezas and, of course, the sacred Langurs; but the majority of them still represent little more than names, to which a locality of origin, measurements and some color description are appended.

The Guerezas, though possibly known to the Romans and for long the basis of a brisk trade in expensive furs, are one of the least known, as a whole, of all groups of monkeys. If you go to spend a year in Africa in order to collect or study mammalian life, Guereza monkeys will probably be the last of the Primates that you will encounter, and you may well miss them altogether, even if you go to the exact localities where they live, and at just the right time. You may walk right below a considerable troupe of them time and time again and never suspect that they are sitting quietly in the foliage above, watching your every move. Most of them are of very ornate color pattern when seen in a cage, but in their own native haunts they often blend so well with their environment that you can be staring right at them and be unable to distinguish their outlines. The most notable examples of this camouflage are the large black-and-white Guerezas of the east part of Central Africa, which are jet-black with vivid white, bushy tails and long capes that actually trail on the ground if the animals are standing on level surfaces. In the trees, these pendant capes may exactly imitate the hanging lichens and mosses that festoon the branches, while the black areas of the animals' pelages blend with the deep shadows; so that, as long as they remain still and silent, their outline is completely obliterated. On the other hand, they may sit defiantly on open branches, when they are as glaringly obvious as a black-and-white skunk on a green lawn.

As was mentioned above, more than forty distinct kinds of Guerezas have been recorded. However, many of these, if not the majority, are still represented in museum collections by comparatively few specimens, and this makes it very difficult to determine the exact status of many of them. After prolonged study of all specimens available to him, Dr. Ernest Schwarz published two reviews in 1928 and 1929 of all the known kinds. In these, he made the then very novel suggestion that all of them fell into only two true species, with exactly half the forms in one, which he called *Colobus badius* and which included all the brown, brown-and-red and black-and-red forms, and the other half in *Colobus polykomos*, all the members of which were black or black-and-white. Moreover, he brought forward much evidence to show that the members of each species, though often looking very unlike, could be linked together via intermediate forms. Nevertheless, even Schwarz indicated that the twenty types in each could, in turn, be grouped under four subheads and that each of these had different geographical distributions. The four under *Colobus badius* he named the *badius, tholloni* and *rufomitratus* subgroups and, for a single form, *verus*. These come respectively from the West African forest block between Senegambia and the British Cameroons and Fernando

Po; from the French Cameroons–Gabun area; from the Congo–to–East African area; and from Sierra Leone. He expressed doubt only about the curious, small, olive-colored form, *verus*, the range of which alone overlapped one of the other subgroups and which he thought might be a valid and separate species. The black-and-white species (*Colobus polykomos*) he divided into what he called the *angolensis, satanus, polykomos,* and *abyssinicus* subgroups. These had in some cases partially overlapping ranges; but this appeared to be adequately explained by the fact that the members of one of them (*abyssinicus*) were montane forms confined to higher elevations and scattered right across Africa, from the northern or British Cameroons in the west to Abyssinia and certain isolated great mountains in the east. The true *polykomos* types all came from the western forest block and from Fernando Po; *satanus,* a pure black form, from Fernando Po and the adjacent Cameroons area, seemed to be only an extreme, dark form of the *angolensis* type; and this latter was confined to the Congo Basin east to Mombasa and south to Nyasaland.

It seems now to be generally agreed that Schwarz's suggestions conform very closely with the true relationships of the various kinds, but sundry emendations in his classification have subsequently been made. The first was Dr. W. C. Osman Hill's demonstration that the little form known as *verus* is not only a separate species but the sole representative of a distinct genus of Leaf-Monkeys—and one, moreover, that appears to be in many respects basic to the whole family. This animal is now known as *Procolobus verus*. Secondly, a few kinds among both *badius* and *polykomos* have been moved from one of Schwarz's subgroups to another. And finally, all of those subgroups have been elevated in status to full species. The results of all of this work are most interesting, since they have supplied a very instructive picture of the manner in which a wide variety of what appear at first to be entirely different animals can evolve from a single basic type.

This is clearly demonstrable with the twenty kinds of black-and-white Guerezas and could, if we had sufficient material to study, probably be extended to include the other-colored forms and then to link both to little *Procolobus*. Dr. Schwarz's theory envisions the original black-and-white form as having lived in what is now Angola, as having been basically a black monkey with the hair on the top of its head growing in a whorl, and as having had a small white brow line, long white whiskers but short beard, a small white shoulder mantle, and a scant brush at the end of the white tail.

At that time, what is now the Congo Basin was a great lake separated from the Atlantic by a narrow isthmus, and these monkeys slowly spread around this lake both up the isthmus to the west and north, and along the opposite shore to the northeast. Some also went due east to the region of Nyasaland and thence north to the east coast and to the Ruanda-Kivu area, in both of which places animals not unlike the original stock are still found. Still others pressed on to the Ituri region. On the west side they fanned out beyond the isthmus and spread around the bulge of Africa and west to Gambia to form the true *polykomos* grouping, with pure white, nontufted tails and shoulder mantles. Today these have wide white brow-bands, and in some almost the whole head may be white, while one has a huge white beard and a white thigh-patch. Schwarz's theory then further supposed that the montane or *abyssinicus* type, without a whorl on the topknot, lacking a white brow line but having a full white and often woolly beard, black shoulders and a tremendous white veil depending from the upper flanks and meeting over the rump, a white hip-stripe, and a bushy, club-shaped tail that may be pure white right up to the roots, was originally developed in West Africa and thence spread east around the northern shore of the Congo Lake, finally reaching the mountains of Abyssinia and the isolated peaks of East Africa. There is some alternative evidence that all the subforms of *abyssinicus* could have evolved from an *angolensis* type somewhere about the eastern Congo and thence spread out in all directions. Then again, somewhat similar coats may have been developed independently by these monkeys wherever they ascended high mountain ranges. Nevertheless, the idea that all the black-and-white Guerezas had a common origin and are closely related seems assured, for even the jet-black species, *C. satanus,* fits into the scheme.

Much as we should like to attempt to do so, space does not permit giving more than a most cursory description of all but a few of the Guerezas. In size they vary from sixteen to as much as forty inches in head and body length, with tails ranging from twenty-six to sixty inches. Some of the largest types are sturdy animals and very thickly furred, so that they look positively enormous. Besides the lack of thumbs they may be recognized by the naked callosities on their buttocks and by their rather short faces. Even those with long, trailing capes and flank veils are extraordinarily agile and swift in getting about the treetops, and they are tremendous jumpers. Though Guerezas are nowhere common, there would appear to be enormous numbers of them in the aggregate, as statistics provided by the fur trade once showed. Since at least the time of Marco Polo's travels, the khans and wealthy merchants in Central Asia had greatly prized certain furs that were described as being naturally shiny and did not need to be dyed, and which had pure white plumes growing on a black mat of short hairs. Mantles with shoulder capes of these skins, when first brought to Venice and Genoa, were, it is recorded, taken apart by furriers in the hope of discovering how the Oriental craftsmen put the long white hairs into the obviously natural black skins. It was not until Europeans themselves began to explore and open up the interior of East Africa that the origin of the skins was found. Curiously, neither the Abyssinians nor the Arabs, both of whom traded for centuries with the peoples of the interior, seem to have placed much value on these skins except as articles of commerce, and it was the latter who transported them from Zanzibar and Mombasa to India, whence they were shipped on to Central Asia.

In the mid-nineteenth century these skins became very popular in Europe and America, and the demand for them was so great that almost every tribe in Africa from Abyssinia to the western Congo, even if it had not as yet seen or even heard of a white man, sent its professional hunters after these luckless creatures. The operations were notably successful because these skins were highly prized by some tribal chieftains for headdresses, capes and garters, and for the adornment of ceremonial shields, so that especially powerful bows were available to shoot them out of high trees. With the introduction of firearms the slaughter naturally increased many fold and with the inevitable result. In 1892 no less than 175,000 Guereza skins reached the European market alone, and all of these had to be almost perfect and without shot holes, so that tens of thousands more must have been slaughtered. That was the peak year, and thereafter the annual take declined rapidly, while the price soared from about one dollar to fifteen dollars per skin. While the trade could purchase a perfect skin for these picayune amounts, articles of clothing or adornment made from or incorporating many of the skins fetched hundreds of dollars on occasion. In ten years the whole business petered out and the monkeys were afforded some form of legal protection, but not before over two million of their skins had been accounted for on the fur market. And these were, of course, all of a few of the montane races of one species (*C. abyssinicus*) of the black-and-white group. There is no reason to suppose that populations of the other species were less numerous.

Among these are some highly colorful types. Some are reddish brown all over, others a brilliant carrot red or orange, others black above and greenish yellow, saffron, orange or brick red below. The hair on their heads may form a tall central crest or, more often, dual crests rising above the ears. Shoulder capes of varying degrees of development may be present, and the tails may have plumes, tufts or a ventral fringe. The typical species, *C. badius,* of which there are four subspecies, is found from Senegal to the northern (British) Cameroons and on the island of Fernando Po.

And, as was noted above, right in the middle of this territory there occurs the small olive-green monkey now known as *Procolobus.* This is distinguished by its exceptionally small head and by the fact that the individual hairs of its body are yellowish green at the base and then grade through various shades of brown till the tips are almost black. It was once thought that the hairs of all Guerezas were plain-colored throughout—unlike those of almost all other monkeys, which are clearly ringed or banded with different colors—but the hairs of certain of the *rufomitratus* group have now been shown to be multicolored and truly banded. *Procolobus* is a rare and very retiring, nondescript little monkey that travels about alone or in pairs and is not averse to descending to the ground to forage. Moreover, it inhabits a wide range of different ecological zones ranging from true equatorial swamp forest to comparatively dry deciduous growth and is, in this respect, quite unlike any other Guereza. Dr. Hill suggests that it is a relic of the sort of animal from which all the other Guerezas evolved, and it even shows a combination of anatomical features sufficiently generalized to make it a candidate for the common ancestry of

both these and the Coloboids of Asia, to which we now turn.

The headquarters of the Coloboids is, like that of the Cynopithecoids, in Asia. In both cases the African and Asiatic types are separated not just by the Indian Ocean but by the vast stretch of deserts and forestless territory extending west from the Indus River in Pakistan to the Atlantic coast of West Africa. Geologists have demonstrated the previous existence of a very large land connection between India and East Africa and of an equally extensive sea north of this, filling roughly the present-day desert belt. At that time, the Congo Basin was first an arm of the Atlantic and, later, a great lake. This ancient geography doubtless accounts for some of the similarities in fauna between the two areas (equatorial Africa and oriental Asia) but it seems to be too ancient to account for the current distribution of monkeys as a whole. However, the most primitive forms of several families of mammals are found in West Africa and the Orient, while they are absent from central and East Africa and sometimes from India also. An interesting example is the Two-spotted Palm Civet of West Africa; another may be the little Olive Guereza. Most of the more *modern* mammals seem to have migrated south into both Africa and the Indo-Oriental region from the north, for the fossilized bones of both tree-dwelling forms like monkeys and plains dwellers like antelope have been found in southern Europe and Central Asia.

The Coloboids of Asia are extremely numerous and varied and must be separated into no less than nine genera. Two of these belong to the Indian subregion, six to the Burma–Indo-China–Malay subregion, and one to the Chinese. The two Indian forms and three of the second contingent may be called collectively Langurs; two of the latter and the Chinese, Snub-nosed Monkeys; and the remaining form, which is confined to the island of Borneo, is well known as the Proboscis Monkey.

Sharing a position of prominence on the Indian scene with the mobsters known to us as Rhesus Monkeys and to the Indians as the Bandar are vast communities of long-limbed, long-tailed, and rather long-furred monkeys that are regarded as sacred. They swarm all over certain towns and most notably the city of Benares, the central point of reverence for the goddess Durga, wife of Shiva. These monkeys are considered to be dedicated to the god Hanuman, and are themselves likewise so called—the word *hanuman* meaning "long-jawed." In this capacity they are not only sacred but absolutely protected from any interference whatsoever by human beings. They are neither tame nor wild, but wander about the country as they please in enormous crowds. And they seem to be quite aware of their immunity, for they may spend some weeks in the jungle and then move into a town where they rob shops and private homes at will and scamper all over man's domains—including his temples, where they are encouraged to reside by the priests, who feed them regularly and plentifully with grain. Foreigners visiting India had better be well acquainted with the position these monkeys hold in the community and in the eyes of those of the Hindu faith, since anyone who kills or even molests one of them lays himself open to peremptory punishment and possible lynching at the hands of any onlookers. While the Indian is above all a man of peace and abhors violence, he has very strong religious convictions, and to avenge the death of a Hanuman is not only his right but his duty. Throughout history there have been some unthinking, unknowing or malicious foreigners who for such an act have met death at the hands of the enraged local populace.

The particular monkey concerned is known to science as *Semnopithecus entellus* and is one of a group of four species of large langurs, of which there are collectively no less than fourteen described varieties. It is a gray animal with black, naked face, ears, hands and feet, but the young are born pure black. All the *Semnopithecus* have prominent bony brow ridges and prognathous jaws, and the hair on top of the head radiates from a central point. In the common *S. entellus* long hairs point forward over the brows like the peak of a cap and are dark brown or black; *S. priam*, which is found from the Madras River south to the southern tip of India and in Ceylon, bears a prominent crest; the northern species, *S. schistaceus*, which inhabits the Himalayas, has long whiskers that cover the ears, and the color of these whiskers and of the top of the head always contrasts with that of the rest of the body. One form of the Himalayan species lives at an elevation of ten thousand feet in Tibet and has a long, shaggy coat. The fourth species, *S. hypoleucus*, is gray with black tail, hands, and feet, and is found along the west coast of southern India. The common species is distributed all across central India from Bombay to Calcutta

and north to the Ganges. The Himalayan forms are in some cases of gigantic size and are quite at home among snow-laden pine trees. They also descend to the ground and romp about in the snow.

The Langurs as a whole may be fairly well divided between those among which the young are born white, or black, or of a pattern known as "cruciger," which is to say with a dark median dorsal line and a cross band of darker pelage over the shoulders. Unfortunately, this nice distinction does not prove to conform exactly with the arrangement of the species between the five genera, but the young of all *Semnopithecus* are pure black and have the naked skin area pale pink. These monkeys also are notable for carrying their tails curved upwards and then forwards over the back when they are traveling along branches or over the ground. In disposition they are fractious beasts and become downright aggressive to other troupes of their own kind or to other animals, and notably the Rhesus, if these animals invade territory to which they consider they have laid claim. They also fight a great deal among themselves, and the adult males really mean business when they do so, even carrying their efforts to the death. This is somewhat unusual among the Coloboids and a rarity among primates as a whole. The most rambunctious are the Hanumans. These, however, can no longer be called truly wild animals because of their intimate association with man for millenia, and one wonders whether they may have developed their aggressive tendencies from this association. Large males grow to a head and body length of thirty inches and have tails three feet long. They never live far from water and spend much time on the ground, especially in rocky places, but they can travel fast in trees and can leap from forty feet above the ground.

The mothers carry their young about with them for some considerable time, clasped to their belly; but when weaned and able to get about by themselves the immature tend to foregather and keep apart from their elders. The Hanuman is distinguished by having a high proportion of twin births; in fact, this seems to be the rule rather than the exception, as it is in other species.

The second genus of Langurs (*Kasi*) are better known as the Purple-faced Monkeys, which indeed they are. Five types have been recognized, but they form only two species—known respectively as *Kasi johni*, which is black with a brown crown and whiskers and is found in the Western Ghats, namely the hilly and mountainous strip that runs up the western side of southern India, and as *Kasi vetulus*, which varies from silvery gray to pure black, invariably has a brown crown to its head and long white whiskers, and is found on the island of Ceylon. These monkeys are of lighter build than the true Langurs and have the naked skin of the face colored bright purple. Males of the Nilgiri Langur (*K. johni*) measure about two feet and have thirty-inch tails. Curiously, this monkey is much hunted both for its beautiful pelt and for its flesh, which is very succulent and is relished by those of the local inhabitants who either are not of the Hindu faith or can bring forward valid reasons for asserting the animal to be devoid of holy attributes.

The remaining langurs are found outside of India proper and are spread over the vast Oriental Region (in the restricted sense) which is to say from the Assam border to southern China and thence south through Burma, Siam, Indo-China, Malaya and the greater Indonesian islands to "Wallace's Line." This demarcation between the Oriental and Australian Regions runs roughly from northeast to southwest between the Saragani Islands, off the extreme southern tip of Mindanao, and Ariago Island of the Kawio group of the Sangi Islands, which string to the north of Celebes; thence through the Celebes Sea and the Straits of Macassar between Borneo and Celebes; and by a complex route between minute unheard-of islands through the eastern Java Sea to the straits that separate the islands of Bali and Lombok (see map). In this area there are certainly no less than fifty quite distinct kinds of "Langurs" that are currently divided among nineteen full species, of three genera. These genera are known popularly as the *Lutongs* or Capped Langurs; the *Surelis*, *Simpais*, or Banded Leaf-Monkeys; and the *Doucs* or Painted Monkeys. The Capped Langurs or Lutongs are primarily mainland forms with outlying species on the islands of Sumatra, Java and Borneo. The Banded Leaf-Monkeys have their headquarters on the islands and only some varieties of one species on the mainland. The Doucs inhabit a more limited territory in eastern Indo-China.

The Lutongs (genus *Trachypithecus*) are represented by twenty-seven recognizable types divided among a dozen species. They are large monkeys, and most but not all of them have the hair on the crown of the head raised into a tall peak or cap-like structure. This hair may lie evenly backwards or stand erect, and it may grow from a single central whorl or from two whorls, one behind the other. The typical Assamese form (*T. pileatus*) is gray above and white below and has a jet-black face and a tall "cap"; those from upper Burma, Siam, Laos, Annam and Cambodia (*T. phrayei* and *ellioti*) are similarly colored, but the skin around the eyes is unpigmented and either staring white or very pale pink. Another species from the Shan States (*T. shanicus*) has no crest, and the head hair is arranged round a single whorl. Still another noncrested form from upper Assam and eastern Bengal (*T. barbei*) is the origin of a very strange story. It appears that this animal has throughout the ages been acquainted with extensive salt springs high up in the mountains, the mineral content of which it relishes, but either through drinking the water, or swallowing the mud through which it bubbles, or eating the small animal life that lives therein, it develops limy concretions in its intestines and gall bladder, varying in size from that of a large pea to a small hen's egg. The Chinese believe that these stones, known (like other types of concretions found in various other animals such as camels, llamas, porcupines, and horses) as "bezoars," are of high medicinal value, and they were still willing to pay as much as ten pounds sterling apiece for them at a time when that currency had enormous purchasing power. These stones still command an extravagant price, but they have become intensely rare because of the merciless slaughter of the monkeys at the points where they congregate at suitable pools.

From Tenasserim to Johore State in Malay there is another noncrested form known as the Dusky or Spectacled Leaf-Monkey (*T. obscurus*) that has, as its name indicates, light areas around the eyes; while to the east in Tonkin there is a black form, *T. francoisi*, with two hair whorls on the head, a tall crest, and vivid white stripes from the corners of the mouth to the ears. Another similar form, *T. laotum*, from Laos, has the whole forehead, cheeks, sides of the head, and throat white. In Annam is still another, *T. delacouri*, with a face like the Tonkin type, but no hair whorl on the head, and pure white thighs. In the same region and notably in Tonkin is a grizzled greenish-gray-brown species, *T. poliocephalus*, with a golden head, buff-white cheeks and a yellow throat that blends into a gray underside. Then, there is a very common species known as the Crested Lutong (*T. cristatus*) that occurs throughout this whole area as well as all over Siam, the Malay Peninsula, on many of the lesser islands, on Sumatra and on Borneo (but not on Java). Finally, on Java and Bali there is still another smaller, darker species, *T. pyrrhus,* without any crest or cap but with long facial whiskers, which is known popularly as the Negro Monkey because it is jet-black all over and has silver spangles. Far away to the west, isolated on the Mentawi Islands off the coast of Sumatra, upon which small archipelago so many strange and unique forms of animals have survived, there is a very distinct species, *T. potenziani,* which is always born a bright gold in color, but which when adult is black above and golden orange below, with vivid white cheeks and throat.

From this very brief review of the twelve species of this single genus, some idea may be gained of the enormous diversity of monkey forms indigenous to this area of the Orient. But still this is very far from the whole story, for there are twenty-seven quite clearly identifiable subspecies of these dozen central types. Then again, large areas of territory inhabited by huge monkey populations have never yet been combed by collectors specifically interested in monkeys. There are estimated to be over a million islands in the East Indies, and tens of thousands on the Asiatic side of Wallace's Line. Considerable numbers of these support indigenous populations of monkeys, and such populations almost invariably change in short order from their parent stock, thus creating distinct races or subspecies. Then again, many of these monkeys show a marked tendency to throw out glaring mutations, such as pure red individuals among those otherwise normally black-coated, or to come out lighter or darker than the norm, or even to display unusual white markings.

The Banded Leaf-Monkeys (*Presbytis*) are now known in an equally great variety of forms, most of which may be regarded as valid subspecies, and these are grouped into nine full species. They are, on the whole, smaller animals that live in small family parties and travel considerably about limited feeding territories in forested country. In many respects they fill the same natural niche in the East Indies that is occupied by the Guenons in the forests of Africa, and they apparently have somewhat the same habits. Little of a specific nature, however, is recorded about their habits, and,

since they are not tolerant of captivity and many of them are rare, little is known of their behavior. Young have been born to a few species in captivity, and the gestation period of at least one kind is affirmed to be 140 days. Nothing is known of their natural longevity or of any breeding cycles they may have. The progressive changes of the growing youngster from birth to maturity have been pieced together in some cases, and it appears that one young at a birth is normal. The baby is carried by the mother for some time, clasped to her belly. They are eaters of leaves, buds and green fruit, and are really very numerous in some localities.

The commonest species, *P. femoralis,* is represented by twelve subspecies, ranging *in toto* from southern Tenasserim south through the Malay Peninsula to Singapore Island, throughout the Rhio and other islands leading to the northeast coast of Sumatra, on the south coast of Sumatra about the Padang area, on the Batu Islands off that coast, and on the western tip of Borneo. They are various shades of brown, darker above and lighter below, and there is a prominent white stripe inside the thigh. The hair on the crown is arranged in two whorls, so that there is a forwardly directed peak like that of a cap, a tall crest, and a tuft sticking out of the back of the head. The young of this, as of all the *Presbytis,* have the "cruciger" pattern of coat explained above. The remaining eight species are island forms.

The best known is probably the Black-crested Leaf Monkey (*P. melalophus*) of central and southeast Sumatra, also known as the Simpai. It is exceedingly variable in color, the back and upper parts ranging from bright red to jet-black and the underside from white to yellow. The cheeks are invariably yellowish white. The hair on the crown forms a transverse crest, but there is no whorl and no brow peak. A closely related form from northeast Sumatra, *P. thomasi,* has a bicolored tail. A common monkey in Java is the Mitred Sureli (*P. aygula*), which has a single crown whorl, a crest at the back of its head and a short brow-fringe. It is a very pretty animal, smooth dark gray above and pure white below from chin to tail tip, with white hands and feet. This species is considerably more rowdy than the average Coloboid and in some places seems to have little fear of man, coming down from the trees and marauding cultivated areas even when people are present. I have seen them eating large tree snails or possibly the contents of the guts of these molluscs.

The remaining five species come from Borneo, the best known being *P. hosei,* which has a head-dress like the Simpai with a prominent white blaze on the forehead. It ranges up to altitudes of 4,000 feet in North Borneo and central Borneo. *P. sabana,* from the hot lowlands of northeast Borneo, has two frontal whorls and a tall crest on the back of the head but no white blaze; *P. crucigera* retains, as its name implies, a prominent back-and-shoulder cross throughout life and is brown in color; *P. rubicunda* from southeast Borneo is a beautiful wine red in color, with black hands and feet, and has a hair-do like the Mitred Sureli. Most unexpectedly for a dark animal, its young are pure white. *P. frontata* has a completely naked forehead, two whorls on the top of the head and a tall crest behind.

The last of the Langurs or normal-nosed Coloboids come from Indo-China and Cochin and are known as Doucs, *Pygathrix nemaeus* and *nigripes.* The two are distinguished by the naked areas of the face being yellow in the former and black in the latter. As the photograph shows they are very curious-looking animals with strange oblique eyes. The head and body measures about two feet and the tail is slightly shorter. There is a very slight brow-fringe, but the hair lies flat back over the head and the plumelike whiskers are neatly brushed back under the ears. The fur is rather short, very thick and glossy, and exhibits a great range of colors and of pattern. In *nemaeus* the top of the head is warm brown, the face is daffodil yellow, and two orange-red stripes run back from the corners of the eyes to enclose the ears. There is a light yellow collar over the neck and just behind this a very dark gray-brown to black belt or second collar. The main trunk, including the arms to the elbows, is a grizzled gray. The thighs and feet are black, and the fingers and palmar surface of the hands are also black, but the forearms are pure white and the lower legs reddish chestnut. The whole tail and a strange triangular saddle across the rump are also pure white. The oddest thing about this coloration is that not only are all the colors very vivid, but they are clearly defined and distinct. Nothing specific is known about the habits of these lovely creatures, though I have been told by an observer that they are quite numerous in the lowland forests of Cochin and that they appear to swim strongly.

At this point there remain but six known Coloboids to be described. These fall into four very distinct genera, all of which have grotesque noses —three of them pointing to the sky and having the nostrils directed straight forwards, the fourth having—in the adult males, at least—a down-drooping protuberance that may reach over three inches in length and actually hang below the chin. The purpose of neither of these extraordinary nasal structures is known, and it is not even clear whether they indicate a close relationship between the four genera concerned. Anatomically all these animals have some points in common, and these features set them apart from all other Coloboids. They are all found in the same general area; and the noses of the young of all of them are much alike, all being decidedly retroussé.

The first is rather misleadingly known as the Mentawi Islands Langur (*Simias concolor*); and there are recognized subspecies of it on Siberut and Pagi islands of that group. They are not langurs; they are not much like the other Snub-nosed Monkeys except for their noses; and they are quite unlike any other Coloboids in that they have tiny, slender, naked tails only about six inches long. They have heavy-set bodies measuring almost two feet, and very short hands and feet but exceptionally long fingers and toes. Altogether, they look more like Macaques, being clothed in short, rather hard brown fur with a grizzled effect over the shoulders, but with black, naked faces, hands, feet, and large buttock pads. They have light gray-brown whiskers brushed back over the ears and then slightly upwards to form, with the long hairs of the side of the crown, a pair of "fins" above the ears. Another set of plumes grows downwards from the lower cheeks and jowls to form fringes on the sides of the throat. The Mentawi Islands (see map), which string along the western coast of Sumatra in the Indian Ocean for over six hundred miles, are separated from the bigger island by only a fifty-mile channel, but each of them is quite different from the next in climate, appearance, flora and, to a considerable extent, fauna, and all are quite different from Sumatra in these respects. Upon them a number of odd types of animals seem to have been stranded in early geologic times, so that their nearest relatives are to be found on the mainland of Malaya rather than on the intervening land mass of Sumatra. There are even some creatures on these islands that are not found anywhere else. The islands are clothed in dense, moist forests that provide a somehow unique natural niche, but in just what manner this differs from similar forests on other islands has not yet been investigated in detail. Nothing is recorded of these Snub-nosed Monkeys except that they are essentially arboreal, despite their rather doglike or macaque-like appearance,

mal, standing somewhere between the Mentawi form and the true Snub-noses of the Chinese regions.

These latter (*Rhinopithecus*) are among the rarest and probably least known of all monkeys. There are three described forms—Biet's Monkey (*R. bieti*) from Yunnan, which is brown, with black head, shoulders and tail and a black band along

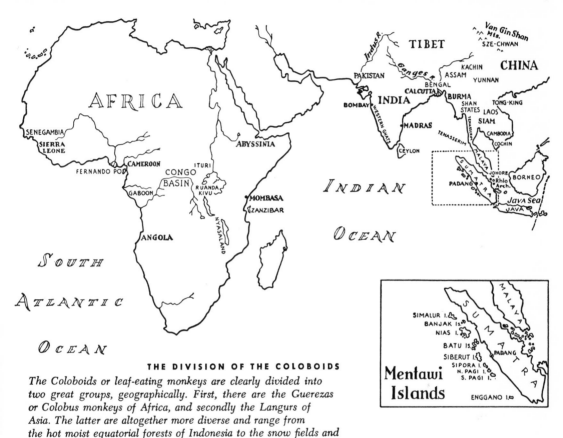

THE DIVISION OF THE COLOBOIDS

The Coloboids or leaf-eating monkeys are clearly divided into two great groups, geographically. First, there are the Guerezas or Colobus monkeys of Africa, and secondly the Langurs of Asia. The latter are altogether more diverse and range from the hot moist equatorial forests of Indonesia to the snow fields and coniferous forests of Tibet and central China. They are, nonetheless, restricted to the west of Wallace's Line, and some of the oddest forms are unique to the Mentawi Islands, which, for some reason, have retained a most odd fauna.

which might otherwise be considered to be an adaptation to a terrestrial habitat.

The second Snub-nosed Monkey, *Presbytiscus avunculus*, inhabits Tonkin and looks much like the Mentawi Islands animal but has a long tail. Its hands and feet are also very short and broad, and the fingers and toes are likewise extremely long and slender. Its nose is even more back-turned and its tip is longer. This monkey was previously regarded only as a species of *Rhinopithecus*, but it has now been shown to be quite a different ani-

the flanks, and white below, about the rump and on the upper surfaces of the hands and feet; Brelich's Monkey (*R. brelichi*), an enormous form, rich brown in color and with a large white cape over the shoulders, found in the Van Gin Shan Mountains of Central China; and another large species, known as the Golden Monkey (*R. roxellanae*), found, apparently, over a rather wide area from Kachin in far Upper Burma, throughout Sikang and parts of Yunnan and Sze-Chwan in China and in extreme eastern Tibet. This magnificent animal appears to vary somewhat in color but is usually a brilliant, shiny, almost iridescent golden orange, with lighter extremities and terminal tail club, slightly darker crown and neck, and a dark band along the flanks and down the fore edge of the legs where the long fur of the dorsal surfaces meets the shorter, softer and sparser fur of the under and inner sides. The face is naked and a brilliant sky or sea blue. All these monkeys seem to vary somewhat in coloration, both individually, by season, by sex, and by age, and the changes pertinent to age and season have not yet been fully worked out. In fact, very little is known about this as well as most other aspects of these wondrous animals.

In size they range from two to over three feet in head and body length, with a tail that is somewhat longer; although they are thus considerably shorter than the largest Guerezas, they are very heavy-bodied and are clothed in long, thick fur to a length, in some cases, of seven inches, and this makes them appear enormous. They all dwell in high mountains and appear to be impervious to cold and altitude, spending much of the year up by the snow line. In some parts of inner China they are treated with considerable respect by the villagers, whom they often outnumber on their periodic or annual migrations, when they are reported to pass from one range to another in vast, steadily moving hordes. Few zoologists and indeed not many travelers have observed these striking primates in their natural habitat. T. Donald Carter of the American Museum of Natural History, who once had the opportunity to do so, tells me that he found them in the high evergreen forests which the natives told him was the habitat that they preferred, but which was at the time of his visit covered with deep snow. The animals were rare, however, because the pelts of the males were in great demand and fetched a high price for their long, silky, golden pelage, which was plucked and woven into materials used for the tailoring of robes for mandarins and high officials.

The *Rhinopithecus* have unusually long hands and feet but short fingers and toes, and by all accounts they spend much time on the ground running along like dogs with their tails held high. They are also at home in the montane forests and bamboo thickets, and, although they still eat predominantly leaves, shoots, and some fruits, they appear to take a somewhat more mixed diet than other Coloboids.

The last of the Coloboids and of the Monkeys *per se* is an altogether bizarre creature now popularly called the Proboscis Monkey and by zoologists *Nasalis larvatus*. It is found only on the island of Borneo and apparently never far from water. It is not only singular in appearance but has the oddest habits and temperament. About the time of writing, four arrived in the United States in good condition as a result of careful feeding during a period of captivity in Java prior to shipment, including the use of new vitamin concoctions and other food boosters, and it is to be hoped that they will survive in captivity, something that has not previously been achieved for more than a few months. In their own country they are exclusively leaf-eaters, eat prodigiously, and are very selective in their feeding. They also combine strenuous exercise, including regular and prolonged swimming in lakes and rivers, with even more prolonged periods of total inactivity, when they may lounge on their backs in the sun or sit on treetops for hours, absolutely motionless. At such times they resent the slightest disturbance, including the approach of any other animals, or any noise made even by their own young. At all times they will drive other animals and especially monkeys from territory they consider to be theirs, and they are at these times most forthright and aggressive. When left alone they are of a profoundly calm and what appears to be contemplative disposition.

They are very large monkeys, the males measuring up to thirty inches, with a tail of similar length, and weighing up to fifty pounds. The females are much smaller, seldom being four feet in over-all length and weighing less than twenty-five pounds. In color they are a rather bright sandy red, darkening on the back to rich chestnut, and lighter below. The face and other naked parts are a mild pink but their faces tend to go red with anger or heat. Their eyes are small and somewhat oblique and give the animals—and notably the adult males—the most ridiculous expression because they are not sunken like those of almost all other higher primates. The whole face is, in fact, more like that of a bird. The noses of the young are flattened, the nares being retroussé, and the tip turned upwards like the Snub-noses; those of the females turn down but are only slightly exaggerated; but the males have veritable trunks, sometimes reaching three inches in length, slightly flattened from front to back, widest in the middle, having a groove down the center line, and hanging down over the mouth to below the chin.

What this grotesque adornment is for has been a natural challenge to evolutionists, but since no reason for it has been established it is regarded as a sexual exaggeration developed by natural selection (of the largest available noses), presumably by the females. It is amusing to note that the Indonesians call this monkey in "kitchen-Malayan"—the lingua franca of the islands—the *Orang blunda,* which means "white man," a term usually reserved in colonial times for the Hollanders because they appeared to the Malay peoples to have excessively long and large noses rendered more prominent by their very pink and white complexions.

Proboscis Monkeys are very clannish and move about in large groups. The gestation period is not exactly known but is believed to be about 166 days. The young weigh less than a pound at birth (.45 kilograms) and their skulls when seen in profile are alarmingly like those of minute adult human beings. They are slow growing, and it is seven years before the adult dentition erupts. They appear to have low fertility and no fixed breeding season.

12

The Superiority of the Apes

GIBBONS, SIAMANGS, ORANGS, CHIMPS, AND GORILLAS

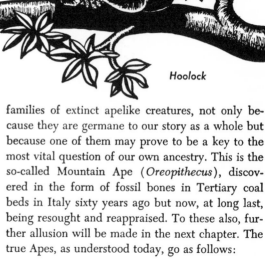

Hoolock

THE PRIMATES were once very simply divided into three great lots, named the Lemurs, Monkeys and Apes. However, as we have seen, the classification of this huge host of diverse creatures for even the most elementary descriptive purposes requires something much more elaborate. Furthermore, neither the name "lemur" nor the title "monkey" really means anything in particular, and the word "ape" proves to be used indiscriminately for a wide variety of entirely different animals. The term "ape" should have a more precise connotation. Unfortunately, it does not, either in popular or scientific parlance.

The creatures in question number twenty-seven known living forms, split between only ten species, but these comprise no less than six genera. They thus constitute a small and compact group. Scientifically, they form a family known as the *Pongidae*, which is not only very closely associated with but perhaps may even be said to blend into another family of Primates—the only one remaining to be mentioned. This is that of the *Hominidae*, which includes ourselves. Of this, however, we will speak further in the next chapter. In listing the Apes, we include, in addition to the living forms, two sub-

families of extinct apelike creatures, not only because they are germane to our story as a whole but because one of them may prove to be a key to the most vital question of our own ancestry. This is the so-called Mountain Ape (*Oreopithecus*), discovered in the form of fossil bones in Tertiary coal beds in Italy sixty years ago but now, at long last, being resought and reappraised. To these also, further allusion will be made in the next chapter. The true Apes, as understood today, go as follows:

	SP.	SUBSP.
A. **LESSER APES** (*Hylobatinae*)		
(1) Gibbons (*Hylobates*)	4	15
(2) Concolors (*Nomascus*)	1	4
(3) Siamangs (*Symphalangus*)	2	3
B. **FOREST APES** (*Dryopithecinae*)		
(1) Asiatic (*Dryopithecus*, etc.)	(extinct)	
(2) African (*Proconsul*, etc.)	(extinct)	
C. **GREAT APES** (*Ponginae*)		
(1) Orangs (*Pongo*)	1	2
(2) Chimps (*Pan*)	1	1
(3) Gorillas (*Gorilla*)	1	2
D. **MOUNTAIN APES** (*Oreopithecinae*)		
(1) Manlike Ape (*Oreopithecus*)	(extinct)	

With this chart before us we may proceed to investigate the members of the family *Pongidae*, or the Apes in the restricted sense. The origin of these creatures is the subject of continuing and most interesting debate. The consensus of scientific opinion today is that they had an origin quite separate from the so-called monkeys in the earliest eons of the Tertiary Period of geological time, some fifty million years ago or more, and possibly somewhere among the diverse forms of primitive Tarsioids. The Dryopithecines are in no way "monkey-like": they are true apes and could well be the ancestors of the present-day great apes. Their ancestors are not known, unless certain bones unearthed in Burma and East Africa (*Amphipithecus* and *Xenopithecus*) represent examples of their ancestral stem. The former are of extremely early date (Upper Eocene Age).

Today there are clearly two stages of apelike creatures in existence—the Lesser and the Greater Apes. The former are rather highly specialized for life in trees, through which they travel by brachiation. As a result their hind limbs are used in a rather special manner, but this, contrary to what might be expected, appears to have promoted their employment as "legs" rather than as a second pair of "arms." These small apes normally run along on their hind limbs with their long arms held above their heads or at other strange angles—both as balancing organs and merely to get them out of the way—when they are not trapezing through the trees, and they do this on horizontal branches as well as on the ground. They are, in fact, more truly bipedal than the Great Apes, and this has given rise to considerable speculation as to the origin of man's upright gait, because the Pithecanthropines have constantly been alleged to display many gibbon-like anatomical characters, and there is now some indication that Modern Man may be descended directly from these Ape-Men (see Chaptre 13). Perhaps our ancestors adopted the upright stance while still living in trees and not when they had to descend to the ground and run about thereon for their living.

Gibbons are today confined to the Oriental Region. There are seven species divided among three distinct genera, and they range from the eastern Himalayas to Hainan, Borneo and Java. They vary in a most bewildering manner and are subject to innumerable regional variations; they show sexual differences of color and sometimes appear in two color types in the same area; they usually change color as they grow older and sometimes do so suddenly and permanently for no apparent reason. Nonetheless, they have certain external features that make it possible to identify them. Using these, we may construct the following key to aid in their identification:

A. With inflatable vocal sacs on throat:
   1. In both sexes   **SIAMANGS**
   2. In males only   **CONCOLORS**

B. Without vocal sacs of any kind:
   1. Rump well furred   **HOOLOCKS**
   2. Rump partially naked:
      a. Light fringe round face:
         i. Hands and feet white   **LARS**
         ii. Hands and feet like body   **AGILES**
      b. No light fringe round face **WOW-WOWS**

The most distinct form of Lesser Ape is also the largest—standing a little over three feet with erect legs—and is known as the Siamang (*Symphalangus syndactylus*). It is a jet-black animal, is clothed in rather long, profuse, but somewhat shaggy fur, has a naked face with a sparse stubble in place of a moustache and beard, and has immensely long arms with the hair on the forearm growing towards the elbow as in the greater apes and ourselves. Both sexes have curious naked, bright red sacs under the chin that may be inflated from the throat and that aid in the production of the most monumental ululations produced by any animal.

The typical form of Siamang is found on the island of Sumatra, but there is a smaller race still living on some mountains in Selangor State on the Malay Peninsula, and there is another dwarf form that was found in 1903 on South Pagi Island of the Mentawi Archipelago off the southwest coast of Sumatra. Besides being diminutive, this variety has rather less webbing between the second and third toes than do its larger relatives, and for these reasons almost alone it has been considered to be of a separate genus named *Brachytanites*. On the other hand, it has also been classed as a species of the True Gibbons and given the name *Hylobates klossi*. If it is not worthy of generic distinction, it should probably better be classed with the other Siamangs as *Symphalangus klossi;* and we so class it herewith, although it does appear to stand somewhere between the Siamangs and the Concolors.

Siamangs as a whole have strange temperaments,

becoming very surly and sometimes truly vicious with increasing age. They do not take kindly to confinement though specimens have lived for up to fifteen years in zoos in America and Europe. The Indonesians, who very frequently keep gibbons as members of their households, seldom keep Siamangs, not only because they usually run away if unchained, but because they are too rough to leave around their children. In their native haunts Siamangs are magnificent. Their home is the upper canopy of the forest, and they seldom if ever come to the ground. At dawn and at sundown they make the mountain valleys literally ring with their tremendous, prolonged, barking hoots that, led off by one and taken up by all others within hearing, mount to a deafening crescendo that makes your eardrums ring and reduces every other jungle creature, even the most raucous birds, to abject silence. This uproar usually stops abruptly, and then echoes go rolling away over the canyons until other, distant troupes pick up the call. Then off they all go again. When disturbed, or sometimes apparently just to amuse themselves, they literally roar through the trees, running along branches on their hind legs with a sort of loping gallop, waving their arms and howling, and when they come to the end of a branch they just sail out into space to seize a branch with the ease of an expert acrobat, and then go swinging along hand over hand in great swoops, covering up to twenty feet between the point of release with one hand and the seizure of another branch with the next. In full flight, moreover, they are actually air-borne longer than they are attached to the trees.

Large males may weigh as much as forty-five pounds, but the single young are exceptionally small and pathetically wizened little things. Their gestation period is believed to be about seven months but is not definitely known, and their life span is estimated to be at least twenty years and possibly more. When a big male blows up his throat sac it may be larger than his whole head.

In no way like the Siamangs, except in that the males have inflatable vocal sacs, are the Concolors of the island of Hainan and the adjacent mainland coast from Tonkin to Annam, Laos and Siam. The four subspecies form a unit that is quite unlike the rest of the Gibbons, and there is little doubt that they should be separated from them as a distinct genus. Moreover the distinction between them and the other Gibbons is not merely that the latter lack

laryngeal sacs. The hair on the top of their heads grows straight upwards to form a central crest in the males and two lateral crests in the females, and there are also anatomical differences between the two groups. Concolors never display a light brow band.

They come in a variety of colors, from pure black to golden or buff. Both males and females are of all colors on Hainan, but on the adjacent mainland all the males are black and all the females buff colored, with the crowns of their heads black. Young males are born black or gray and then go black, but young females are always gray, then go black, and finally turn buffy. The western form, found in Thailand and Laos, also comes in a black and a buff form in both sexes and has gray babies, but the black form has a pure white chin, whiskers and throat, and the buff has a black cap. The Annam form is always black but has a rusty chin and throat. In habits Concolors are agile and rowdy. They are said to take a considerable amount of small animal food such as tree frogs, snails and insects. Some individuals will eat eggs but others seem to be terrified of the sight of them.

The first of the smaller, more typical Gibbons is known as the Hoolock (*Hylobates hoolock*). This has a more northerly range than any other, being found in the eastern Himalayas from Assam to Upper Burma and thence east into Yunnan Province in China. Southwards, it reaches Tenasserim in the Malay Peninsula, northern Thailand and Laos. It is fairly easy to recognize, since it always has a light, and usually a pure white, horizontal band across the brow while the rest of the body is unicolored. The males are invariably jet-black, but the females turn from black to gray and then to a smoky or buffy color with age. The young of both sexes, however, are born gray, then go black.

In popular accounts Gibbons are almost invariably said to be docile and loving in captivity, but this seems to be at complete variance with the findings of most experts. In the wild they are excitable and nervous creatures, and amazingly alert, even when they are supposed to be asleep. They have wonderful vision and very good hearing, and they are adept at making themselves scarce. They live in family parties of various sizes according to the species, ranging from a pair with young to twenty or thirty. Within the family they are fairly peaceable and seem to show much concern and compassion for any of their own kind that may get into difficulty, but the full-grown males and females fight wickedly among themselves, so that there are never more than one of each in the group, though old vanquished males may be allowed to tag along and young females to breed within the group at the same time as the current matron. According to Dr. C. R. Carpenter, who made prolonged and careful studies of whole populations of gibbons in northern Siam, the sexes appear to have equal standing, and either may lead the family to and from feeding trees. Each group maintains a territory varying in size from thirty to one hundred acres, according to the height of the trees and thus the amount of available room to feed—because, being aerial dwellers, it is the volume of their estates, not the area, that counts. There are some neutral zones between these territories, and on these more than one troupe may feed but not sleep, and one gang usually dominates and takes precedence over other gangs that go there. When two gangs meet they indulge in "whooping" contests, from which the weaker group always retreats in the face of the threats of the stronger.

Gibbons will fight extra-tribally, and with most unpleasant vigor and results. Many zoo men have lived to rue the day they introduced new arrivals to a large cage already occupied by these animals, for the whole lot may fly into a melee to the death. Both sexes will fight each other, or pairs will form alliances and fight together, and they will all attack other species, including even Siamangs. Similarly, while they often make extremely gentle and loving pets, they have somewhat unreliable dispositions, especially in temperate climates and when kept indoors. The jaws of a gibbon are a terrifying sight, since both the upper and lower canines are recurved, razor-edged tusks, the upper ones reaching down outside the lower jaw almost to the chin on either side. They are also lightning-fast creatures, and their attacks are sudden and premeditated. Their bite can be really dreadful. They are intelligent enough to harbor pet peeves, and they are furtive and cunning in their attacks, invariably taking their victim unawares.

Gibbons eat mostly green nuts and fruits, but they take some leaves and shoots and nibble on certain flowers. They also eat large quantities of termites, tree ants and other insects, snails, tree frogs, young birds and eggs. They also catch adult birds—and on the wing, to boot, and often in mid-air while swinging from one branch to another.

When so brachiating they may carry items of food in their feet with the legs flexed up against the body. They often feed while hanging by one hand, using their teeth to pare the food and their other hand to pick it. They drink by dipping the hairy backs of their hands into water and then licking it off with a swiftly repeated motion. They also drink dew or rain dripping from leaves or their own fur, which is immensely dense and impervious. Strangely, however, all gibbons quickly become water-logged if completely immersed, and they are quite incapable of swimming.

The remaining species—other than the Concolors and Hoolocks—form a close-knit group and are three in number. Two of these come in two distinct forms and the third in no less than eight recognized but at least partially interblending varieties. Together, they are distinguished from the Hoolock, as the key indicates, by a rather noncommittal detail —namely, the amount of hair on the rump. All gibbons have hardened, naked seat-pads that develop after birth. These are almost hidden in thick fur in the Hoolock but are very prominent and completely exposed in all the remaining gibbons. Further, these latter never have a light band across the brow, but instead may bear a complete light ring round the face. They consist of the Lars, the Agile Gibbons, and the Wow-Wows or Silvery Gibbons.

The Lars (*Hylobates lar*) live on the mainland, from Lower Burma south throughout the Malay Peninsula, and east through Siam. One form is the commonest gibbon seen in captivity. This has a body varying from black to buffy gray, a black face surrounded with a complete white ring, and white hands and feet. It is known as the White-handed Gibbon. Another form—from Siam—varies considerably in color, but the light ones invariably have a black cap and a black patch on the chest.

The so-called Agile Gibbons (*H. agilis*) have the hands and feet of the same color as the rest of the body. They come in two clearly recognizable forms and are found on the mainland of the Malay Peninsula and on the island of Sumatra, where they are the only gibbons apart from the Siamang. In their lightest color phase the white ring round the face may be only very slightly lighter than the rest of the head fur.

All the remaining gibbons belong to a species named *Hylobates moloch* and popularly and variously known as Wow-Wows or Wau-Waus, or as

Silvery or Gray Gibbons. They are island forms, of uniform color, without light brow bar or facial ring. The best known are the pale gray forms from Java, which are very common as pets in Indonesia, and which have been carried about from island to island for centuries by the seafaring Malayan peoples of the East Indies. Despite this and the consequent possibility of repeated introduction of one form into the territory of another, several distinct subspecies of Wow-Wows can be recognized, notably on Borneo, Palawan, and other islands. But all the Wow-Wows occur in various color varieties.

The headquarters of the Primates today is undeniably the Oriental Region. It is the home of the Tupaioids and the Tarsioids and of a Lorisoid; and there reside also a greater variety of monkeys than anywhere else on earth, while it is now the territory of all the Lesser Apes, and was once the home of one of the great groups of Ape-Men. It also still has a Great Ape, originally called by the Dutch the Orang Utan—from the Malayan *orung*, meaning "man," and *ootan*, meaning "wild"—in the absence of any one widely known native name for these great anthropoids.

It is interesting to note that the name Orang Utan, although composed of Malayan words, is not the Malayan name for these apes and is unknown in Indonesia except among foreigners. These apes are known by a wide variety of native names in the various areas of Sumatra and Borneo where they are found, according to the local languages. The true Malay language is highly complex, almost impossible for foreigners to master, and is spoken only in a limited area on the Malay Peninsula. The language used as the lingua franca throughout Malaysia is known as "kitchen Malay" and is equivalent to "pidgin English." It is full of foreign words and is greatly simplified, has no grammar, and is used by foreigners to communicate with all the numerous peoples of a vast area, all of whom have their own languages, such as Javanese, Sundanese and Madorese on Java alone. In this jargon, these apes are most often called *monyet merah besar*, or "big red monkeys," to distinguish them from *Lutong Merah* or the Red Langurs. Another fairly well known local name for them is *Mias*.

Orangs (*Pongo pygmaeus*) are now found in certain isolated and separate areas strung along the lowland swamp-forest belt that runs around the western coast of Borneo, and in the forests of Achin, which constitute the extreme western tip of Sumatra. They are nowhere common, but are now happily somewhat protected though still in danger of total extinction. Although separated widely, the two populations are believed to represent but one species; however, Orangs vary almost as much as men in their adult appearance. Although they are comparatively rare in zoos, almost everybody knows what they look like. However, there would be few people who would not be greatly confused if they were confronted with a series of portraits of different individual Orangs. A most remarkable example of such a portrait is shown in Plate 76—a photograph that, were it not from the files of the American Museum of Natural History, might well be rejected as a hoax perpetrated by some make-up artist—and this not so much because of the height and breadth of the forehead as because of the intensely human expression, especially in the eyes. Furthermore, old males—and to a lesser degree old females—are often grotesque parodies not only of men but of all anthropoids, because of huge cheek pads, composed of fat and fibrous tissue and covered in dark, naked, pimply skin, that form flanges on either side of their faces. Moreover, their eyes are comparatively very small and close together, and their noses are bridgeless, so that the former sink into the middle of an almost circular, somewhat concave face. The muzzle, which forms a prominent forward-projecting mound in the young, shrinks back into the plane of the face in the adults, and is often hidden by heavy, drooping moustachios and a full, pendent beard of patriarchal form.

The body of the Orang is rather sparsely clothed in long, reddish hairs, some of which may measure over a foot in length. The proportions of the body are most singular, the legs being comparatively very short and rather weak, the shoulders huge and wide, the torso rather long and barrel-chested, the head enormous, the upper arms short and the forearms excessively long. The toes are very long, large, and finger-like, but the great toe is very small and thumblike; the hand is elongated, with very long fingers and a small, hooklike, opposable thumb. The skull is large and, in old males, develops a transverse crest that runs over the top from above one earhole to the other, for the attachment of immense muscles that extend downwards to the jaws and over the neck to the shoulders, and in which the skull itself is completely embedded. The jaws are actually wider in front than at the back;

and, looked at from the side, the lower jaw forms a right angle like an exaggerated pair of pump pliers held upside down and pointing forwards. All mammalian jaws are arranged upon this plan, but in the Orang they have reached the ultimate in gripping, pinching and crunching efficiency. Another oddity of these creatures is the possession of immense throat pouches that can be inflated with air from within from the larynx and have a capacity of up to six quarts. These may be single or double structures and sometimes extend down under the skin to the bottom of the breastbone, into the armpits, and over the neck to the back of the head and the shoulder blades. Those of females are much smaller, but both sexes are born with them. Their purpose is not known for sure, though they would, at first sight, appear to be sound-augmenting devices. Another suggestion is that they form, when inflated, a sort of air cushion to help support the great weight of the head or to cushion its action when the jaws are being used to rip tough objects.

Orangs are large animals, the average weight of thirteen adult males having proved to be slightly over 165 pounds, with a maximum of just 200 pounds. They are thus the heaviest creatures that normally live in trees, and this tends to support the theory that our ancestors, though as large as we, could have also been arboreal. Despite their weight, Orangs can get about the trees at a most unexpected rate, though, *because* of their weight, using for the most part the middle branches. They are deliberate in their movements and extremely cautious, using both feet and both hands and reaching out for a firm hold with only one at a time before letting go with the other three. However, they can also swing along by their arms alone, like gibbons. A remarkable film taken by the Martin Johnsons, famous big-game photographers, of the capture of a large adult male in Borneo also shows them making considerable leaps outwards and downwards from tall bare trees to massed foliage on lower tree heads. A creature weighing 150 pounds with an arm span of eight feet sailing through the air at a height of 60 feet from the ground is a most astonishing sight.

On the ground these apes appear very awkward, stumping along on their short, bowed hind limbs and with their arms widely splayed and partly bent, with the elbows pointing outwards; but in an emergency they can move along quite rapidly by using the arms like crutches and swinging the body and legs along between them in a slightly sidewise, crablike fashion. Unsuspecting hunters and cameramen have several times been more than startled at the speed of their approach or departure on the ground. They can also walk upright for limited distances, and the young can thus waddle along at a good clip, holding their arms crossed overhead.

The purpose of the immense arms of this creature seems obvious, but that of the tremendous biting mechanism of huge teeth, vicelike jaws and mountainous muscles is not readily explicable. There is little first-hand observation recorded upon the feeding habits of Orangs in the wild, but all experienced and well-informed native hunters in the countries where they are found seem to concur in the belief that they are predominantly fruit-eaters. At least one zoologist has recorded them, in Sumatra, as also eating leaves and some bark, and the very wide diet that they will accept in the unnatural conditions of captivity would seem to indicate that it is at least possible that they take some animal food in the wild. On the other hand, gorillas have an almost equally impressive jaw mechanism—but, while it has been discovered that their food consists of the leaves of seedlings, a few very small fruits, and certain tiny berries which the great creatures eat solemnly, one at a time, they also consume vast quantities of bark and other roughage that they have to rip apart with their teeth and hands. The Orang also relishes the fruits of the durian, a large, wood-hard object covered with pyramidal bosses that grows on a tall tree in the animal's native haunts. These fruits come to edibility for a limited season each year, and, although their white, stringy, custard-like contents—which is almost completely filled with huge pits—has been described as smelling like "a mixture of rotten onions and sewage," they are the downfall of a considerable portion of the human populace, which relishes them to such an extent that they sometimes eat them to excess, and as a result, break out in boil-like skin eruptions. To get at the contents of a durian requires a good sharp machete or axe and considerable strength and patience. Orangs appear to be able to open them without much trouble, using their teeth alone.

Unfortunately, the complete life histories of only a handful of Orangs are on record. Taking the classic case (reported by Dr. G. Aulmann of the Dusseldorf Zoo in Germany), the period of pregnancy of the mother was 275 days, a week more than the human period of gestation and four weeks longer than that of the Chimpanzee. The baby weighed three pounds five ounces and was nursed for six years. It did not attain its complete set of adult teeth until its tenth year, and it continued to grow until its twelfth year. The mother was highly solicitous of her offspring but was willing to allow humans whom she knew and trusted to handle it within limits.

In their own country, it appears that Orangs go about in family parties but that on occasion adult males may live alone, while two or three females and their youngsters of various ages may travel together. They move about a fair-sized territory in search of fruits in season, and this may entail movements that almost amount to migrations from high altitudes to the lowlands, but it seems that the same parties stay in the same general area for years, if not forever.

Like other great apes and men, Orangs are rather individualistic, so that it is difficult to make any hard and fast statements about their behavior. Nevertheless, it seems that they customarily sleep under crude shelters which they build of leaves and twigs on platforms in trees. The construction of these dwellings calls for an hour or two of rather hard labor on the part of the apes each evening and is accomplished by bending branches together into a fork in the tree, then breaking off small twigs and piling these over the former to make a platform, and then covering this with smaller branches and leaves. They are also reported either to cover themselves with a blanket of foliage or to burrow down into the platform and therein curl up on their sides to sleep, much as do human children on a cold night. From all accounts, Orangs seem to lead extraordinarily placid lives, if unmolested. Like other animals and, one must suppose, ourselves, the greater part of their waking hours is concerned with obtaining a sufficient supply of food; and they eat a prodigous amount. Unlike gibbons, which often go barging about the forests, whooping and yelling for no apparent reason, Orangs seem to prefer to just sit quietly or to move about slowly when not in pressing need of food. In captivity they give an impression of being contemplative and relaxed.

Young Orangs look remarkably "soulful," but this is probably a purely human interpretation of their physiognomies and expressions, for they display a combination of the riotous behavior of young Chimpanzees and the brooding quiet of baby Gorillas. They may become quite gay on occasion, and a young male once in the London Zoo had to be restrained when ladies were around from what could only be described as precocious behavior. At other times they will sit quietly for hours watching the world with solemn, concentrated attention.

The Chimpanzees, which are of African origin, are altogether different in temperament and to some considerable extent in physical make-up. They are not so big as Orangs—the average weight of males is about 110 pounds and of females about 90 pounds—and their proportions are different. The head is comparatively small, the shoulders are wide, and the torso very long but not nearly so barrel-chested as that of the Orangs. Their legs are longer in proportion to the body and the arms are shorter; the feet are smaller and the hands larger but not so long. Their great toes are very large and are used as thumbs. Chimpanzees are also covered with rather sparse, lank hair, but the amount and texture of this varies considerably; it never grows so long as that of the Orangs.

Chimpanzees are extraordinarily varied in size, build, skin color, pelage and, above all, in facial conformation and expression. Adults may be thin or fat, hairy or bald, and adult males weighing over 180 pounds have been recorded. A visitor to the zoo in Rochester, New York, in the year 1953, might have seen two of the most astonishing Chimpanzees ever exhibited at the same time: one was a gigantic male, densely clothed in long silky black hair all over, with beetling brow, large ears and immensely long arms; the other, in the adjoining cage, was an obese female, almost without hair all over and having a pinkish gray skin, small ears and unusually stubby arms. Looking at them side by side, one could hardly believe that they could be classed as of the same species, and the sight caused one to reconsider the range of variation in bodily structure possible within a so-called species.

The Chimpanzees are altogether very unexpected creatures: one can hardly call them either animals or human beings, for, the more we come to know of their ways both in the wild and in captivity, the more unconventional they seem to be. However we judge character, or upon whatever criteria we may make our assessment of it, the Chimps are undeniably extroverts and, to us, imbued with a most disturbing insight. For this reason, and because they are on the whole fairly easy to keep healthy in our environment, an enormous amount of careful experimentation has been done with them, and very large numbers have now been kept under more or less continuous observation for extended periods under all manner of conditions. As a result the prevailing opinion seems to be that there are very wide limits to their capacity.

The account of the activities of a young female that lived for four years with the well-known photographer, Miss Lilo Hess, in America, accounts of which appeared in *The Illustrated London News* in 1956, may serve to demonstrate this. The Chimp in question learned to use a screwdriver not only to extract screws from door hinges and other contrivances, but also to insert them into a piece of wood in order to hold this in place across a stool that had broken in half. What is more, the ape also drove nails with a hammer, and persisted in the task until the stool could be placed on its legs again, and sat upon. The holding of a screw on a plank with one hand while a screwdriver is applied and turned with the other entails combinations of coordinated muscular actions of a most complicated and advanced nature, and when any living thing persists in doing this for hours, despite many failures to achieve its objective, and when that objective is something so esoteric as rendering a broken stool serviceable again, as a *usable stool, per se,* we can but compare the combination of actions and determination involved as an exhibition of "intelligence" of a human order.

Many other things that Chimpanzees have done, or have been induced to do under experimental conditions, are also hard to believe, and many of them indeed seem to be at least comparable to the efforts of a man in similar circumstances, and sometimes even to better them. Notable among such was the case of a hungry man left in a bare room with an assortment of simple items including a long stick and a desirable banana suspended from the roof, but out of reach. He promptly swatted at the banana with the stick until he had battered it down. A hungry Chimpanzee was then introduced to the room, but he, after contemplating the problem, erected a structure under the banana, climbed up this, and retrieved the fruit, *whole and undamaged.*

The Chimpanzee has, today, the widest distribution of any living ape, being found from Gambia in the west all across central tropical Africa north of the Congo to the southern border of the Eastern Sudan, and thence south to the Lake Mweru forests, wherever there is tall closed forest. It also occurs in certain isolated areas south of the Congo. In other words, its range almost coincides with the distribution of the tall equatorial forest belt of Africa. However, it is primarily a lowland-dweller, and there are certain subtypes of forest in which it does not live. There has been much, and still is some, debate as to how many kinds of Chimpanzees can be identified. Although there are manifestly black-skinned forms and others that, especially when young, have pink skins, and although some are bald and others have profusely haired heads, and despite the fact that the majority from any one region may show marked racial similarities, it is now clear that they are all of one "species"—at least to the extent that Men are. A group of Chimpanzees of any age caught in the same area may display almost the whole gamut of recorded differences, whereas others of the same age and sex brought together from widely separated countries may look almost identical. Further, Chimpanzees also change radically in appearance as they mature, and they may put on excessive weight, go bald, change hair color to a limited extent, or develop black skin blotches or a completely dark countenance.

It should also be stressed that Chimps, like Orangs, and to a much greater extent Gorillas, show marked "racial," or what might perhaps better be called "national," as well as family likenesses, and this sometimes to an even greater degree than do most humans. Inbreeding is probably more frequent among Chimpanzees than among even tribalized humans, and now that the great forested areas of Africa are being sliced up into a number of isolated patches, these apes are being ever more subdivided racially. To what extent this is tending to "fix" recognizable peculiarities among limited populations of Chimpanzees is not known, but it is something that is already obvious among Gorillas.

Chimpanzees are gregarious, living and moving about in loose family parties of about half a dozen individuals; but two or more such parties may join up for spells. Females outnumber males by about three to one, and it seems that they are polygamous. Also, young seem always to outnumber the adults, and all females are almost invariably carrying babies. Although great climbers, Chimpanzees are not truly arboreal and spend a great deal of their time on the ground, upon which they walk about rather sedately on all fours, with their fingers half flexed to carry the weight of the forebody on the knuckles while the feet are placed firmly on the ground like our own. In this position, Chimpanzees have about the same stance as Rhesus monkeys, and the forebody is carried only slightly above the haunches. They can move unexpectedly fast over level ground by a kind of loping gallop with a slightly sidewise or crablike motion, and on slopes they, like the Orangs, use their arms as crutches. They seldom walk erect unless carrying something, and then they waddle along with bent knees, out-turned feet and swinging shoulders. They climb trees with consummate agility, but they seldom travel by them, preferring to descend to the ground and progress thereupon by easy stages; yet they can brachiate extremely well if occasion necessitates, and can even negotiate aerial chasms of considerable extent by leaping with outspread arms and legs and landing on foliage, as do monkeys.

Like Orangs, Gorillas, and ourselves, they make "nests." These are of two kinds—sleeping platforms in trees or on the ground, and resting cubicles on the ground in which they take daytime siestas. These nests are crude affairs, in both instances made by bending small branches or saplings inwards to a vague central point and then piling other sprigs and sprays of foliage upon these. They have been observed making an arch above their daytime rests, apparently to ward off excessive sunlight, which they seem to dislike. There seems to be valid evidence that they are sometimes active at night when there is bright moonlight, but they are always light sleepers and may be heard calling and moving about even on dark nights. Normally they become active just before dawn and devour food in enormous quantities for a couple of hours immediately after the sun is up; then they move about, feed in a desultory manner for some hours, rest during midday, move again in the afternoon, and feed once more—and ravenously—in the evening before making their beds and settling down to sleep. They appear to be essentially green-nut-eaters, though they take a very large variety of fruits, some leaves, shoots, buds and possibly some green bark. No one appears ever to have recorded them as eating any animal food, though in captivity they will eat almost anything that human beings will, allowing, of course, for individual preferences.

Chimpanzees are very rowdy creatures, and in all manner of ways. They have a remarkable vocabulary that manifestly forms a primitive kind of language. Almost anybody who has lived with a Chimp can obtain a response from any other one by imitating some of the sounds he learned from his previous association. But this is far from all. One can achieve results of a concrete and specific nature fairly easily by making appropriate noises to chimps, and they in turn can make an astonishing number of requests by vocalization. Further, in addition to noises produced by the mouth, they customarily drum with the hands or feet on the ground, tree trunks, hollow logs and other convenient objects. Though these drummings are not rhythmical, they appear to have "meaning," just as do the completely unrhythmical and, to the westerner, incomprehensible "talk" of the communication drums (as opposed to instrumental drums) of the African. Herein lies a whole field of investigation that has, as yet, hardly been touched upon with respect either to the Chimpanzee or to Man. Then again, Chimpanzees can communicate by a whole gamut of facial manipulations—drawing back the lips, pouting, smacking the lips, chattering the teeth and so forth—in some respects more expressive than the efforts of the average member of our own race and often much more insistent. The over-all racket that they make in their own country is quite inconceivable to anyone who has not encountered it. A party of half a dozen Chimpanzees indulging in a get-together may be heard for miles, and sounds as if a whole tribe of men were on the warpath.

The average gestation period among Chimpanzees is, as far as has been observed in captive specimens, 236 days. The whole process of birth, growth of the child, and its care by the mother is, among Chimpanzees, very like that in our own kind, but of course conducted upon strictly natural principles. The young Chimp at first clings to the mother and is almost as helpless as a human child though a better clinger. As it grows, it at first outstrips the human in most ways, but then slowly falls behind in many others. Physically it reaches puberty and maturity more swiftly. Several detailed studies of every phase of the growth of a Chimpanzee have been made by several groups of scientists, employing every possible known testing and recording device; and baby Chimps have also been brought up with human children. Others have been observed continuously throughout their whole natural lives so that a great volume of information is available upon them. This is summarized in an informative and most readable book by the famous anthropologist, Dr. Earnest Hooton, entitled *Man's Poor Relations*. In this work, written in 1941, the longevity of Chimpanzees is given as about twenty to twenty-six years in captivity. Since then, however, it has become known that this may be exceeded, and Professor Yerkes long ago stated that he considered a fifty-year maximum not unreasonable. This coincides with the opinions of the native peoples of Africa who, in places where Chimpanzees abound, contend that they have a life span identical to "men in olden times," meaning before the introduction of modern medical aids to health, which appears to have been between forty and fifty years, given exceptional good luck and health.

So finally we come to the mighty Gorilla, and with this creature we meet the Primate that is probably the best known but the least understood of all. There is hardly anybody left, even in the remotest parts of the civilized world, who has not heard of a Gorilla, and the very name of the creature has entered our own language and many other languages as a word denoting certain human and subhuman attributes of a most unsavory nature. Piled upon this basis of opprobrium there is now a fantastic accumulation of misrepresentation, misinformation and misinterpretation; and the visual interpretation of the poor creature is no less inaccurate than the written one. And all this despite innumerable most painstaking studies of the creatures in their own habitats, and even more long-term studies of captive specimens. Today quite a number of Gorillas of almost all ages—about fifty at the time of writing—may be inspected in the great zoos of America, Europe and Japan, but unfortunately the appearance of these, and particularly of the large males, only augments the generally accepted belief that they are ravening beasts intent only upon tearing every other living thing limb from limb. Nevertheless, from all reliable reports on their behavior in Africa and from the observations of everybody who has come in contact with them in captivity, they appear to be rather quiet and retiring creatures that prefer to keep out of the way of other animals, and most especially of man, and that seem to ask only to be left to their own placid devices.

This is not to discount the enormous strength of the Gorilla nor its fighting potential if aroused by molestation, fear or general aggravation. Adults may become very morose and surly, but almost everybody who has been closely associated with them seems to agree that this attitude is simulated rather than real. They are, in fact, the exact antithesis of the rowdy, boisterous Chimpanzees, preferring to feign indifference rather than to show emotion, and adopting a lordly air of superiority to cover their disconcertion. On the whole, the young are very friendly towards everybody, though babies are inexpressibly quiet and soulful. Half-grown youngsters usually become cheery and playful and, if in good health, like nothing better than a good rough-and-tumble. They show great affection for their own kind and literally cling to each other, both mentally and physically, for companionship. Mature gorillas have romped with their keepers or other trusted human friends and, although four times their weight, seem never to endanger them deliberately.

One of the most famous of all Gorillas that ever lived among human beings was raised in a top-floor apartment in London by a lady named Miss Cunningham. He lived not as a captive animal nor even as a pet, but more as a member of the household, and he acted accordingly. It happened that the writer lived on the next street and could watch the Gorilla—"John Daniel," or, as he was everywhere known, "Johnny Gorilla"—at play daily on a balcony. Apart from one occasion when he was apparently playing hide-and-seek with some human friends, I never saw him act in an unorthodox manner, at least, that is, from the human standpoint. On this occasion, he came dashing out of a French window and scampered straight up the steeply inclined roof to its ridge where he squatted, grimacing at the gaping crowd that rapidly filled the street below. This animal, if we can call him such, was more than half grown before his owner was persuaded to place him in the London Zoo, where he was given a large outdoor lion cage, in which he used to play with a small boy every afternoon, to the delight of enormous crowds. He never hurt anyone, though he gave a few unsuspecting folks a terrible fright when they encountered him unexpectedly. I remember my own shock when I first saw him stepping from a taxicab on our street.

Even if obtainable and even if the price were not prohibitive, one would hardly recommend a Gorilla as a chosen companion for a human child, yet all the evidence seems to show that such a choice would not be nearly as dangerous as is popularly believed, and further, that it might in some respects prove downright beneficial. Gorillas are not, in fact, dangerous animals when they have been brought up among humans. There is much evidence to show that they are not much more so in their own native haunts, despite the beliefs held about them since Roman times—beliefs fostered by almost all early travelers in Africa, many Africans even in some countries where they live, almost all movies and comic-strip artists, and all writers of fiction. Naturalists, animal collectors and scientists, starting with Paul du Chaillu, who was the first European to see them alive and to report scientifically upon them, have battled these misconceptions for almost a century; but, alas, the general impression still remains that they are the most horrible and dangerous creatures in the world.

Although the tribal African is a consummate naturalist, he often disseminates wondrous tales, especially among white men, for various and sundry reasons of his own. One of the reasons for his doing so that is often overlooked is his not always ungrounded fear that the subject of discussion may, if he tells the truth about it, result in some new taxation being clamped upon it, with consequent loss of income to himself. Thus, he often makes out that the fauna of his land is very terrible and should be avoided as much as possible. Some of the tallest tales about Gorillas were originally of native origin. Nonetheless, there are Africans who know these creatures very well and who are willing to impart their real knowledge about them to a serious inquirer.

We were once privileged to stay amongst such tribesmen some years ago, and everything they told us confirmed the accumulated modern scientific opinion about these apes. Only in a few details and in one particular did the two accounts differ: the natives asserted that the father of a troupe of Gorillas, after driving off a party of men by rushing at them and looking fierce, might actually creep around and launch a surprise attack on the retreating humans. They also absolutely insisted that the Gorillas invariably grabbed the last-but-one man of the retreating line, but that they then did nothing more than seize a leg and bite the man's thigh. In this area, the native people also went even further than our zoological acceptance in respect to the Gorilla's standing in nature, for they insisted that he, *unlike* the Chimpanzee, is not an animal at all, but is a kind of sub-man who has slipped backwards into a more primitive way of life. Strangely, they also asserted that male Gorillas never molested human females, and they stressed the retiring habits of these creatures, their desire to keep away from men—if not from his cultivated banana and other vegetable fields—and their extreme reluctance ever to carry through a frontal attack upon him.

Gorillas are found in two widely separated areas in the equatorial forest belt of Central Africa. One is a strip of mountainous territory in the eastern Congo, west of Lakes Edward and Kivu and stretching south to the northern end of Lake Tanganyika. The other is of considerably greater extent but is actually made up of a number of separate smaller units, and covers a block of territory lying between the Atlantic on the west, the Congo River on the east, and the northern edge of the closed forest on the north—which, at this point, runs roughly along the seventh parallel of north latitude. However, they are not found uniformly throughout this whole area, which encompasses the French Cameroons, Rio Muni, the Gabun and a strip of French Equatorial Africa. Then, a considerable population of them live on an isolated mountain range in the southern British Cameroons near the Nigerian border. Not only are they confined to closed-canopy forest; they are also absent from large tracts of apparently suitable country, but for no reason that we know of.

The eastern Gorillas are considerably different from the western but both are regarded today as forming a single species.

Some five hundred years B.C. a Carthaginian admiral named Hanno made a remarkable voyage round the bulge of western Africa and reached the forested shores of what is now the Guinea coast. On his return he reported that there were enormous "wild men," which he called Gorillas, on some islands off that coast and on the adjacent mainland. Later, three skins of females were said to have been sent back to Carthage, but it is not clear whether the creatures in question really were Gorillas, or whether the gallant admiral had really encountered these animals at all. Nothing truly definite was discovered about them until two thousand years later. During this time, however, vague and usually very fanciful reports of a vast ape, or of a wild "man" other than the Chimpanzee existing in West Africa, constantly filtered through to Europe; but it was not until 1847 that the Gorilla was introduced to zoological literature in a proper manner. This was in the Proceedings of the Boston Natural History Society, in which two doctors named Thomas Savage and Jeffries Wyman de-

ERNEST P. WALKER

61. Dusky Lutong (*Trachypithecus obscurus* subsp.)
One variety of a widespread gray-coated species of
Capped Langur that is commonly called the
Spectacled Leaf-Monkey. It is found in Tenasserim.

62. Dusky Lutongs (*Trachypithecus obscurus* subsp.)
A mother and twins of another subspecies of the
Spectacled Leaf-Monkey from Johore State in
Malaya. These monkeys are of considerable size and
rather rowdy behavior, but are retiring and nervous
in captivity and demand a specialized diet.

63. Proboscis Monkeys (*Nasalis larvatus*)
One of the oddest in appearance, and in some respects in behavior, of all Primates. These large, leaf-eating Coloboids of Borneo take sun baths, swim for fun, and are indifferent to humans, but drive lesser animals from their domains.

64. Siamang (*Symphalangus syndactylus*)
A Gibbon-like ape of large size from the island of Sumatra and parts of the Malay Peninsula, it stands between the Lesser and Great Apes. It has large naked air sacs under its chin, which can be inflated from the throat.

65. Study of a Wow-Wow (*Hylobates moloch*)
The Gibbon or Lesser Ape of Java that is so popular as a pet and is regarded by the Indonesian householder as one of the family. It has subhuman intelligence and alarmingly human reactions.

66. Wow-Wow Walking
(*Hylobates moloch*)
Gibbons walk and run on the hind legs and carry their long arms akimbo to get them out of the way and for balance. If they are wearing belt and chain, they will hold the slack off the ground when in a hurry.

ROY PINNEY

67. Agile Gibbon and Baby (*Hylobates agilis*)
This species has a redundant English name, since all Gibbons are unbelievably agile. It comes in various coat colors and inhabits Sumatra and the Malay Peninsula. The mothers carry and tend their young just as we do.

YLLA: RAPHO GUILLUMETTE

Young Orang Utan
(Pongo pygmaeus)
The great ape of Borneo and Sumatra is the least manlike and, in certain respects, most specialized in habits of all the Simioids. Most peculiar of their features are the complex, inflatable air sacs that can be "pumped up" from the lungs and may extend all around the throat and onto the shoulders.

CY LA TOUR AND WORLD JUNGLE COMPOUND

69. Young Orang Utan and Chimpanzee
A study in racial tolerance, juvenile understanding, and mutual protection. These two individuals would of course never have met had it not been for human agency.

IAN: MONKMEYER PRESS PHOTO

70. *Chimpanzees*

The Chimpanzee shares emotions with men as well as other creatures, and displays them in facial expressions similar to our own.

71. A Half-grown Female Chimpanzee
(*Pan satyrus*)
The lesser of the two Great Apes of
Africa, the Chimp is an active, rowdy,
and emotional creature.

72. One-year- and Two-year-old Lowland Gorillas
The Gorilla—the greatest of the Great
Apes—is found in two distinctly different racial forms in Africa, known as the
Mountain (from the Kivu region of the
eastern Congo) and the Lowland
(from the Cameroons–Gabun area).

A Trio of Young Gorillas
Gorillas show marked
family likenesses, as seen
by the brownish "skull-
caps" of this group. They
are terrestrial creatures
that climb trees only to
collect food, to sleep or to
escape danger.

75. Adult Male Lowland Gorilla
(*Gorilla gorilla gorilla*)
The Gorilla is essentially a vast, quadrupedal, vegetarian Primate. Despite his terrifying mien and immense size he is peaceable and almost gentle.

74. Young Chimpanzee
The discerning Chimp is often just as afraid of a camera as a primitive human tribesman who is unaware of the ways of the tourist.

76. "Missing Link?"
Although it may look like a fake or a museum exhibit, this is an authentic photograph of a young male Sumatran Orang; it is, nonetheless, cause for serious thought.

scribed a great ape from the Gabun River. Dr. Savage had been stationed on that river as a missionary and had collected a number of skulls from the garbage piles of the natives, who were addicted to gorilla flesh as food. He never saw a live Gorilla but accumulated much information about their alleged habits, some of it highly colorful.

The real introduction of the Gorilla was finally engineered by that remarkable little Franco-American, Paul du Chaillu, who so excited and aggravated the learned world in the latter part of the last century by his vivid lecturing and disarmingly charming books about his travels in Africa. He was the first white man known to have killed a Gorilla, and in 1860 he produced its remains, together with other skulls, skeletons and skins, to prove to the scientific world that this greatest and most manlike of apes really existed. It is now hard to believe the reception he got and the furore he created in doing so, and more especially that such an uproar took place less than a hundred years ago, for the unfortunate Du Chaillu was not only accused of exaggeration and faking but even of not having ever been to Africa, and this by the supposedly most learned people of the time. Reading all this nonsense today gives one pause to think, especially if one happens to be standing in one of the magnificent houses in one of our great modern zoos, designed entirely for the comfort and display of one of these creatures.

At the turn of this century, a German explorer named Captain Oscar von Beringe killed a gorilla at an altitude of nine thousand feet on Mt. Sabino on the other side of the vast Congo Basin, almost a thousand miles east of any place where they had till then been found. This was the first specimen of the eastern form ever heard of, and it proved to be very different—notably in the size and arrangement of its great toe, which is placed more like our own and is less opposed—and is now named after him as *Gorilla gorilla beringei* (as opposed to the rather ponderous name of *Gorilla gorilla gorilla* to which all the western forms are now assigned). After this event, all known preserved specimens were reappraised, and within a few years were split up into no less than sixteen species, with numerous subspecies. Many of these forms were, however, established on individual abnormalities of skull conformation or coat color. Finally, in 1929, Dr. Harold Coolidge proposed the above-mentioned arrangement of two races or subspecies

in a single species. It is perhaps unfortunate that the popular names of "Lowland" and "Mountain" Gorilla have been chosen for the western and eastern varieties respectively, because a considerable proportion of the western live in high mountains and the farthest western outlier actually in montane forest exclusively, at a height of from four to eight thousand feet. Moreover, that isolated group (which used to be named *G. g. matschiei*) shows certain features that were once put forward as distinguishing the true Mountain Gorilla from the Lowlands form.

The truth of the matter seems to be that Gorillas vary to an astonishing degree. Not only do they change radically during growth and to a far greater extent than do humans, they may be skinny or obese, and all their bodily proportions may vary to a far greater extent than is the case among Chimpanzees and almost as much as among Orangs. Further, their faces and expressions also vary greatly, and their skulls come in an astonishing range of shapes. Some years ago we lined up nine adult male Lowland Gorilla skulls, picked at random from the collection of the British Museum, and published photographs of them, taken together, from the front and from the side. From the frontal aspect it is hard to believe that they do not represent nine quite different kinds of animals. If covered with skin they would have varied far more than a selection of the wildest abnormalities in all the human races on earth today. On the other hand, it has been noted that Gorillas display marked family likenesses just as we do, and the author has personally observed this in an advanced form among the isolated far western population. In one family unit, all members had bright red topknots; in another, all were black all over; in another, all had silvery gray saddles across the midback. Details of the proportions of the Gorilla will, therefore, not be given here, and we will content ourselves with pointing out some of the differences between them and the other living great apes.

In this respect, Gorillas are, first of all, by far the largest of the apes, full-grown males certainly weighing up to 600 pounds (the weight of the great M'Bongo of the San Diego Zoo, who died in 1941) and possibly up to 700 pounds when fully fed and in good health in the wild. Gorillas can vary in weight in an extraordinary fashion and in very short order, according to the amount of food they have taken in just before being weighed. Females are considerably smaller than males. The total arm span of M'Bongo, measured across his back from fingertip to fingertip, was 97½ inches, or a little over eight feet, but a specimen we obtained in West Africa, which is now in the British Museum, measured across the *front* of the body 110 inches from tip to tip of the outstretched arms. This grand old man had a face measuring over a foot in length, a four-foot torso, and legs over two feet long if he wanted to or had been able to straighten them out, and thus exceeded six feet in "height," though this is not uncommon among Gorillas, for they have immensely large bodies and not altogether unsturdy legs. Their feet are comparatively small, their arms are not only long but immensely muscled, and their hands are very big but are proportioned much like our own. The head, though big, is, compared to that of other apes, small in proportion to the body.

Gorillas are distinguished from other apes by their large, flaring nostrils which point upwards, their rather widely set eyes, their pointed heads and their tiny ears. They have been said to be born with light skins which gradually darken through brown to black within a few weeks, but all the youngest ones recorded have had jet-black skins. The body is rather thickly clothed in short, firm hairs, but there are usually considerable naked areas, especially on the chest, which in adult males is usually glistening, naked, black skin. Even obese old males can stand on their hind legs alone, but they are normally quadrupedal, walking on their finger knuckles and on the flats of their feet. This gives them a curious, slightly tilted, sway-backed stance well shown in the photograph. The head is almost buried in the immense shoulder muscles, and the elbows turn slightly outwards in walking.

The Gorilla is, as far as is known, a complete vegetarian and has an enormous daily intake, but this is of two distinct kinds. The actual food consists of shoots, the leaves of tiny seedlings, lots of different kinds of berries, some bark, roots, and grains, and certain fruits; but they also engulf roughage in bulk, and this consists of large quantities of fibrous material such as the stems of young banana trees, when they are available on a native plantation. It has been found that such roughage is absolutely needed by captive gorillas, and it is now customary to give them foliage, which they devour almost like elephants.

Thus far, only one Gorilla has been born in cap-tivity—at the Columbus (Ohio) Zoo, in December 1956. In this case, the period of gestation was 259 days. But the exact dates at which the young attain various stages of their growth not entirely known. However, a few have been raised from what appeared to be extreme infancy, and from these cases some pertinent points have been ascertained within fairly close limits. They appear to be a little under four and a half pounds when born; at a year they weigh about fourteen pounds. They seem to cut their first teeth when they are but two months old. They appear to be full grown at about twelve years, but there are various criteria by which we may judge this. We know nothing of their longevity; but again, informed people native to their homelands assert that Gorillas live just about the same length of time as human beings—and, as we have noted above, the average life expectancy of those people was, until recently, only about forty-five years. This estimate, however, seems to be rather too high for Gorillas.

Gorillas travel about in aggregated family parties usually presided over by a single large male; but double parties have been recorded, and sometimes several families will be seen feeding together at the same place, all mingling and getting along most amiably. Old lone females, and what appear to be young "married" couples living in isolated bliss, have also been reported. Their daily routine appears to be very regular, and they generally give every appearance of being extremely conservative in all their ways. They start moving about shortly before dawn but do not descend from the trees, in which they usually but not invariably build platforms, until the early morning mist is well illuminated. Then the old man, who usually sleeps on the ground or on a heavy platform near the ground, starts grumbling, tapping on the ground or on his bare chest or his hollowed cheeks. After considerable milling around on the part of the youngsters, who grunt a great deal, the whole group then moves off, headed by the old man but well deployed. They go directly to the same feeding ground day after day until the food supply runs low or they lose interest in the dietaries there obtainable, when they make a double move either in the morning or the afternoon, and then prepare new sleeping quarters. During the middle of the day they lounge about and the adults take naps.

To any who have watched Gorillas undisturbed in their tangled, moss-covered mountain fastnesses, there is something both majestic and ineffably sad about these great worried apes. They are lordly and magnificent in their bearing, and they seem, as certain African folklore has it, to have a regal disregard for all other living things except leopards, against which they may take the most strenuous and terrifying action. Even this they do with a sort of condescension, as if they knew that a warning should be enough. They raid man's plantations, but with an air of possessiveness, and the "old man" will rush, roaring, at the luckless farmer who happens to be weeding his yams when they arrive there. At this time, the animals shield their bodies by pulling bushes together in front of them, instead of pushing them apart like all other animals, but they never, it seems, carry through these simulated attacks, provided the man stands his ground. If, however, the man gives ground or turns his back to run away, Gorillas may give chase and take a swipe at the fugitive with their enormous, horny fingers, ripping flesh from a man's back.

Although they are now rigidly protected in all territories, quite a number are caught alive as babies every year (and this usually entails the killing of the mother and often of several others), and many more are killed by primitive tribesmen for food. They need protection, and everything should be done to encourage the creation of the largest possible reservations for their comfort and continued survival. But we may here sound a note of hope. The famous film producer and animal photographer, Armand Denis, tells me of certain areas where he found Gorillas not just common but exceedingly numerous, and he mentioned a place where, on a twenty-mile trek, he was hardly ever out of earshot of a party.

13

The Descent of Man

MEN-APES, APE-MEN, SUB-MEN, AND US

Ape-Man

N**O DISCUSSION** of the Primates, nor of the Monkey Kingdom, as we have called this great association of related mammals, would be complete without at least some mention of ourselves and of our close relatives who became extinct only in comparatively recent times.

There was a time when, in the western world at least, the very idea that we might be related to these other forms of life was repugnant. Apart from any other consideration, it was deemed sacrilegious, since it is a basic tenet of our faith that God created man in His own image. Then, there was another reason for being reluctant to associate Man with the group of mammals known as Primates, or even to accept him as a member of the class of Mammals as a whole, or, for that matter, as an animal at all. Apes and Monkeys are not indigenous to Europe or North America, and have not been since preglacial times as far as we know. They were known to the ancients, and they played some part in European folklore and heraldry, but always as exotic outsiders. The mere suggestion, therefore, that we could have blood relationship with them, even at some very remote time, rather naturally offended the susceptibilities of people of European origin, for they considered them as mere bestial parodies of ourselves, perpetrated upon us by Nature as some sort of hereditary awful warning.

It is not only the findings of modern science, starting with the writings of Charles Darwin and his numerous interpreters, that have changed our opinions on this question. Rather, it is a complete revolution in our basic thinking that has brought about a reappraisal of our fundamental concepts. Today, we not only accept the oneness of Nature as the creation of a superior power, but also, in lieu of demanding a separate creation for ourselves, we have come to accept, and to accept with considerable humility, a small allotted place in something much greater.

That we are associated with the other Primates seems now to have been quite clearly demonstrated by the discoveries of many sciences. Most notable among these is, of course, that of anthropology, and most particularly of the energetic branch of that pursuit which goes out and digs for physical clues. Embryologists may demonstrate the recapitulation of an endless evolution of ancestral themes in a single embryo, and anatomists may show the exact matching of every part of our body to that of an ape, but nothing speaks so clearly as the actual remains—even if they be only fossilized bones—of creatures that stand exactly halfway between men and apes, and that might thus be called "missing links." No sooner had Darwin put forward his basic idea that we were descended from such nonhuman creatures than this search began, and it has continued ever since. It has now produced sufficient concrete results for us to put forward a considerably more than tentative suggestion as to the steps by which we descended, ascended, or at least evolved from nonhuman ancestors.

To make the position clear, though at the risk of oversimplification, we can define five stages between an Ape and a Man. These may be called those of an Ape, a Man-Ape, an Ape-Man, a Sub-Man, and finally of a true Man. As it so happens, both existing and extinct apes and men, together with certain intermediate forms, are now associated as the *Hominoidea,* and this group contains two families, that of the apes (*Pongidae*) and of the men (*Hominidae*). The general subdivisions of the former were given in brief at the beginning of the last chapter in the form of an abbreviated chart. In this was included a group of extinct creatures, unearthed in Italy, to which the scientific name *Oreopithecinae*—meaning mountain apes—has been given. The discovery of these creatures provides us with much food for thought, for among them may lie the clue to our ancestry.

In 1869 parts of skulls, jaws, teeth and sundry other bone fragments of an apelike creature, showing several astonishingly human features, were found embedded in coal of what is called the Miocene Age—estimated to be some ten million years old—in a mine in Tuscany, in Italy. They were named *Oreopithecus* by their discoverer, Dr. Paul Jervais, who either mistakenly or in order to obviate awkward questions identified them as the remains of "monkeys." This resulted in their being neglected until 1954, when Dr. Johannes Hurzeler of Switzerland by chance decided to study them in greater detail. The latter scientist immediately recognized that they were the bones of apes and, what is more, that their human-like features are more than incidental. Thorough study of these remains is being prosecuted in the United States at the time of writing, and a new investigation of the coal mine where they were found, which is still in operation, is being undertaken by Dr. Hurzeler and Dr. Helmut de Terra of Columbia University.

Whole skeletons are alleged to have been found in these mines, but to have been broken up along with the commercial coal because nobody showed any interest in them. The original finds consisted of parts of lower jaws with a few teeth, and some pieces of arm and leg bones. From these it is obvious that some anthropoid with a short face inhabited Italy long before any such creature so far known from anywhere else. Until more bones are examined these creatures cannot be precisely placed in the scheme of primate life, but one publication (*Science News Letter,* March 24, 1956, p. 182) has made so bold as to state that "the

creature may not have been in the direct line of descent of modern man or, in fact, of any now existing animal," but that "anthropologists want to know much more before accepting this ancient creature as a man or the direct ancestor of modern man." In other words, or in plain language, this means that there is a possibility we might have, in these bones, not only an ancestral ape but one of a type from which manlike creatures (and ultimately man himself) could have evolved. On the other hand, *Oreopithecus* may still prove to be only a side branch, or a sort of "experiment" by Nature, in the higher primate form—a form that, though having a short face and upright front teeth like men, just died out and gave rise to nought. The revival of this discovery is, nonetheless, of the greatest interest, and at the time of writing it has assumed even greater significance because it has just been announced that Dr. de Terra has discovered another jawbone.

What position this creature will finally be assigned in the Anthropoid family tree remains to be seen, but it is definitely an ape, and it has certain features that either actually are or at least look like those otherwise found only among the *Hominidae.* At the moment, *Oreopithecus* must remain in the family of the Apes. There is a possibility, though, that it might one day have to be moved up into that of the *Hominidae.* If this occurs, the split between the two families will have to be moved backwards in time some ten million years.

The discovery of the so-called Australopithecines is a different story. The first evidence of the past existence of these creatures came to light in 1925, and the remains were immediately recognized as being those of an astonishingly manlike ape. However, in this case the age of the remains was estimated to be only half a million years at the most, and the discovery was neither "buried" and forgotten, nor glossed over because it did not seem to fit into the established scheme of things.

When the skull of the first of them—that of an immature individual—embedded in a piece of limestone from a cave-floor deposit at Taungs in Bechuanaland, South Africa, was discovered by Professor Raymond Dart, it was thought that a new form of extinct ape had been found; but when the specimen was closely studied it was recognized that it displayed a number of traits that were decidedly human. Since, however, the skull was that of an infant, nothing could be said with certainty as to the conformity of the creature had it grown to adult size. No further fossils were found till 1936, when Dr. Robert Broom of the Transvaal Museum at Pretoria began to bring to light a whole series of skulls and subsequently other bones of similar creatures from limestone deposits, which appeared also to have been formed in caves, at Sterkfontein and Kromdraai, some forty miles west of Johannesburg. These creatures were obviously most closely related, but apparently not of the same species or even genus as the young *Australopithecus,* and Dr. Broom named them the "One Related to Man" (*Paranthropus*) and the "Near-Man" (*Plesianthropus*)—and he used the suffix *anthropus* or "man," rather than *pithecus* or "ape," deliberately.

These creatures proved to have brains of only the absolute size of existing apes, and thus slightly smaller than half that of modern man. In comparison to the size of their bodies, however, this was really considerably greater than that of the great apes, because these creatures were of very small stature—only about the size of the present-day Pigmies of the Congo. The face projected like that of an ape, and the canine or eyeteeth were very large. Thus the whole skull, seen from the side, looked much like that of a Chimpanzee, but at the same time it showed many human characteristics, notably the form and position of the transverse ridge across the back of the skull for the attachment of the neck muscles. This was low down like that of primitive men, instead of high up like that of the apes. Although the sum total of human features far outnumbered the simian in these skulls, there was at first considerable reluctance to accept their owners into the human family without a closer look at the rest of the skeleton, and they were therefore classed as a subfamily of the apes. It was argued that they might be a very primitive form of apelike creatures which branched off the main family tree, became isolated in South Africa, and developed independently a number of characters that, in the aggregate, came to look like those of humans. Their remains are not thought to be very old, geologically speaking—possibly only of early Pleistocene age, less than one million years ago.

In 1950, however, this suggestion was rendered unnecessary, and the true position of the creatures concerned was established as being well within the family of men by the discovery of limb bones, part of a shoulder blade, some vertebrae and ribs,

and, what was much more important, a whole hip girdle. The last proved to be very definitely human in construction, and there is no bone structure in our bodies more distinct from that of the apes than this. Further, from the shape of these bones it was manifest that the creatures walked erect like us. This was also confirmed by almost every feature of the limb bones and the shape of the back of the skull. Here, then, were creatures with the brain capacity of Apes, the faces of Apes, the teeth of men with a few minor, apelike aspects, but walking erect, having small, delicate arms, and about the stature of modern pigmy races. Presumably they might still be called apes if you choose brain size as your criterion for drawing the line between the two, but in almost all other respects that we know so far, they match up to the definition of men. We may call them Men-Apes, but they definitely belong in the human family.

There is no doubt about the position of a third group of manlike creatures to which the name of Man, per se, *cannot* be given. This is the *Pithecanthropinae,* or literally the Ape-Men, the remains of which have been found, so far, only in China and in the island of Java. Thus, we may construct a more detailed chart of the human family as follows:

    I. Man-Apes (*Australopithecinae*)
      (1) Southern Man-Ape (*Australopithecus*)
      (2) Half-Man (*Paranthropus*)
      (3) Near-Man (*Plesianthropus*)

    II. Ape-Men (*Pithecanthropinae*)
      (1) Giant Ape-Man (*Gigantopithecus*)
      (2) Great Ape-Man (*Meganthropus*)
      (3) Typical Ape-Man (*Pithecanthropus*)

    III. True Men·(*Homininae*)
      (1) Sub-Men (*Homo neanderthalensis,* etc.)
      (2) Ancient Man (*H. sapiens acheulensis*)
      (3) Modern Man (*H. sapiens sapiens*)

In this, the status of the various kinds of True Men is shown in a way that is actually one of three or four possibilities—as will be discussed later.

Sixty-five years ago a Dutch anthropologist named Dr. Eugene Dubois brought to light, from a riverbank deposit in central Java, a considerable part of the skull and parts of the skeleton of a creature that appeared to be almost exactly halfway between an ape of somewhat gibbon-like structure and a man. This was the first *Pithecanthropus,* and it created the greatest excitement and a considerable amount of controversy. Estimates of its brain capacity, which were arrived at from taking casts of the inside of the skull, came out at 900 cubic centimeters, which is almost exactly halfway between that of the largest ape at 500 cc. and the average modern man at 1350 cc. The shape of the brain itself, and to a great extent that of the skull also, was likewise intermediate. A leg bone, however, showed that the ape-man stood upright.

No further bones of anything like this creature were found until 1927, when a Canadian anatomist named Dr. Davidson Black was excavating some caves in northern China about forty miles from Pekin. He found some teeth that looked to be intermediate between those of men and apes, and he assigned these to an extinct form of Ape-Man which he named *Sinanthropus,* or Chinese Man. Two years later an almost complete skull with similar teeth, and subsequently parts of more than forty individual skeletons, including fourteen skulls, came to light. They came from deposits that were laid down half a million years ago. Dr. Black's studies were carried on after his death by Dr. Franz Weidenreich, who eventually pointed out that these remains resembled those of the Javanese *Pithecanthropus,* of which, in the meantime, a lot more material had been discovered by a German anthropologist, Dr. G. H. R. von Koenigswald, at and around the same locality in Java where Dr. Dubois had made the initial find. The sum of their investigations finally showed, without a doubt, that there was a type of true Ape-Man inhabiting the Far East half a million years ago, and that it came in at least two varieties, one more manlike than the other. The more primitive types were found in Java, the more advanced in north China, but both were *Pithecanthropus.* The most unexpected fact to come to light, however, was that these creatures used fire and made stone implements. They also stood upright, and the size of their brains varied considerably, from as little as 850 cc. to 1300 cc., which is almost the size of the average Modern Man. Yet their skulls remained truly apelike, with enormous, bony brow ridges, jaws jutting forward, no chin and large canine teeth. Whatever their appearance, they must, nevertheless, be classed as *Hominidae* because of their tool- and fire-making activities.

During the prosecution of their searches, Doctors Weidenreich and von Koenigswald brought to light also the remains of two other really astonishing creatures that cause one to reconsider the whole question of our ancestry. First, in Java, a small portion of a lower jaw with three teeth of an obvious Pithecanthropine was found, but this was of such enormous size that it could only be construed as belonging to quite a different creature, which was accordingly called *Meganthropus* or the Great Man. That "there were giants on the Earth in those days" has always been one of man's most cherished beliefs, and perhaps we might even say wishes, but there was no concrete evidence that any such oddities had ever existed until the appearance of this bit of a very old jaw. Even this, however, did not constitute the remains of a *real* giant in the popular concept; but something else that turned up later in a Chinese drugstore in Hong Kong certainly did.

Since time immemorial the Chinese people have made use of enormous numbers of different natural substances, such as herbs, earths, the horns of animals and so forth, for medicinal purposes. Among this assortment are the fossilized bones and teeth of various animals that may often be found in deposits laid down on the floors of caves. There are certain large cave complexes in southern China that have thus been dug for ages, and the fossils found therein may be spotted by a particular kind of yellow clay in which they have been buried and which fills the cracks and interstices of their surfaces. In 1935, Dr. von Koenigswald, while browsing through such material offered for sale by a druggist in Hong Kong, noted three molar teeth of human form but of really gigantic size. They were far larger than the corresponding teeth in the largest Gorilla known. The author was privileged to hold one of these teeth in his hand while its discoverer held a normal human example of the same tooth for comparison; it was like holding a tennis ball next to a golf ball. Its owner must have been a true giant or have had a head and jaws that no human neck muscles could hold aloft. The owner of these colossal teeth was unfortunately named *Gigantopithecus,* which means the Gigantic Ape, but it was without a doubt a form of Ape-Man and, as the famous Professor W. E. LeGros Clark has said, would better have been called *Gigantanthropus,* or the Giant Man.

Thus we see that three of our five arbitrary stages in the progression from an Ape to a Man have already been bridged. This, of course, is not to say that the Men-Apes were directly descended from apes as we know them today nor that they, in turn, are the direct ancestors of the Ape-Men. Both are offshoots of the main stem of development, but they are extremely close to it, and they show that the man-types developed their hands and walked erect and probably started making tools and using fire before the development and increase in the size of their brains began. It is to be hoped that intermediate stages between apes, men-apes and ape-men will one day be discovered. Also, we would like to know more about the origin of the apes themselves. And in these respects, we should await with more than casual interest the investigations of the Italian *Oreopithecus* mentioned above.

Then comes the question of the link between the Ape-Men and True Men, and here we find that the gap has already been bridged to a considerable extent by various specific discoveries. These have, however, taken a rather unexpected turn that has only recently been interpreted for us. Starting with the discovery of a brain box and some ribs of an odd, manlike creature in a cave near Dusseldorf in Germany, and continuing through a long series of disinterments of similar skulls and skeletons in various parts of southern Europe, in the Near East, and of related forms in South Africa and Java, a picture has been built up of a kind of sub-man who lived in caves and made exquisite stone implements, of a type known as the Mousterian, at about the time of the onset of the last cold phase of the current Ice Age. This type, now known as Neanderthal Man (*Homo neanderthalensis*), had a long narrow skull, rather pointed at the back, enormous bony brow ridges, a chinless lower jaw, and heavy, human-shaped teeth. He stood erect but appears to have had a somewhat bent-kneed stance and to have done a lot of squatting. All reconstructions of him look like moronic plug-uglies, but several anthropologists have pointed out that, if you shaved him, dressed him in modern clothes and sent him off down a sidewalk in a large modern city, nobody would pay any attention to him. Nevertheless the Neanderthalers were not Modern Men, and there are valid grounds for the suggestion that they should be placed in a separate genus. The details need not be elaborated upon, but it has now been demonstrated that the Neanderthalers formed a distinct offshoot of the human stock and one that gradually evolved from rather manlike to consider-

ably "un-manlike" creatures, and thus diverged progressively from True Man. Further, they were a numerous and various lot with sundry races in Europe—including a near giant, of which a single jawbone was found at Heidelberg in Germany in 1907 and was named *Homo heidelbergensis;* a very distinct species in Rhodesia, of which a fine skull was retrieved from a deep, shaftlike cave and which is known as *Homo rhodesiensis;* and another form in Java called *Homo soloensis.*

Even more interesting than the worldwide deterioration (as it may be called) of the Neanderthalers are two further discoveries about them. The first was made in Palestine, where, it now appears, Neanderthalers and Modern Men lived side by side in a series of caves. Cross-breeds between the two have been found. Second, and much more important, is that the remains of various kinds of Modern Men have been found in deposits that are much older than those in which any Neanderthaler has been found. Modern Man, in fact, appears to have been around for an enormous length of time, and it is now apparent that it was he who produced what is called the Acheulian form of stone tools, a culture that lasted from approximately 400,000 to 130,000 B.C., from the end of the second throughout the third and up to the beginning of the last of the four recent glaciations. There were men making stone tools even before this and going back over half a million years, but we do not yet know who these persons were. This "Modern Man" of the Acheulian period had a skull, teeth and skeleton almost exactly like ours, but what is of the greatest significance is that there are examples known that show exceptionally thick skulls and certain other features that seem to point to the Pithecanthropine group of Ape-Men. This is perhaps the most interesting outcome of all research on man's origin—the suggestion that we may stem from a type of Sub-Men that was, in turn, derived from Ape-Men of the Pithecanthropine type.

Acheulian Man was sufficiently different from the men who live today to be distinguished as a subspecies. There are those who would elevate all the major races of men existing today to specific status, or make them at least full subspecies; on the other hand, there are those who would class all Modern Men together and make even the bent-legged Neanderthalers only a subspecies of *Homo.* The intermediate view is probably the soundest at the present stage of our knowledge. This is to split

Man into two genera; the Neanderthalers, with several species; and Modern Men, with but one, divided into a number of subspecies, most if not all but one of which are extinct. And incidentally, anent the matter of extinction, certain decidedly curious facts may be given passing recognition.

There have for many years now been rumors of some anthropoid creature as yet uncaptured in certain areas of the Himalayas. This is known to the native human inhabitants of that area as the *Yeti,* or *Match Kangmi,* and to our popular press as "The Abominable Snowman." Quite a number of reputable explorers and mountain climbers have reported finding tracks of humanoid appearance in the snow fields of the area, and several have photographed these. The Tibetans assert that the creatures who make these tracks are about four feet tall, are clothed in long, gingery blond fur, and are of human form but decidedly of nonhuman temperament. They assert that they live in the dense rhododendron forests just below the snow line.

In 1952 a cave near Florence in Italy, which had been sealed by eleven feet of flowstone for tens of thousands of years, was blasted open and the footprints of Neanderthal men were found, as fresh as the day they were made, in the clay that floored the cave. Along with them were imprints of Cave Bear and of Modern Men, both of which are perfectly distinct and quite different. The footprints attributed—and on very solid grounds—to the Neanderthalers closely resembled in outline those of the Yetis found in the Himalayas, whereas neither are anything like those of Modern Man, on the one hand, nor of bears, the larger Langurs, or any other mammal, on the other. It is not impossible to suppose, therefore, as some have, that a species of Sub-man, Ape-Man, or Man-Ape could have survived until today in the virtually unexplored and for the most part uninhabited vastnesses of the eastern Himalaya among the dense rhododendron forests up near the snow line. The Neanderthalers certainly inhabited Europe during the last major advance of the ice, when conditions at sea level seem to have been much as they are today near the snow line in the Himalayas.

So, finally, we come to the primate creature that has named itself *Homo sapiens,* or the "Wise." About this appellation and its validity there may be doubt, but it cannot be denied that, today, this mammal alone is capable of giving other animals names and of doing many other things that the others manifestly do not do. The most important of these, from a biological point of view, is probably his ability to alter the environment in which he lives. Many animals do this to a limited extent by building shells around themselves or nests in which they may lurk. There are others, like ants and beaver, that actually go out and change their local countryside, but there are none that can alter the face of whole continents, upsetting their drainage system, underlying water table and vegetation, the conformity of their seacoasts and ultimately their very climate itself, as modern man does. But Modern Man is odd and unique in many other ways.

There are mammals, like the opossum, which will eat almost anything—and their digestion is like that of an acid vat—but there is probably no mammal that customarily takes such a wide variety of substances in its diet as does Man. He eats almost every kind of animal (unless its flesh is actually poisonous, which is extremely rare), worms, insects, scorpions, spiders, jellyfish, starfish and sea urchins, shellfish of all kinds, crabs and other crustaceans, sea squirts (bêche-de-mer), fish, amphibians (frogs), reptiles (snakes and iguanas, turtles and tortoises), birds and every kind of mammal, including on occasion his own kind. Of vegetable matter his diet is just as varied, ranging from seaweed and diatoms to the kernels of pine cones and funguses, every kind of fruit, leaves, seeds, nuts, bark and grasses. Of minerals he takes quite an assortment also, and apart from eating earth—which is a far from rare abnormality—he uses salts of several kinds. When lost on polar icecaps, men have lived for weeks by chewing tanned leather, and during famines in China, by boiling earth and drinking the water. One scientist drifted across the Atlantic on a raft, living exclusively on fish and drinking only the water squeezed from their bodies, and a man trapped in a coal mine maintained life for a time by chewing on the coal.

Partly as a result of this wide food tolerance, partly because of his habit of wearing clothes, and partly because he appears to be by nature a most adaptable and hardy creature, Modern Man has spread all over the earth, living in all manner of climates and in the most unlikely places, from Arctic ice floes to treetops and the center of burning deserts, in caves, in jungles, and on piles over lakes or miles out upon the open sea. Most important of all, however, is his nest-building ability that makes it possible for him to live almost anywhere on this

planet and that may one day see him infesting
others. Buildings of all kinds (including the Empire
State and the Great Pyramid of Egypt), and carts,
cars, ships and planes, which are really only little
movable houses, are actually "nests"; and heating
and air-conditioning are really only adjuncts to
them, like the ventilating shafts of nests of ants or
the holes in sponges.

Then again, man has devised another aid to survival, namely agriculture. This is a very odd procedure that has only otherwise been developed by
one or two types of animals—notably by the Leaf-
cutting Ants or *Atta* of tropical America. This, he
probably discovered by dwelling on the banks of
great rivers like the Nile, which flowed through a
hot, dry desert and down which seasonal floods
rolled. Only thus could an unversed, nonthinking
creature come to realize the alternation of genera-

tions between a little seed, that looks like a tiny
pebble, and the green, flowering plant that sprouts
from this, and realize that, by hoarding the former
and planting it at the right time, he would get, first,
plants and then, from these, more seeds. Once man
grasped this simple fact he was on the road to
civilization; but this is another story and not our
province.

Today, man may be divided roughly into four
great groups or Races, customarily called the
Australoid, the Caucasoid, the Mongoloid and the
Negroid. All are of ancient lineage, but the Australoid appears to be the oldest and the Negroid
the youngest. There has been much intermingling
between them, and there are many large populations of mixed racial origin that are themselves of
most venerable age. The Australoids appear to
have originated about the Indian Ocean on the

Asiatic side and to have once inhabited Persia and India, Indo-China and Indonesia, and then to have spread to Australia and Tasmania.

The Caucasoids seem to have sprung up in western Eurasia and thence spread all over the world, sending a main branch east in very ancient times, that filtered into India via Persia and then on, via the East Indies, to the farthest Pacific islands. Then, much later, in historic times, a great host went west to America to found the modern nations there, and, finally, a third went again to the south Pacific to found modern Australia and New Zealand. A subbranch, the Semites, meanwhile spread in waves outwards from Arabia, covering the northern half of Africa and wide areas in the Near East.

The Mongoloids arose in eastern Eurasia and have also been constantly spreading outwards in all directions, reaching Europe in the west and India and Indonesia in the south and continuing in wave after wave throughout thousands of years far into the Pacific area. A great host of Mongoloids also streamed over the northern land bridge between Siberia and Alaska into North America, and thence spread south to the very tip of South America—in which continents they are known as American Indians, or better, as Amerindians.

The Negroid race appears to have arisen only comparatively recently in the lower eastern Sudan and then to have spread west to the Atlantic, north to the Sahara, and east to the Indian Ocean. It is important to realize that the true Negro peoples only reached South Africa at the same time that the Europeans did so, in the fourteenth and fifteenth centuries of our era. The people that lived there previously and are now almost extinct may form a separate, fifth, race. This apparently once ranged from central Europe to Indonesia and has been misleadingly called the Proto-Negro (meaning simply "that which was before the Negroes came"). It is still at the cultural level of the Late Stone Age, and today we know its members in Africa as the Bushmen and the Hottentots, and in Malaya as the Saka.

At one time it was believed—at least by European Caucasoids—that living man formed a sort of vast pyramid with a great mass of virtual Sub-Men at the base near the apes, and the white-skinned Caucasoid Aristocrats, few in number, at the top. The order of descent went something as follows: Nordic Europeans, Latin or Mediterranean Europeans with light skins, Middle Eastern peoples with

somewhat darker skins, the Indians and certain "Islanders" with dark skins but Caucasoid features, Mongoloids of all kinds, then Negroids of all divisions, and beneath them all, and only one stage removed from apes, the poor Australian Blackfellows. Modern research, modern communications, a lot of education and some common sense have shown all this to be nonsense.

Apes as we know them today, and particularly the Great Apes, are distinguished by having profuse, rather lank, straight hair, long torsos and short legs, and no "lips"—*i.e.* noneverted lips. On these criteria, the type of man that comes closest to the apes is the Caucasoid, while the Negroid is the farthest removed therefrom; the Australoid shows some of both features, and the Mongoloid the most exceptional combination of long straight hair but very little of it, a long torso and comparatively short legs, and partially everted lips. Actually, none of these characters have much if any real significance, since there is much evidence to show that all of them may be nothing more than adaptations to particular climatic conditions or mere genetic variations. Skin color seems to have even less significance. Narrow nostrils, moreover, may be designed only to keep out cold or to conserve moisture in deserts, and wide flaring ones to get rid of excess moisture in a hot damp climate. The typical extremely long leg, with powerful thigh, long light calf, long foot and a pronounced extension of the heel backwards, which is so finely developed in certain Negroid peoples, may well be nothing but a specialization for running on open plains and for jumping—and it is notable that the greatest jumpers in the world are a tribe of central Africans and that the feet and heels of the greatest of all ballet dancers, Nijinsky, had by chance just this form. The existing races of men are, in fact, each just somewhat specialized varieties of a common theme.

By overprinting a number of photographs of all kinds of people of the same sex, age, and general build and size, of all races, one scientist produced a remarkable composite picture of Modern Man. The resulting composite person could perhaps most easily be matched in the more elegant part of Mexico City than anywhere else today, since he had wavy dark hair, only a little facial hair concentrated in the moustache and on the lower chin, a broad forehead and rather wide face with somewhat high cheekbones, a beautifully chiselled, semi-full mouth, a straight, rather long nose with slightly flared nostrils, small ears (the age was about thirty years), and light brown eyes. Only the possible fifth race, known as the Proto-Negroid, appears to be truly different, the hair of its members growing in isolated patches and being very short, tightly curled, and friable, the skin coppery, the skull very short, the nose bridge almost absent, and the legs bent. Members of this race also often show the curious development of excess fatty tissue on the buttocks known as steatopygy, and they display some other odd characteristics.

Further, neither the form of the skull—long, medium, or short—nor of the body—tall, little-muscled and skinny, athletic, or obese with large, fat stomach and sloping shoulders—nor even the blood type has anything to do with race, though there are groups of people who may display one type of these categories predominantly, such as the Basques, who have a very high percentage of one particular blood type. There are, in fact "long, thin pinks and short, fat blacks," as a certain impolite West Indian song relates.

Finally, modern man has developed a certain biological procedure to an extraordinary point. This is the rearing of his young. The gestation period of man is long, the period between birth and weaning is comparatively short, but then his young are "nursed," nourished, protected and controlled by the parents for a longer time than those of any other animal. Further, man being gregarious and having developed a social life and specialized educational system for training his children, the period of dependence of the latter is often extended still further under the aegis of the tribal group or society, and now that the State makes still other demands on the young in the form of military or other regimentation, men may be nearly halfway through their allotted life span before they become truly independent.

Men are communal but not, except in a primitive tribal stage, truly gregarious, since the individuals in any one group do not necessarily remain the same. Most are sedentary, but many peoples have been truly nomadic, and some of these once indulged in regular seasonal migrations. They appear to be basically polygamous, but monogamy is at present very widespread as a purely social custom, and polyandry is still known. Being communal, they are normally peaceable creatures, but they become highly aggressive if their nests or feeding territory are encroached upon, when they indulge in all types

of what is called by animal behaviorists "distance threat and deflection," usually starting from the farthest distance possible in the form of howling contests accompanied by grimaces just like gibbons and monkeys, and sometimes ending in actual fights. Since the development of civilization, which is really nothing more than a truly social life, Men have taken up the practice of warfare just like ants and other social insects.

Language is thought by some to be a distinction of our species, but probably is not. That animals communicate with each other by sounds is common knowledge, but the extent of these sounds is only just coming to be realized with the preliminary exploration of the subsonic and supersonic ranges of air-borne waves, and their import as a means of communication among animals has, so far, hardly been studied at all. As a learned French cleric once reported of the Basques, "They have a language which they say they understand, but I frankly don't believe it." This is unfortunately all too true also of our present attitude to the "language" of animals, for it is now known that they can communicate in several other ways besides by sounds, including even by electromagnetic media. Man alone, as far as we know, has developed methods of recording his communications, and this may serve better than any other single characteristic to set him apart from the other animals. Yet, even here, the same thing is accomplished in primitive ways by many animals—like minks, which leave apparently quite clear information for others of their own kind along their regular hunting and migrating circuits by rubbing the secretion from their anal glands on stones and other objects.

In the final analysis, there is really nothing about Man or his basic behavior that is unique, so that the honest sociologist, with even an elementary knowledge of zoology, is almost as hard put to it to draw the line between men and the other primates as are the anatomist and the systematist.

Today, it regrettably appears to be considered not only unscientific but generally inadmissible for anyone claiming an interest in scientific technique to express awe, or to admit marvel, in the face of Nature. Today, although science itself is increasingly admitting its own inadequacies and its appreciation of the amount that it does *not* know, there is growing up a shockingly complacent and almost insufferable popular attitude to what used to be called the wonders of nature. The fact that a shrew burrowing under the surface soil in your yard may be your blood relative is now considered no more marvelous than that some of the molecules we breathed today may be part of a hydrogen bomb that blows one of our cities off the surface of the earth next year—and is probably now just as seldom actually believed. A cartoon in a famous magazine of humor just before the Second World War showed a dejected little professor standing between two towering storm troopers in front of Adolf Hitler. The caption below stated simply: "Mein Fuhrer, this man claims he can make butter out of milk." There could hardly be a better commentary on the present state of culture created by the Primate called Man.

Yet, for those who can still bring themselves to admit it, there is a great deal in Nature that is so much more marvelous than any of our own accomplishments that it leaves us completely humbled and without recourse except to something much greater than we can comprehend. Why should there be 750 different kinds of primate mammals on this piffling little planet? Why should certain Insectivores have given rise to animated parachutes, but others to nimble-fingered little mites with large brains? Why did the staring lemurs get left in Madagascar and the Tarsiers die out in North America? Why didn't the Rhesus discover agriculture or the Neanderthaler civilization? Why does man slaughter his own kind? Is there not a pattern in all this that is still beyond our understanding?

Even if it can never be vouchsafed to us to comprehend the meaning of life, there is no reason why we should not endeavor to understand its mechanism, and where better to start than with the study of ourselves, our cousins and our ancestors —in short, with that great assemblage of life that we call the Monkey Kingdom. For, if we can once come to understand ourselves, all else might then become fairly obvious.

Systematic List of Living Primates

THE FOLLOWING LIST combines the findings of a considerable number of published reviews of separate groups. The most recent revisions were, as far as possible, adopted as the ultimate criteria. This was not done throughout because much current research is not yet published, but the results of some of this (*vide*: No. 24 in the bibliography) have been incorporated herewith by permission of the specialists concerned. This list purports to be as complete as current knowledge permits; but with any such catalogue there must be considerable individual disagreement. Under each of the twelve major headings are listed the references (as numbered in the bibliography) to the publications covering that group. The right-hand column of figures in the systematic list itself gives—though perhaps somewhat approximately—the number of subspecies that appear to be currently recognized. The numeral "1" indicates that the species is presently monotypic. Certain *family* and *subfamily* headings are placed in brackets and are anglicized to emphasize that they are not as yet established in the accepted taxonomy.

TUPAIOIDS

(*Bibliographic Refs. 6. 12. 32. 45. 46*)

Tupaiidae (Mivart, 1868)		Sub-Primates
Ptilocercinae (Lyon, 1913)		Feathertails
Ptilocercus (Gray, 1848)		Feathertails
lowi (Gray, 1848)	2	Feathertails
Tupaiinae (Lyon, 1913)		Tupaias
Tupaia (Raffles, 1822)		Typical Tupaias
glis (Diard, 1820)	53	Common Tupaias
splendidula (Gray, 1865)	1	Little Painted Tupaia
carimatae (Miller, 1906)	1	Carimata Island Tupaia
mülleri (Kohlbrugge, 1895)	1	Müller's Tupaia
montana (Thomas, 1892)	2	Montane Tupaias
javanica (Horsefield, 1822)	2	Javanese Tupaias
minor (Gunther, 1876)	5	Lesser Tupaias
gracilis (Thomas, 1893)	3	Slender Tupaias
picta (Thomas, 1892)	1	Great Painted Tupaia
dorsalis (Schlegel, 1857)	1	Striped Tupaia
nicobarica (Zelebor, 1869)	1	Nicobar Tupaia
cuyonis (Miller, 1910)	1	Cuyo Island Tupaia
palawanensis (Thomas, 1894)	1	Palawan Island Tupaia
möllendorffi (Matschie, 1898)	1	Möllendorff's Tupaia
Tana (Lyon, 1913)		Great Tupaias
tana (Raffles, 1821)	7	Common Greater Tupaias
cervicalis (Miller, 1903)	2	Batu Island Tupaias
chrysura (Günther, 1876)	1	Labuan Tupaia
paitana (Lyon, 1913)	1	North Bornean Tupaia
besara (Lyon, 1913)	1	West Bornean Tupaia
tuancus (Lyon, 1913)	1	Banjok Island Tupaia
lingae (Lyon, 1913)	1	Lingga Island Tupaia
sirhassenensis (Miller, 1901)	1	Natuna Island Tupaia
bunoae (Miller, 1900)	1	Tambelan Island Tupaia
Anathana (Lyon, 1913)		Indian Tupaias
ellioti (Waterhouse, 1850)	1	Madras Tupaia
wroughtoni (Lyon, 1913)	1	Bombay Tupaia
pallida (Lyon, 1913)	1	North East Indian Tupaia
		Mountain Tupaias
Dendrogale (Gray, 1860)		Cambodian Tupaia
frenata (Gray, 1860)	1	
murina (Schlegel & Müller, 1843)	1	Pigmy Tupaia
melanura (Thomas, 1892)	1	Bornean Mountain Tupaia
		Philippines Tupaia
Urogale (Mearns, 1905)		Everett's Tupaia
everetti (Thomas, 1892)	1	

183

LORISOIDS

(*Bibliographic Refs. 1. 12. 14. 22*)

Galagidae (Hill, 1953) — Long-tailed Lorisoids
Galaginae (Mivart, 1864) — Bushbabies
Galagoides (Smith, 1833) — Dwarf Bushbabies
demidovii (Fischer, 1808) — 7 — Demidoff's Bushbabies
Galago (E. Geoffroy, 1796) — Typical Bushbabies
crassicaudatus (E. Geoffroy, 1812) — 11 — Thick-tailed Bushbabies
senegalensis (E. Geoffroy, 1796) — 9 — Lesser Bushbabies
alleni (Waterhouse, 1837) — 1 — Allen's Bushbaby
Euoticus (Gray, 1863) — Needle-clawed Bushbabies
elgantulus (Le Conte, 1857) — 1 — West Needle-clawed Bushbaby

inustus (Schwarz, 1940) — 1 — East Needle-clawed Bushbaby

Short-tailed Lorisoids

Lorisidae (Gregory, 1915) — Lorises
Lorisinae (Flower & Lydekker, 1891) — Pottos
Periodicticus (Bennett, 1831) — Pottos
potto (Müller, 1766) — 5 — Pottos
Arctocebus (Gray, 1863) — Angwantibos
Calabarensis (Smith, 1860) — 2 — Angwantibos
Loris (E. Geoffroy, 1796) — Slender Lorises
tardigradus (Linnaeus, 1758) — 6 — Slender Lorises
Nycticebus (E. Geoffroy, 1812) — Slow Lorises
coucang (Boddaert, 1785) — 10 — Slow Lorises

LEMUROIDS

(*Bibliographic Ref. 22*)

Lemuridae (Gray, 1821) — True Lemurs
Cheirogalageinae (Gregory, 1915) — Lesser Lemurs
Microcebus (E. Geoffroy, 1828) — Mouse-Lemurs
murinus (J. F. Miller, 1777) — 2 — Lesser Mouse-Lemurs
coquereli (Grandidier, 1867) — 1 — Coquerel's Mouse-Lemur
Cheirogaleus (E. Geoffroy, 1812) — Dwarf Lemurs
trichotis (Gunther, 1875) — 1 — Hairy-eared Dwarf Lemur
major (E. Geoffroy, 1812) — 4 — Greater Dwarf Lemurs
medius (E. Geoffroy, 1812) — 2 — Fat-tailed Dwarf Lemurs
Phaner (Gray, 1870) — Fork-crowned Lemur
furcifer (Blainville, 1841) — 1 — Tanta
Lemurinae (Mivart, 1864) — Greater Lemurs
Hapalemur (I. Geoffroy, 1851) — Gentle Lemurs
griseus (Link, 1795) — 2 — Gray Gentle Lemurs
simus (Gray, 1870) — 1 — Reed Lemur
Lepilemur (I. Geoffroy, 1851) — Sportive Lemurs
mustelinus (I. Geoffroy, 1851) — 1 — Weasel Lemur
ruficaudatus (Grandidier, 1867) — 1 — Red-tailed Sportive Lemur

Lemur (Linnaeus, 1758) — Typical Lemurs
catta (Linnaeus, 1758) — 1 — Ring-tailed Lemur
variegatus (Kerr, 1792) — 3 — Ruffed Lemurs
macaco (Linnaeus, 1766) — 1 — Black Lemur
fulvus (E. Geoffroy, 1812) — 7 — Brown Lemurs
mongoz (Linnaeus, 1766) — 2 — Mongoose-Lemurs
rubriventer (I. Geoffroy, 1850) — 1 — Red-bellied Lemur
Indriidae (Burnett, 1828) — Monkey-Lemurs
[Propithecines] — Long-tailed Monkey-Lemurs
Propithecus (Bennett, 1832) — Sifakas
diadema (Bennett, 1832) — 5 — Diademed Sifakas
verreauxi (Grandidier, 1867) — 5 — Verreaux's Sifakas
Avahi (Jourdan, 1834) — Woolly Lemurs
laniger (Gmelin, 1788) — 1 — Woolly Lemur
[Indrines] — Short-tailed Monkey-Lemurs
Indri (E. Geoffroy & G. Cuvier, 1795) — Dog-Lemurs
indri (Gmelin, 1788) — 1 — Indri
Daubentoniidae (Gray, 1870) — Rodent-Lemurs
Daubentonia (E. Geoffroy, 1795) — Aye-ayes
madagascarensis (Gmelin, 1788) — 1 — Aye-aye

TARSIOIDS

(*Bibliographic Ref. 23*)

Tarsiidae (Gill, 1872) — Tarsioids
Tarsius (Storr, 1780) — Tarsiers
syrichta (Linnaeus, 1758) — 3 — Philippine Tarsiers

bancanus (Horsfield, 1821) — 4 — Malaysian Tarsiers
spectrum (Pallas, 1778) — 5 — Celebesean Tarsiers

HAPALOIDS

(*Bibliographic Refs. 7. 16. 24. 28. 38*)

Hapalidae (Wagner, 1840) — Marmosets
[Hapalines] — Marmosets and Tamarins
Cebuella (Gray, 1866) — Pigmy Marmosets
pygmaea (Spix, 1823) — 2 — Pigmy Marmosets
Hapale (Illiger, 1811) — Tufted Marmosets

jacchus (Linnaeus, 1758) — 1 — Common Marmoset
flaviceps (Thomas, 1903) — 1 — Buff-headed Marmoset
chrysoleucus (Wagner, 1842) — 1 — Silky Marmoset
santaremensis (Matschie, 1893) — 1 — Santarem Marmoset

Species	No.	Common name
penicillata (E. Geoffroy, 1812)	2	Black-plumed Marmosets
aurita (E. Geoffroy, 1812)	1	White-eared Marmoset
petronius (Ribeiro, 1924)	1	Montane Marmoset
leucocephala (E. Geoffroy, 1812)	1	White-fronted Marmoset
humeralifer (E. Geoffroy, 1812)	1	White-shouldered Marmoset
albicollis (Spix, 1823)	1	White-necked Marmoset
Mico (Lesson, 1840)		Naked-eared Marmosets
argentata (Linnaeus, 1771)	3	Silver Marmosets
Marikina (Lesson, 1840)		Bald-headed Tamarins
bicolor (Spix, 1823)	1	Piebald Tamarin
martinsi (Thomas, 1912)	1	Martin's Tamarin
Tamarin (Gray, 1870)		Black Tamarins
tamarin (Link, 1795)	2	Negro Tamarins
midas (Linnaeus, 1758)	3	Red-handed Tamarins
inustus (Schwarz, 1951)	1	Dusky Tamarin
Tamarinus (Trouessart, 1899)		Moustached Tamarins
nigricollis (Spix, 1823)	6	Black-necked Tamarins
weddelli (Deville, 1849)	1	Deville's Tamarin
fuscicollis (Spix, 1823)	1	Brown-handed Tamarin
illigeri (Pucheran, 1845)	2	Red-mantled Tamarins
tripartitus (Milne-Edwards, 1878)	1	Gold-mantled Tamarin
mystax (Spix, 1823)	1	Typical Moustached Tamarin
pluto (Lönnberg, 1926)	1	Black Moustached Tamarin
graellsi (Espada, 1870)	1	Rio Napo Tamarin
pileatus (I. Geoffroy and Deville, 1848)	1	Red-capped Tamarin
labiatus (Humboldt, 1812)	3	White-lipped Tamarins
imperator (Goeldi, 1907)	2	Emperor Tamarins
melanoleucus (Ribeiro, 1912)	1	White Tamarin
Leontocebus (Wagner, 1840)		Maned Tamarins
rosalia (Linnaeus, 1766)	1	Golden Lion-Tamarin
chrysomelas (Kuhl, 1820)	1	Gold-headed Tamarin
chrysopygus (Mikan, 1820)	1	Gold-rumped Tamarin
Oedipomidas (Reichenbach, 1862)		Pinchés
oedipus (Linnaeus, 1758)	1	Cottontop Pinché
spixi (Reichenbach, 1862)	1	Geoffroy's "Marmoset"
leucopus (Gunther, 1876)	1	White-handed Pinché
Callimiconinae (Dollman, 1933)		Titi-Tamarins
Callimico (Ribeiro, 1912)		Titi-Tamarins
goeldii (Thomas, 1904)	1	Goeldi's "Marmoset"
[Callicebines]		Titis
Callicebus (Thomas, 1903)		Titi-Monkeys
torquatus (Hoffmannsegg, 1907)	6	Necklaced Titis
cupreus (Spix, 1823)	14	Rusty Titis
ollalae (Lonnberg, 1939)	1	Golden Titi
moloch (Hoffmannsegg, 1807)	4	Devil-Titis
cinerascens (Spix, 1923)	1	Ashy Titi
gigot (Spix, 1823)	4	Light-thighed Titis
personatus (E. Geoffroy, 1812)	4	Masked Titis

PITHECOIDS

(*Bibliographic Refs. 7. 16. 24. 28. 45*)

Species	No.	Common name
Cebidae (Swainson, 1835)		New World Monkeys
Aotinae (Elliot, 1913)		Night-Monkeys
Aotus (Humboldt, 1812)		Douroucoulis
trivirgatus (Humboldt, 1812)	10	Douroucoulis
Pitheciinae (Mivart, 1865)		Half-Monkeys
Pithecia (Desmarest, 1804)		Sakiwinkis
monachus (E. Geoffroy, 1812)	4	Bonneted Sakis
pithecia (Linnaeus, 1766)	2	Mat-faced Sakis
Cacajao (Lesson, 1840)		Uakaris
calvus (I. Geoffroy, 1847)	1	Bald Uacari
rubicundus (I. Geoffroy, 1848)	2	Red Uacaris
melanocephalus (Humboldt, 1812)	1	Black Uakari
Chiropotes (Lesson, 1840)		Bearded Sakis
chiropotes (Humboldt, 1812)	1	Red-backed Bearded Saki
satanas (Hoffmannsegg, 1807)	1	Black-bearded Saki
albinasa (I. Geoffroy & Deville, 1848)	1	White-nosed Bearded Saki
Cebinae (Mivart, 1865)		Typical New World Monkeys
Saimiri (Voigt, 1831)		Squirrel-Monkeys
sciurea (Linnaeus, 1775)	7	Common Squirrel-Monkeys
oerstedi (Rheinhardt, 1872)	2	Oersted's Squirrel-Monkeys
madeirae (Thomas, 1908)	2	South Brazilian Squirrel-Monkeys
boliviensis (d'Orbigny, 1834)	4	Pacific Squirrel-Monkeys

CEBOIDS

(*Bibliographic Refs. 7. 8. 16. 24. 26. 28*)

Species	No.	Common name
Cebidae (Swainson, 1835)		New World Monkeys
Cebinae (Mivart, 1865)		Typical New World Monkeys
Cebus (Erxleben, 1777)		Capuchins
capucinus (Linnaeus, 1758)	5	Black-and-White Capuchins
albifrons (Humboldt, 1811)	13	Cinnamon Capuchins
nigrivittatus (Wagner, 1847)	5	Capped Capuchins
apella (Linnaeus, 1758)	16	Tufted Capuchins
Atelinae (Miller, 1924)		Hand-tailed Monkeys / Spider-Monkeys
Ateles (E. Geoffroy, 1806)		Spider-Monkeys
paniscus (Linnaeus, 1758)	2	Black Spider-Monkeys
belzebuth (E. Geoffroy, 1806)	2	Marimanda Spider-Monkeys
fusciceps (Gray, 1866)	2	Brown-Headed Spider-Monkeys
geoffroyi (Kuhl, 1820)	8	Central American Spider-Monkeys
rufiventris (Sclater, 1871)	1	Colombian Spider-Monkey
Brachyteles (Spix, 1823)		Woolly Spider-Monkeys
arachnoides (E. Geoffroy, 1806)	1	Woolly Spider-Monkey
Lagothrix (E. Geoffroy, 1812)		Woolly Monkeys
lagotricha (Humboldt, 1811)	6	Common Woolly Monkeys
infumata (Spix, 1823)	1	Dusky Woolly Monkey
lugens (Elliot, 1907)	1	Black Woolly Monkey
thomasi (Elliot, 1903)	1	Thomas' Woolly Monkey
hendesi (Thomas, 1927)	1	Hendes' Woolly Monkey
caroarensis (Lönnberg, 1931)	1	Caroari Woolly Monkey
Alouattinae (Elliot, 1904)		Howler Monkeys

Alouatta (Lacépède, 1799)		Howler Monkeys
villosa (Gray, 1845)	1	Silky Howler Monkey
palliata (Gray, 1848)	8	Mantled Howler Monkeys
seniculus (Linnaeus, 1766)	9	Bearded Howler Monkeys
fusca (E. Geoffroy, 1812)	3	Brown Howler Monkey
belzebul (Linnaeus, 1766)	4	Black Howler Monkeys
caraya (Humboldt, 1812)	1	Carayanese Howler Monkey

CERCOPITHECOIDS

(Bibliographic Refs. 1. 3. 15. 37)

Cercopithecidae (Gray, 1821)		Long-tailed Monkeys
Cercopithecinae (Blanford, 1888)		African Long-tailed Monkeys
Allenopithecus (Lang, 1923)		Swamp-Monkeys
nigroviridis (Pocock, 1907)	1	Allen's Swamp-Monkey
Miopithecus (Geoffroy, 1842)		Talapoins
talapoin (Schreber, 1774)	4	Talapoin Monkeys
Cercopithecus (Brünnich, 1772)		Guenons
nictitans (Linnaeus, 1776)	12	Spot-nosed Guenons
petaurista (Schreber, 1774)	3	Lesser Spot-nosed Guenons
ascanius (Audebert, 1799)	7	Black-cheeked Guenons
cephus (Linnaeus, 1758)	3	Moustached Monkeys
erythrotis (Waterhouse, 1838)	3	Red-eared Guenons
erythrogaster (Gray, 1866)	2	Red-bellied Guenons
mitis (Wolf, 1822)	20	Diademed Guenons
l'hoesti (Sclater, 1898)	3	Mountain Guenons
hamlyni (Pocock, 1907)	1	Hamlyn's Guenon
neglectus (Schlegel, 1876)	5	De Brazza's Monkeys
diana (Linnaeus, 1758)	3	Diana Monkeys
pogonias (Bennett, 1833)	3	Crowned Guenons
wolfi (Meyer, 1890)	4	Wolf's Guenons
mona (Schreber, 1775)	7	Mona Monkeys
aethiops (Linnaeus, 1758)	20	Savannah Monkeys
Erythrocebus (Trouessart, 1897)		Red Monkeys
patas (Schreber, 1774)	3	Patas Monkeys

CYNOPITHECOIDS

(Bibliographic Refs. 1. 12. 14. 34)

[Cynopithecids]		Dog-Monkeys
[Cercocebines]		Long-tailed Dog-Monkeys
Cercocebus (E. Geoffroy, 1812)		Mangabeys
aterrimus (Oudemans, 1890)	1	Peaked Mangabey
albigena (Gray, 1850)	3	Crested Mangabeys
torquatus (Kerr, 1792)	3	Capped Mangabeys
galeritus (Peters, 1879)	3	Plain-headed Mangabeys
[Macacines]		Macaques
Silenus (Goldfuss, 1820)		Lion-tailed Macaques
silenus (Linnaeus, 1758)	1	Wanderoo
Zati (Reichenbach, 1862)		Bonneted Macaques
sinica (Linnaeus, 1771)	3	Toque Monkeys
radiata (Geoffroy, 1812)	2	Bonnet Monkeys
Cynamolgus (Reichenbach, 1862)		Long-tailed Macaques
irus (F. Cuvier, 1818)	21	Crab-eating Macaques
Rhesus (Lesson, 1840)		Rhesus Monkeys
mulatta (Zimmermann, 1780)	4	Common Rhesus
assamensis (McClelland, 1839)	2	Montane Rhesus
cyclopsis (Swinhoe, 1862)	1	Formosan Rhesus
Macaca (Lacépède, 1799)		Pig-tailed Macaques
nemestrina (Linnaeus, 1766)	5	Pig-tailed Monkeys
Lyssodes (Gistel, 1848)		Stump-tailed Monkeys
speciosa (F. Cuvier, 1825)	5	Red-faced Macaques
fuscata (Blyth, 1875)	2	Japanese Apes
Magus (Lesson, 1827)		Moor Macaques
maurus (F. Cuvier, 1823)	3	Moor Macaques
Simia (Linnaeus, 1758)		Tailless Macaques
sylvana (Linnaeus, 1758)	1	Barbary Ape
[Cynopithecines]		Baboons
Cynopithecus (E. Geoffroy, 1835)		Celebesean Baboon
niger (Desmarest, 1820)	1	Black Ape
Mandrillus (Ritgen, 1824)		Drills
sphinx (Linnaeus, 1758)	1	Mandrill
leucophaeus (F. Cuvier, 1807)	1	Drill
Papio (Erxleben, 1777)		True Baboons
comatus (E. Geoffroy, 1812)	4	Chacma Baboons
cynocephalus (Linnaeus, 1766)	5	Yellow Baboons
doguera (Pucheran, 1856)	7	Anubis Baboons
papio (Desmarest, 1820)	2	Olive Baboons
Comopithecus (J. A. Allen, 1925)		Hamadryad Baboons
hamadryas (Linnaeus, 1758)	1	Hamadryad
Theropithecus (E. Geoffroy, 1843)		Gelada Baboons
gelada (Rüppell, 1835)	1	Gelada

COLOBOIDS

(Bibliographic Refs. 1. 12. 14. 17. 18. 19. 21. 35. 41. 43. 44. 48)

Colobidae (Blyth, 1875)		Leaf-eating Monkeys
Colobinae (Elliot, 1913)		African Leaf-eaters
Procolobus (Rocheburne, 1887)		Primitive Guerezas
verus (van Beneden, 1838)	1	Olive Guereza
Colobus (Illiger, 1811)		Guerezas
badius (Kerr, 1792)	5	Brown Guerezas
tholloni (Milne-Edwards, 1886)	2	Congo Guerezas
rufomitratus (Peters, 1879)	11	Red-crowned Guerezas
angolensis (Sclater, 1860)	6	Black-and-white Guerezas
satanus (Waterhouse, 1838)	1	Black Guereza

polykomos (Zimmermann, 1780)   3 White-tailed Guerezas
abyssinicus (Oken, 1816)   9 Mountain Guerezas
   Langurs
[Semnopithecines]
Semnopithecus (Desmarest, 1822)
   Typical Langurs
schistaceus (Hodgson, 1841)   5 Himalayan Langurs
entellus (Dufresne, 1797)   1 Hanuman Langur
priam (Blyth, 1844)   3 South Indian Langurs
hypoleucos (Blyth, 1841)   6 White-fronted Langurs
Kasi (Reichenbach, 1862)   Purple-faced Monkeys
johni (Fischer, 1829)   1 Black Langur
vetulus (Erxleben, 1777)   4 Silvery Langurs
Trachypithecus (Reichenbach, 1872)
   Lutongs
pileatus (Blyth, 1843)   5 Capped Langurs
pyrrhus (Horsefield, 1820)   3 Negro Monkeys
cristatus (Raffles, 1821)   2 Crested Lutongs
phrayei (Blyth, 1847)   3 Phraye's Lutongs
barbei (Blyth, 1847)   1 Barbe's Lutong
shanicus (Wroughton, 1917)   1 Shan States Lutong
obscurus (Reid, 1837)   7 Dusky Lutongs
potenziani (Bonaparte, 1856)   1 Red-bellied Lutong
francoisi (Pousargues, 1898)   1 Tonkinese Lutong
laotum (Thomas, 1921)   1 Laotian Lutong
poliocephalus (Trouessart, 1911)   1 Gray-headed Lutong
delacouri (Osgood, 1932)   1 Delacour's Lutong
Presbytis (Eschscholtz, 1821)   Banded Leaf-Monkeys
femoralis (Martin, 1838)   12 Thigh-striped Leaf-Monkeys
melalophus (Raffles, 1821)   1 Black-crested Leaf-Monkey

thomasi (Collett, 1892)   1 Thomas's Leaf-Monkey
aygula (Linnaeus, 1758)   2 Mitred Leaf-Monkeys
hosei (Thomas, 1889)   1 Hose's Leaf-Monkey
sabana (Thomas, 1893)   1 Lowland Borneo Leaf-Monkey
cruciger (Thomas, 1892)   1 Cross-marked Leaf-Monkey
rubicunda (Müller, 1841)   1 Red Leaf-Monkey
frontata (Müller, 1838)   1 Bald Leaf-Monkey
Pygathrix (E. Geoffroy, 1812)   Doucs
nemaeus (Linnaeus, 1771)   1 Yellow-faced Douc
nigripes (Milne-Edwards, 1871)   1 Black-faced Douc
[Rhinopithecines]   Strange-nosed Monkeys
Presbytiscus (Pocock, 1924)   Tonkinese Snub-nosed Monkeys
avunculus (Dollman, 1912)   1 Tonkin Snub-nosed Monkey
Simias (Miller, 1903   Short-tailed Snub-nosed Monkeys
concolor (Miller, 1903)   1 Mentawi Islands Langur
Rhinopithecus (Milne-Edwards, 1872)   Typical Snub-nosed Monkeys
roxellanae (Milne-Edwards, 1870)   1 Tibetan Snub-nosed Monkey
bieti (Milne-Edwards, 1872)   1 Yunnan Snub-nosed Monkey
brelichi (Thomas, 1903)   1 Brelich's Snub-nosed Monkey
Nasalis (E. Geoffroy, 1812)   Proboscis Monkeys
larvatus (Wurmb, 1781)   1 Proboscis Monkey

SIMIOIDS

(*Bibliographic Refs. 12. 14. 20. 33*)

Pongidae (Elliot, 1913)   Apes
Hylobatinae (Gill, 1872)   Lesser Apes
Hylobates (Illinger, 1811)   Gibbons
moloch (Audebert, 1797)   8 Wow-wows
agilis (F. Cuvier, 1821)   2 Agile Gibbons
lar (Linnaeus, 1771)   2 White-handed Gibbons
hoolock (Harlan, 1834)   3 White-browed Gibbons
Nomascus (Miller, 1933)   Concolors
concolor (Harlan, 1826)   4 Concolors
Symphalangus (Gloger, 1841)   Siamangs

klossi (Miller, 1903)   1 Pigmy Siamang
syndactylus (Raffles, 1821)   2 Great Siamangs
Ponginae (Allen, 1925)   Great Apes
Pongo (Lacépède, 1799)   Orang Utans
pygmaeus (Linnaeus, 1760)   2 Orang Utans
Pan (Oken, 1816)   Chimpanzees
satyrus (Linnaeus, 1758)   1 Chimpanzee
Gorilla (I. Geoffroy, 1852)   Gorillas
gorilla (Savage & Wyman, 1847)   2 Gorillas

HOMINOIDS

(*Bibliographical Refs. 27. 49*)

Hominidae (Gray, 1825)   Men
[Hominines]   True Men

Homo (Linnaeus, 1758)   Typical Men
sapiens (Linnaeus, 1758)   1 Modern Man

Analysis of the Taxonomy of Living Primates

	Families	Subfamilies	Genera	Species	Subspecies
1. TUPAIOIDS	1	2	6	31	99
2. LORISOIDS	2	2	7	10	54
3. LEMUROIDS	3	5	10	21	44
4. TARSIOIDS	1	1	1	3	12
5. HAPALOIDS	1	1	10	43	85
6. PITHECOIDS	1	3	5	13	38
7. CEBOIDS	1	3	5	22	92
8. CERCOPITHECOIDS	1	1	4	21	105
9. CYNOPITHECOIDS	1	3	14	25	83
10. COLOBOIDS	1	3	11	44	112
11. SIMIOIDS	1	2	6	10	27
12. HOMINOIDS	1	1	1	1	1
	15	27	80	244	752

The Numerical Constitution of Living Primates

By Species		By Subspecies	
1. Coloboids	44	1. Coloboids	112
2. Hapaloids	43	2. Cercopithecoids	105
3. Tupaioids	31	3. Tupaioids	99
4. Cynopithecoids	25	4. Ceboids	92
5. Ceboids	22	5. Hapaloids	85
6. Cercopithecoids	21	6. Cynopithecoids	83
7. Lemuroids	21	7. Lorisoids	54
8. Pithecoids	13	8. Lemuroids	44
9. Lorisoids	10	9. Pithecoids	38
10. Simioids	10	10. Simioids	27
11. Tarsioids	3	11. Tarsioids	12
12. Hominoids	1	12. Hominoids	1

BIBLIOGRAPHY

1. Allen, G. M. (1939). A checklist of African mammals. *Bull. Mus. Comp. Zool.* LXXXIII.

2. Allen, J. A. (1925). Primates collected by the American Museum Congo Expedition. *Bull. Am. Mus. Nat. Hist.* 47.

3. Booth, A. H. (1955). Speciation in the Mona monkeys. *Journ. Mamm.* 36.

4. Boulenger, E. G. (1936). *Apes and monkeys.* London: Harrap.

5. Burton, M. (1949). The psychology of apes. *Story of animal life.* 2.

6. Butler, P. M. (1956). The skull of *Ictops* and the classification of the insectivora. *Proc. Zool. Soc. Lond.* 126, Pt. 3.

7. Cabrera, A. & Yepes, J. (1940). *Historia natural ediar, mammiferos sud-americanos.* Buenos Aires.

8. Carpenter, C. R. (1934). A field study of the behaviour and social relations of howling monkeys. *Comp. Psychol. Mono.* 10, No. 2, Serial no. 48.

9. —— (1935). Behaviour of red spider-monkeys in Panama. *Journ. Mamm.* 16, No. 3.

10. —— (1940). A field study in Siam of the behaviour and social relations of the gibbon (*Hylobates lar*). *Comp. Psychol. Mono.* 16, No. 5.

11. —— (1942). Societies of monkeys and apes. *Biological Symposia*, 8 (50th Anniversary; University of Chicago).

12. Chasen, F. N. (1940). A handlist of Malaysian mammals. *Bull. Raffles Mus.*, No. 15.

13. Duncan, F. M. (1947). *The monkey tribe.* London: Sampson, Low, & Marston.

14. Ellerman, J. R. & Morrison-Scott, T. C. S. (1951). *Checklist of Palaearctic and Indian mammals.* London: British Museum.

15. Elliot, D. G. (1913). A Review of the Primates. *Am. Mus. Nat. Hist. Mono.* Series 1–3.

16. Hershkovitz, P. (1949). Mammals of northern Colombia. Preliminary Report No. 4: Monkeys (*Primates*) *Proc. U.S. Nat. Mus.* 98.

17. Hill, W. C. O. (1934). A monograph on the purple-faced leaf-monkeys. *Ceylon Journal of Sci.* (B), XIX.

18. —— (1936). Supplementary observations on purple-faced leaf-monkeys. *Ceylon Journ. of Sci.* (B), XX, Pt. 1.

19. —— (1939). An annotated systematic list of the leaf-monkeys. *Ceylon. Journ. Sci.* (B), XXI, Pt. 3.

20. —— (1949). Gibbons. *Zoo Life.* 4.

21. —— (1952). The external and visceral anatomy of the olive colobus monkey (*Procolobus verus*). *Proc. Zool. Soc. Lond.* 122.

22. —— (1953). *Primates* I. *Strepsirhini.* Edinburgh: University Press.

23. —— (1955). *Primates* II. *Haplorhini.* Edinburgh: University Press.

24. —— (in preparation). Systematic list of the *Hapalidae* and *Cebidae*.

25. Hooton, E. (1942). *Man's poor relations.* New York: Doubleday.

26. Kellogg, R. & Goldman, E. A. (1945). Review of the spider-monkeys. *Proc. U.S. Nat. Mus,* 96.

27. Le Gros Clark, W. E. (1950). *History of the primates.* London: British Museum.

28. Lima, E. da C. (1945). *Mammals of Amazonia.* Rio de Janeiro: Mus. Parense Emilio Goeldi.

29. Lydekker, R. (1893). *The royal natural history.* London: Warne.

30. —— (1905). Colour evolution in guereza monkeys. *Proc. Zool. Soc. Lond.* II.

31. —— (1916). *Wild life of the world.* London: Warne.

32. Lyon, M. W. (1913). Treeshrews: An account of the mammalian family *Tupaiidae*. *Proc. U.S. Nat. Mus.* 45.

33. Miller, G. S. (1933). The classification of the gibbons. *Journ. Mamm.* 14.

34. Pocock, R. I. (1931). Revision of the macaques. *Journ. Bombay Nat. Hist. Soc.* XXXV.

35. —— (1934). Monkeys of the genera *Pithecus* and *Pygathrix*, etc. *Proc. Zool Soc. Lond.*

36. Pournelle, G. (1954). *Zoonooz.* 27, No. 12.

37. Sanderson, I. T. (1940). The mammals of the North Cameroons forest area. *Trans. Zool. Soc. Lond.* XXIV, Pt. 7.

38. —— (1950). Marmosets, nature's imps. *Zoo Life*, 5, No. 2.

39. Schlaikjer, E. M. (1938). The living dead. *Natural History*, XLI, No. 3.

40. Schultz, A. H. (1942). Growth and development of the proboscis monkey. *Bull. Mus. Comp. Zool.* LXXXIX, No. 6.

41. Schwarz, E. (1910). On *Cercocebus aterrimus* and *Cercocebus albigena*. *Ann. & Mag. Nat. Hist.* (8), V.

42. —— (1928a). Bemerkungen über die roten Stummelaffen. *Zeitschrift für Säugetierkunde.* III, 3.

43. ——— (1928b). The species of the genus *Cercocebus, Ann. & Mag. Nat. Hist.* (10), 1.

44. ——— (1929). On the local races and distribution of the black and white colobus monkeys. *Proc. Zool. Soc. Lond.* II.

45. Simpson, G. G. (1945). The principles of classification and a classification of mammals. *Bull. Am. Mus. Nat. Hist.* 85.

46. Taylor, E. H. (1934). *Philippine land mammals.* Manila: Bureau of Science.

47. Walker, E. P. (1954). *The Monkey Book.* New York: Macmillan.

48. Washburn, S. L. (1944). The genera of Malaysian langurs. *Journ. Mamm.* 25, No. 3.

49. Weidenreich, F. (1945). Giant early man from Java and South China. *Anthropo. Papers, Am. Mus. Nat. Hist.* 40, Pt. 1.

Index

NOTE: Numerals within parentheses refer to the numbers of black-and-white plates.